ALOIS JIRÁSEK

Legends of Old Bohemia

ALOIS JIRÁSEK

Legends

of

Old Bohemia

WITH ILLUSTRATIONS BY
JIŘÍ TRNKA

TRANSLATED BY
EDITH PARGETER

PAUL HAMLYN · LONDON

DESIGNED AND PRODUCED BY ARTIA, AND PUBLISHED BY
PAUL HAMLYN LTD.,
WESTBOOK HOUSE, FULHAM BROADWAY, LONDON,
FOR GOLDEN PLEASURE BOOKS LTD.
© 1963 BY ARTIA
PRINTED IN CZECHOSLOVAKIA
S 1302

Table of Contents

EDITOR'S NOTE ON PRONUNCIATION

Czech words are pronouced phonetically, as they are written, with the stress on the first syllable. An accent (ˇ) above a letter softens its sound: (č = ch, š = sh, ň = ñ, ě = ie, ť = tj etc.). Czech vowels are as follows: a = but; e = let; i, y = pit; o = pot; u = put; á = arm; é = bear; í, ý as in seed; ó = ball, ů = rule.

Legends of Old Bohemia

*Come and listen to a tale of the olden days. Hear the story of the people of ancient
Bohemia, how they came into the borders of their native land, and settled along the Elbe and
the Vltava and the other rivers of their country.*

*Hear also those further stories which have come down to us out of the darkness of the
ages, the surviving fragments of the wonderful tales of bygone generations, who bowed before
the gods in the gloom of ancient groves, and sacrificed to the springs in quiet valleys, to the lakes
and the rivers and the holy, living fire.*

Let us turn our minds back to those early years, before these people came and settled here.

There were no towns, the villages were but few and small, and even these existed only in certain districts, where the poor remnants of the former inhabitants still survived, speaking a strange tongue. The soil was still almost entirely untouched by the plough. Everywhere the land was wilder and more desolate: plains, plateaus and valleys alike.

Vast primeval forests grew dense and black along the mountains on the frontiers, and from the ridges of these highlands extended down the slopes in wide belts mile on mile into the interior. Even there, in the hinterland, stretched many a wilderness of ancient, dark woods, and between them gleamed the clearer green of luxuriant meadowlands covered with thick, tall grass. There were plenty of stretches of unstable ground both in the open country and in the forests, treacherous marshes quivering with the cries of water fowl, silent, black and enchanted swamps, in which trembled the mirrored images of ancient trees, their gigantic trunks bearded with grey mosses.

Human footsteps were rare here, but everywhere the woods teemed with animals. With no-one to hunt them, they multiplied until the soil could barely support them. In the deep forests the bear made his home, hunting through the trees for hollow boles filled with honey-comb by the bees that swarmed everywhere and set the trees humming.

The wild boar rooted in the loose forest soil, and through the thick, tangled undergrowth crept the fox and the wild cat. The agile lynx crouched in ambush in the branches, piercing the twilight of the woods with his keen eyes, and through the thickets echoed from the distance the bellowing of the gigantic aurochs, extinct wild ox, as he made his way to the spring. The stag ran freely through the woods with his flock of hinds, while great numbers of does grazed in the meadowlands; but plentiful hordes of wolves, too, roamed in pursuit of their prey through the forest and the open country.

High in the sunny sky above the comb of the forest uplands sailed the king of all birds, the golden eagle, and all his kin. Among the rocks and the woods nested countless birds of prey, the kite and the falcon, merlin and sparrow-hawk and all the family of the hawks, and all the lesser birds of prey, with the owl and the eagle-owl.

Brooks, rivers and lakes teemed with fish, and the otter, a dweller in the dim recesses of the ancient alders and willows overgrown with wild hops, had good hunting, while the beaver laboured undisturbed at his skilful building.

To the voice of the winds and the rustling of the trees, brooks murmured and rivers roared, and in their white sand the sun picked out gleaming grains of pure gold.

The depths of the earth were still untouched, as no-one had yet broken in to them to tear out their treasures of ores and precious metals.

Everywhere strength and wealth ran riot. The earth, generous and fruitful, waited only for an industrious people who would make use of her rich gifts.

And they came, and cultivated the uncultivated; they mastered her by hard, laborious toil, and made her holy by their sweat and blood, which they shed later in many a war in defence of their work and tongue, and the land they had tamed.

Out of the maternal regions of the Slav lands came these people, our ancestors, with their leader Czech.

Come, then, let's begin their story.

The Story of Czech

I

Beyond the Tatras, in the plains along the river Vistula, extended from time immemorial the land of the Croats, a part of the original great fatherland of the Slavs.

In this Croatian land lived a numerous race, similar in language, code and manner of life.

And it happened that there arose among them quarrels and bloody wars about boundaries and villages. Tribe took arms against tribe, cousin fought against cousin, and they destroyed one another.

At this time two brothers of a powerful family, both chieftains, Czech and Lech, decided that they would abandon this native country of theirs, so beset by wars. They said to themselves: 'We'll go and seek out for ourselves new settlements, where our tribe can live in peace and attend to its work.'

From the times of their forebears they had already been accustomed to till the soil diligently, to cultivate all kinds of grains, and keep horses, and herds of cattle and other stock.

As they had resolved, so they did. Calling together their kinsfolk they made sacrifice to the gods, took up the images of their forefathers, and bidding farewell to their native soil, turned towards the setting sun, into unknown regions. One tribe followed behind another, every one of the numerous families, with all their friends and relations. In front went the scouts and bodies of armed men, in the midst the chieftain Czech, an old, grey-bearded man but still strong and stalwart, his brother Lech, and around them the rulers and the elders of the tribes, all on horseback. Behind these came the old men, women and children, either in rough carts or on horseback, and the herds of cattle, and more armed men brought up the rear. Thus they passed first through regions inhabited by tribes akin to them, until they crossed the farthest frontiers of the Croat land, forded the river Oder, and came into mountain country which was unknown to them.

There they still found some settlements where the people spoke as they did, and even beyond there were still traces of their tongue, in the country bordering the river Elbe.

Before they crossed the second river they found the land more deserted, and saw only very few villages. They lay widely scattered from one another, and their inhabitants spoke a foreign tongue and were dressed in skins. They were few in numbers, but bold and courageous, and they blocked the way of the strangers with weapons in their hands. Czech and Lech and their company conquered them, destroying their poor dwellings, in rough huts or in holes dug out of the ground, and they continued their advance, passing from forest to forest.

It was a harsh journey they undertook through the deep thickets, a laborious march by grasslands and swamps full of reeds, timothy grass, great clumps of mosses and various bushes. In the evenings they kindled a fire and kept it fed until dawn, so that its glow, striking deep into the forest darkness, might frighten away the cunning and ferocious beasts of prey.

So they came to the third great river, the Vltava, where it flowed through this wilderness; and when they had forded this river, too, all the company began to complain that there was no end to this toilsome journey, and no permanent resting-place for them anywhere.

Then the chieftain Czech pointed to a high mountain, which loomed before them blue above the broad expanse of the plain, and said:

'Come, let us go as far as the foot of that mountain, and there the children and the flocks can rest.' So they did, and made camp at the foot of the mount, to which they gave the name of Říp. The chieftains and the tribal elders examined the soil around them and saw that it was fertile. In the morning at first light Czech arose and made his way, he alone, through the silent forest still full of the night's darkness, to the very crest of Říp.

When he emerged on the summit of the mountain it was morning; and behold, before him lay outstretched a vast open landscape, extending as far as eye could

see, level and clear right to the blue mountains, forest and heath, fields and meadows. Through its verdant green the rivers wound gleaming like spilled silver.

And forefather Czech rejoiced over this pleasant and lovely land, and meditated as he looked upon it how the gods had granted it to his people, and how the future generations of his tribe would make their home here.

When he came down from the mountain he proclaimed what he had seen. The next day many of the people went out round about the hill to view all the surrounding country. And what they saw pleased them well: waters full of fish, a fruitful soil, every aspect of this land; and they agreed that it was suitable for settlement.

The third day, therefore, when the sun began to rise over the forests, Czech called his brother and the elders, and bade them summon all the people. Climbing with them to a point from which they could look out over the country, he spoke to them thus:

'Now you will complain no more, for we have found a land where we can halt our march and found our settlements. Look, this is that land for which you have been searching. Often have I spoken of it to you, and promised that I would lead you into it. This is that promised land, teeming with beast and bird, flowing with milk and honey. Here you will have an abundance of all, and it will provide us a firm defence against our enemies. Behold, such a country as you have desired! All it lacks is a name. Consider, then, with what name it should be named.'

'Yours! Let it bear your name!' cried out an old man with a long white beard, the oldest of all the elders. His cry rang out as though inspired by the gods, and immediately everyone, elders and people together, shouted aloud as with one voice:

'Yours! Your name!'

'Let it be called after you!'

Gratified by the wish of the whole people, Czech fell on his knees and kissed the earth, the new homeland of his seed. And having kissed it, he rose, deeply moved, and raising his hands cried out a blessing over the wide landscape:

'All hail, sacred land, promised to us! Guard and cherish us, keep us from illness and injury, and multiply us from nation to nation to all eternity!'

Then joyfully he laid upon the ground the images of the forefathers, which they had brought with them from their first homeland wrapped in a white veil, and kindled a great fire. And in gratitude and for a blessing they offered up a burnt offering, and rejoiced together every one.

Then there followed hard and strenuous labour. When they had divided up the land they began to cultivate it. Where there was thick forest they felled it, or destroyed it with fire, clearing large areas, the grassland and meadows they dug, and the second year they began to break up the soil with the plough.

At once they also set to work to build dwellings of wood, roofed with straw. Each tribe set up its own houses apart, on its own land.

Gardens, fields and meadows composed a village, the communal property of all the families of one tribe, and to these were added forests, pastures, rivers and lakes for all to share. To one village, one tribe.

Their dwellings, with the cowsheds and stables, with sheds and yards behind them in the enclosure of fences plaited from wands or built with wooden beams, they grouped about a circular village green. Year by year the fields around the settlement increased, and year by year the earth yielded a richer harvest. Rye, wheat, barley, oats and millet rippled in thick growth over the broad acres. Above them in clearer green shone the strips of supple flax and tall hemp, beside the beds full of vari-coloured poppies.

The meadows and lime-woods trembled with the humming of bees, for in addition to the wild swarms in the forests the people kept them in straw hives, or in wooden ones hollowed out of old tree-trunks. Every year the herds of cattle and sheep and pigs increased, and in the paddocks where the mares grazed, within the enclosure of the village, lively foals played and beautiful fillies cropped the grass.

An elected headman ruled the members of the clan and their property. In the name of the clan he began and ended the prayers, offered sacrifices, welcomed guests, settled disputes arising within the tribe, and allotted every man his share of the work. Everyone had his own task, everyone his own trade. The women looked after the households, spun, wove linen and cloth, sewed dresses and other garments: tunics, gowns for both women and men, trousers, cloaks, furs and fur-lined coats.

The men pastured the flocks and herds and protected them from wild beasts, worked in the fields, hunted and coursed the wild animals in the forests, thinning their numbers on principle with arrows, lances, snares and pit-traps, into which they trapped wolves which worried the flocks most.

The scene was lively and busy both in the villages and out in the fields. From the pastures rose the music of whistles, or the long shepherd's pipe, in the fields and meadows and orchards rang out the songs of the young folk at work. Only at the hour of midday, in the time of the deepest silence, no-one ventured to sing outside. For then the witches of noon came out and drifted in their white veils like a pale shadow across the plain to human dwellings, to the danger of unguarded children. The ugly wild women roamed abroad, with great heads and eyes on different levels, bewitching men into frenzied weeping; and the graceful wood-nymphs appeared with wreaths on their golden hair, their slender forms swathed in white draperies. Of these the people went in dread, as they did of the wood-witches that lull people to sleep and steal their eyes, and of the wandering souls in the wan blue flames that drift on fens and marshes. And in terror they passed by the lake or the woodland pool, where in the shadow of ancient trees and bushes the water-goblin lay in wait, changing his shape at will, and where the pale water-nymphs in their green gowns lured men to destruction.

But most of all they feared Perun, the lord of the thunder, and his lightning, 'the messenger of the god', and other powerful demons which weaken the human body, soften the bones and darken the mind. They prayed to them, they brought gifts to the wells, black hens or doves. They offered sacrifices in particular to Veles, so that he would protect the herds from sickness, and give them his blessing.

In the enclosure of the villages they could be more at ease. Here their dwellings were protected by the domestic gods, the forefathers, the souls of the ancestors, whose images stood in a consecrated place beside the hearth. The mischievous gnome, too, a little godling with claws on hands and feet, brought luck to the house, and so did the imp who guarded the farm and watched and fed the stock, though in the night he disturbed the sleep of the household. And while the domestic snake, the familiar spirit still brooded under the oven or beneath the threshold, luck and blessing would not desert the dwellers or the dwelling.

When the leaves fell in the autumn and thick mists shrouded the countryside, when the earth was motionless under frost and the snow covered all the land, the families gathered in spacious rooms with beamed roofs and closed shutters.

The great stone oven kept them warm, and the fire on the hearth gave them light. Its red glow flickered over the walls, where hung shields covered with dark, stretched hides, nets, bows, wooden quivers sheathed in badger-hide, short swords, powerful lances and heavy stone maces, where the antlers of stags and the horns of bison cast crooked shadows over the walls.

By this wavering light the women spun, the men repaired their tools and farm implements, sharpened their weapons or rested after their strenuous hunting. And there was talk then, many and varied tales to tell, and old songs to sing. The hunters told of combats with bear and bison, or of wild, hairy men who were scarcely ever seen themselves, but led other people astray and set them wandering into the forest solitudes and swamps, so that many a hunter thus deluded had never returned from the woods.

Or an old man with snowy hair and white beard would wander in memory back to the distant regions of his first homeland, remembering the disputes and battles of those early times, the stout heroes, the mighty chieftain, and how he would rise at midnight before a battle and go out from his army and begin to howl like a wolf, and how suddenly a wolf would echo his howling, and then many wolves would join the cry.

And then the talk would be of strange apparitions and visions in the darkness of the night, in marshes, in the open fields or the forest solitudes, of fire-birds passing like flame through the dark night, of evil witches guarding the water of life and death, of white fates appearing at the cradles of new-born children, of enchantresses, of good and evil omens; and in holy dread they would all listen to the secret prophecies of the clan and the race.

When the fire had burned out they lay down on beds spread with skins, committing the village with prayer to the guardianship of the ancestors, whose spirits brooded with watchful care over the lands and dwellings of their descendants.

The village in its enclosure of fences, covered deep in snow, grew silent in the deserted night; only the barking of the wakeful dogs echoed into the distance as often as they caught the scent of a wolf on the prowl, light green eyes gleaming. Now and then an otter would whistle briefly from the river.

In this season of snow and ice, of long twilights and longer nights Morana held sway, until the god of the sun began to shine upon the face of the earth with a warmth more prolonged and more friendly. Then the fetters of ice broke and dispersed from the face of the water; and then there was rejoicing in every village and every heart. With exultant song they made their way to the water, to brooks and rivers now running freely, cast into them the image of winter and death, and with a joyful outcry welcomed Vesna, the lovely goddess of spring.

When the sun in his course stood at the zenith, shining upon broad acres waving with growing corn, and meadows shimmering with flowers, the people everywhere celebrated the sacred festival of the solstice. The night preceding the longest day was full of wonders for them. Flowers sprinkled with its dew acquired magical properties of prophecy and healing, and were a protection, like wormwood, the mother of all herbs, against demons and evil spirits which were particularly formidable on this secret night, and also against witches, who swarmed on the hilltops and in their obscure dens. In the half-darkness of this night great fires glowed on the hills and peaks. Their light gleamed far into the distance, and far into the distance drifted the songs of the garlanded virgins and youths who danced round them, praising the strength and power of god's sun, the giver of life, and of love which is the sun of life.

After the summer solstice came the harvest, then the cool autumn followed, and on its heels came winter. Year flowed after year. The clans increased, the seed of Czech multiplied. Distant tidings had drawn after them new groups of settlers from their first fatherland, so that the tract of country on which they had first settled was no longer great enough to support all of them. So the clans divided, new generations moved away on every side, towards midnight and midday, rise and set of sun, along the rivers and the mountains, and founded new settlements.

And they built castles and fortresses for their headmen and chiefs, as defences at the frontiers, and for protection generally, especially in order to provide a safe shelter for the women and children and the old men, and a place where they could drive in the herds and flocks if an enemy should invade their land. They chose the sites for their castles on spurs of land by rivers, or in the plain among the forests, among waters and swamps, so that there should be no way of approach to them but by one narrow causeway of faggots. Round the site they constructed high circular ramparts, often three-fold, with vast parapets built of hard logs, and with tall strong-points at intervals along them and guarding the gates.

The chieftain Lech, Czech's younger brother, had a great and numerous tribe, and he, too, resolved to move on farther towards the rising sun. Czech and all his people were reluctant to let him go. But they took leave of Lech with a friendly blessing, and begged him not to go too far from them, for if some danger should ever threaten him from an enemy he might look to them to come to his aid like his own clan.

Lech said to them:

'Oh, my dear brothers and sons, and you men of the Czech lands! Never will I forget that I am of your stock. Therefore I have no will to go so far from you that you should receive no tidings of me, nor I of you. I will give you a sign, so that you may know in what regions we have settled. On the third day after our departure go up on to the summit of Říp, before the day breaks. At that hour I will light a great fire in the forest, and where you see afar the blaze of the fire and the smoke of the burning, there you may know I have taken up my abode.'

When, therefore, on the agreed day before dawn they climbed to the summit of Říp and looked all round them, they saw in the hazy distance between the points of sunrise and midday a red glow, penetrating the thick twilight and spreading across the sky. As the day broke, they saw in that same direction black clouds forming beneath the glowing sky, the smoke of the enormous fire which the chieftain and his tribe had kindled. In those parts Lech remained and settled, and at once began to build a castle there, surrounded with great ramparts; and because of this smoke-sign, they say, they named it Kouřím, that is, the Castle of Smoke.

III

Almost thirty years had passed since the time when the chieftain Czech had entered into the Czech lands. And when the old man reached his eighty-sixth year the tale of his days was completed, and he died. They held a solemn funeral ceremony over him, and all lamented him crying:

'You were our chieftain and our father, you led us into this land, you were a true and faithful guardian to your household and all your kin. Alas, alas for us, who will rule and protect us now?'

There was not one among them who did not grieve for his death. His soul had departed into paradise, so they believed, into the realms of eternal spring, there to live on with all the honour and dignity to which the dead man had been accustomed on earth among his own people. Therefore they clothed his dead body in new garments, a draped cloak, a gown girdled with a broad belt gleaming with little chains and ornaments of metal, trousers dyed in a fine colour, and slippers. On his head, with its long white hair and long white beard, they placed a splendid cap of sable.

Before evening they set the corpse, dressed like this, on a tall pyre, having first draped the top of the wood with embroidered cloths. The pyre was built in a woodland grove darkened by old, bushy limes and oaks, close to the meeting of three roads for the repose of his soul. Then they brought mead and fruit and fragrant herbs and laid them beside him. They brought also a loaf of bread, with meat and a bow, and set them before him, and brought his arms, lance and sword, mace and black shield, and laid all these by his side. And when they had killed a cock and a hen and thrown them on to the pyre, the closest relative of the dead chieftain approached, kindled a brand of wood, and holding it in his right hand, drew near to the pyre, walking backwards. Until he had fired it he kept his left hand behind him. Then, when the wood had caught fire, the others drew near with burning pine-flares, and threw them into the pyre.

As the strong wind drew them, the flames crackled and blazed high, and the smoke rolled upwards until it obscured the majestic figure of the dead chieftain, enthroned for the last time before a gathering of his people. And all about him they wept and lamented, and the women sang songs of mourning.

As the pyre burned out they gathered the bones and the ashes, and placed them in an urn, and laid it, together with the ornaments and weapons of the dead man, in a grave; and over the grave they raised a monument, a tall round barrow. When they returned from the funeral through the dark wood at the hour of twilight, they gathered stones and twigs and leaves from the earth and threw them back over their heads, and no-one looked back as he did so.

And when, long afterwards, they revisited that place and that barrow, they wept and bowed down, blessing their chieftain; and his name was handed down from generation to generation.

As long as the chieftain Czech ruled over the land, order and discipline held sway everywhere. The people were honest and loyal to one another. They had no bolts on the cowsheds, and they never barred their doors. There was no crime they looked upon as more grave than theft and robbery. Every man was provided for within his clan, and no-one could be reduced to poverty except he who would not work, and was exiled from his tribe as a result.

But when the people, after the death of Czech, were left without a ruler, they fell into bad ways. Disputes and quarrels arose, usually over boundaries and village property, oppression and violence broke out, and many among them began to fight among themselves. And when this evil state of affairs spread from day to day, the elders of the tribes met together at Czech's burial mound, and paying homage to the memory of the dead, said to one another:

'We'll look for a chieftain who will rule over us, and give judgement according to law.'

They decided that they would send to Lech, the brother of Czech, and ask him to be chief over the people. But Lech had decided not to remain long at the castle of Kouřím, so he refused; but he recommended to them as ruler and judge the headman of a powerful clan, whose name was Krok. This man lived at the castle which was named after him, among the forests above the river Mže, not far from the village of Zbečno. Not only was he well endowed with goods and gear, but in wisdom and wit he excelled above all others, so that not only from his own clan but from all the villages in the surrounding countryside men came hurrying to him like bees to a hive, to ask for his judgements. So the people listened to Lech's advice, and with one voice chose Krok to be judge and leader of the whole race.

Seating him on a chair above the grave of Czech, they placed Czech's cap upon his head; the staff which their old chieftain had carried they laid in his hand, and did reverence to him.

In the meantime Lech had sent out messengers into the regions towards the rising sun, to look for a new country. When they returned they announced that beyond the mountains, beyond the river Oder, they had seen a vast open country, fertile and uninhabited by man. Lech, hearing how they praised this land, took his leave of Krok, and gathering his family and his companions about him, made his way into the regions indicated by the messengers. And there he settled and remained, and built the castle of Hnězdno, that is, the Place of Nests, so named because of the great numbers of eagles' nests he found there, and the castle of Krakow, which he named after his son.

From this time on, Krok ruled the Czech land, and gave judgement for his people and taught them wisdom. As chieftain he had his seat at Budeč. In his reign there was a school at this place, where instruction was given in the service of the gods, in the old songs, and in prophecy and the magic arts. In those days sorcery was held to be the highest of the arts, and he was held in esteem as a distinguished person and dear to the gods who could boast of possessing the spirit of prophecy. The wise Krok was among those who could see with the eye of his mind into the darkness of the ages.

Once, when he wished to gaze into the events of the past and the future, he ordered that for the space of three days no-one should be admitted to his presence. When he was alone he entered into the spacious hall of his fortress at Budeč, and having prayed, made offerings to the gods of the forests, mountains and waters. It was that secret and holy night of summer when fires blazed on all the hills and peaks, and through the quietness the winds carried abroad the songs of the young men and maidens.

Krok prayed, and invoked all the gods and spirits to answer him and give him knowledge of things to come. And he learned much in that time of his prophetic inspiration, and these secret omens, both bright and dark, he inscribed on birch bark and kept for his daughters. Then he called in his nobles and headmen, and told them one of the things which the inspiration of the gods had caused to be drawn out of the darkness of the future to illuminate his mind and consciousness.

'This place,' he said, 'shall no longer be my abode, for Budeč will not suffice, nor will it long endure. We must seek out another dwelling place.'

To this they all agreed, and Krok, summoning his messengers at once, ordered them:

'Tomorrow before sunrise ride out from here, and set your course between the noon and the rise of sun until you come to the river Vltava. There seek, until the gods lead you to the suitable place.'

So they went as he had ordered, and searched in those regions, until they

stood on the right bank of the Vltava, on a rocky spur among thick forests. Through the azure twilight flowed the quiet flood of the broad river, in which was mirrored the high rock on which the envoys stood fronting the setting sun, and the grassy meadows on the opposite shore, and the dark groves above them on the steep slopes of the hills.

Beneath these slopes the river flowed on, turning to the east, and its rapids murmured and roared aloud there in the deep silence of the primeval forests. As the envoys looked round them at the rocky spur and the wooded countryside the gods touched them, and they all cried aloud on the rock with one voice:

'This is the place appointed!'

So also said Krok and all the elders, when they came there on swift horses to examine the spot and its surroundings. And there they built a castle, the master-work of the carpenters, from mighty logs of old oak and pine, a dwelling with vast halls supported by mighty columns, and quiet, retired rooms, a spacious castle with courtyards, and a place of assembly for councils or gatherings of the people when they met to sacrifice to the gods, or to enthrone their chieftain, or to listen to his judgements and decrees.

Where the sheer rock did not protect the site they dug out deep ditches for the defence of their castle, and surrounded it with earthworks raised by a rampart of beams and by strong towers. With similar towers they fortified the gate-house enclosing the heavy gate, which was bolted with a great beam of wood.

In the forest only a little way from the castle, beneath old beech-trees, gushed forth a strong spring, from which flowed a plentiful supply of clear water. They named this spring Jezerka, and the castle that stood on the high rock they called Vyšehrad, that is to say, the lofty castle. This castle became celebrated and sacred through all the tribes of the Czech people, and the legend of its founding travelled through the neighbouring tribes, and reached even the regions where a foreign tongue was spoken.

With all ceremony they led Krok and his family into the castle, and paid great honour to him, for they loved their wise chieftain, under whose rule blessing had returned to the entire country. On all sides they could see the daily work going forward in peace. Lance and arrow and all other weapons made war on no enemy but the beasts of prey. The people cultivated the soil industriously, felling and burning the forests so that the fields and villages were always on the increase.

Everywhere there was plenty, both in the barns and in the sheds and stables; peace remained inviolate as long as Krok governed the land, and that was more than twenty-three years.

When he went to his fathers, the entire people mourned for him. His ashes and his arms they laid in a grave beside the barrow of Czech. The wise judge left after him three daughters: Kazi, Teta and Libuše. Their tender youth had been spent at Budeč, where they had learned wisdom with other maidens and youths of their clan, and with some also from other clans, like the young Přemysl of the Stadice family.

Both then and thereafter the daughters of Krok excelled their companions and all others, as slender lilies surpass the flowers of the meadow; in wisdom they outshone all, and in nobility of mind and grace of face and form, for they were tall and beautiful, and the admiration of all who beheld them.

Of these three, Kazi knew all the herbs and plants and their properties. By means of them she could heal many and diverse sicknesses; more, with a mere word she could subdue pain, laying a blessing on the sufferer in the name of powerful gods and spirits. With her word of power and the magic of her blessing she often compelled even the fates to bow to her will, and returned life to those who had already drawn their last breath. After her father's death she took up her abode for the most part in a castle which stood on the mountain of Osek near the river Mže, and it was called after her the castle of Kazín.

The second daughter was Teta, who as the name tells founded Tetín, a very strong castle on the summit of a steep rock above the river Mže. Fearing the gods and demons, she was tireless in performing the ceremonies in their honour, and she taught the people also to do reverence to them and make the various sacrifices as due. She herself often ascended the mountain of Pohled, above Tetín, at sunset, and there she prayed to a frowning idol set upon a rock beneath ancient oaktrees, and often burned sacrifices there, either by day or in the deep of the twilight.

But the daughter whom all the people regarded with the greatest devotion was Libuše, although in years she was the youngest. She was so graceful, so chaste of body, so warm and friendly and yet so grave in her manner, so firm and prudent in speech, that even the rough and turbulent men subdued their voices and tempered their words when she passed by in her loveliness, and even old men, experienced and jaded by age, praised her, saying:

'She is more lovely than her mother, and wiser than her father.'

And with holy dread they spoke of her, saying that she burned into ecstasy, that her face and her eyes were transfigured, when the spirit of prophecy kindled in her, when she gazed into the twilight of the future, and saw the shape of things to come.

After the death of Krok, the noblemen and headmen and the assembly of the people met in a sacred grove by the spring Jezerka. The daughters of Krok also came there to the meeting. Beneath the shade of the old beeches, limes and oaks, the elders of the clans and their people all agreed as one man, without any dispute, that the sovereignty should remain in the family of Krok, in the person of his youngest daughter, Libuše.

The ancient wood rang with the joyful shout of acclaim, and the roar of the people's voice carried as far as the river and into the darkness of the forests. With rejoicings they led the young princess, garlanded and flushed with emotion, from Jezerka to holy Vyšehrad. Beside her walked Kazi and Teta, her sisters, and their maidens, before them and behind went the stalwart nobles and headmen of the clans, distinguished by blood and repute.

Leading Libuše into the great courtyard of the chieftain's castle, they seated her upon a stone chair beneath a spreading lime-tree, where her father, the wise judge and ruler, had sat. The young princess had her own castle, called after her Libušín, which she had founded and built beside the forest which extended as far as the village of Zbečno. But from the time of her enthronement she took her seat at Vyšehrad, and from there she ruled all the people with wisdom.

In the fortress of Vyšehrad, Libuše's sovereign seat, there was a green garden, embelished with all manner of trees and shrubs and rare flowers. But strange to relate, all its paths were winding and deceitful; they twined in various directions, wound confusedly on themselves, met and separated among the bushes, beneath the trees and between the flowers and lawns, all so similar in appearance that a stranger in this enchanted garden, full of secret corners and places deceptively alike, would not be able to find his way out.

In this garden Libuše loved to linger with her maidens, but still more frequently she walked there alone, in the morning when every flower and leaf glistened with dew in the sunrise, or towards evening, when the trunks of the trees flamed with the red glow of the sunset, or when later their crowns and thickets darkened in the twilight, and the pale paths were lost in deep shadow.

In such an hour the young princess, her tall figure draped in a white robe, her hair flowing freely, seemed herself a pale shade, walking with a slow and grave step, or standing with her lovely face upturned to the sky, as though lost in a dream in the silent glimmering of stars or moon.

And here one day she brought her sister Kazi, who had ridden from Kazín on a swift horse to pay her a visit. The garden, the lawns and the pathways already lay in shadow, only the tops of the trees, the rampart of great beams and the tall towers which surrounded the scene in the background, darkened by the weathering of rain and sleet, were flooded with the radiance of the last light. The sun had sunk into the dark forests drowned in bluish mists on the hills beyond the Vltava. In the calm and silence of this hour a sudden clamour burst forth at the gate. The sound of it carried as far as the princess's garden, growing ever clearer and louder. The shouting of men drew near like an abrupt storm. Through the hubbub of strong, resonant voices penetrated a shout of triumph, and on that sign someone blew a long blast on a horn. The call of victory rang from the instrument, and resounded through the length and breadth of the castle with a joyous clangour.

The sisters, startled as they talked together, stood listening. And in a moment the castellan came rushing in to them in great excitement, and begged them to come and see what was happening in the courtyard.

There, through the great open space, accompanied by a shouting procession of the castle guard and many other people, strode a stalwart young man, his hands clapped to the nape of his neck as he carried some heavy burden. His flushed, sunburned face was bent forward, and from beneath his cap, tumbling about his cheeks and forehead, fell a flood of dark, curly hair.

The princesses stared at him in astonishment, and gasped to see his burden: a great wild boar, alive, which he grasped by its pointed ears and bore on his back, belly upwards.

This young huntsman, without a spear, and with his sword still thrust into its sheath in his broad belt, his shoes fouled with mud and his close-fitting breeches all streaked with mire, carried this frightful load as though it had been a small saddle-bag. He walked firmly and confidently, his legs did not tremble under him nor did his step falter.

All round him young men and old were shouting with exultation, and pointing their fingers and spears at the old, powerful 'reaper', bristling reddish brown, with a gigantic head and a black muzzle, from which jutted the terrible tusks, curved and gleaming. The boar heaved and struggled, kicking with his black hooves, gnashing his teeth, while his bloodshot eyes rolled in fury.

All the shouting throng fell silent when they saw Libuše and Kazi. The bold huntsman, who was Bivoj, the son of Sudivoj, halted at the foot of the steps which mounted between thick columns before the door of the great hall.

On these steps stood the princesses. Bivoj at the head of his attendant train, the ferocious beast on his back, greeted Libuše and her sister, and said:

'Here I bring you this evil beast that has done us so much injury, the wild boar of the mountain of Kavka. If it's your will, he shall die before your eyes.'

When Libuše assented with a gesture, all the men cried out and seized their swords and lances. But Bivoj cried above their clamour:

'I shall stand against him alone. I caught him, let me also kill him. You form a circle in case he should try to break away. And first, lay a spear at my feet.'

As he said, so they did. The men took their stand in a wide circle all around, weapons in hand. Not a man among them took his eyes from Bivoj, who gazed all round him, and at last fixed his shining eyes on the princesses who stood on the steps above him. He looked at Libuše, but longer yet at her sister, who was gazing in excitement at this gallant young man. She had seen him for the first time in the wood by the spring Jezerka, and had often thought of him since. Now she delighted in his manliness, his strength and audacity, yet her heart contracted with dread and she blinked involuntarily as Bivoj, straddling his legs, heaved the boar with all his strength over his head before him, so that the ground shook and echoed to the impact. But before the boar had struck the earth Bivoj had stooped, and snatching up the heavy spear with its glittering point, grasped it firmly in both hands and crouched waiting.

The old, formidable 'reaper' lay sprawled on the ground for a moment as though stunned. Then his belly heaved, the comb of long bristles on his back stood up like a mane, the whites of the eyes in the black mask gleamed. In a flash he bounded from the earth, and blind with rage, looking neither to right nor left, with sharp tusks jutting white from his gaping jowl, he flew like an arrow straight at Bivoj.

All around there fell an awed silence as the wild boar made his frenzied onslaught. But then came sudden cries from among the men, and from the women and children of the castle household. The men shouted and waved their weapons, as the boar flew full on to Bivoj's spear. A stream of blood poured from the beast's gaping maw; he reared up for the last time, and then crashed to the earth as though mown down before the scythe. Blood flowed from him, and flooded the ground around him.

Bivoj tugged out the spear from his defeated foe, and set his right foot on the body of the dying beast. Then he wiped the sweat from his brow and cheeks, and said to the princesses:

'Now he'll terrify no more of our people, and do us no more injury!' and he stamped on the boar's head.

The sturdy castellan, approaching him before the princesses, said to him:

'The gods give you greeting! You have delivered the countryside. This was a wicked beast, a killer, six years old. And dangerous,' said he, pointing to the dead boar, 'a terror and a menace all about the mountain of Kavka. The damage he has done! To the corn—he's rooted up whole acres of grain—and to our animals, especially the huntsmen's dogs and the horses. When Božej's Svatoslav rode out after him, this "reaper" here ripped up his horse. He's given more than one man his death-wound, too. He was a terror to everybody. Even the men ran and hid from him. Until Bivoj here—'

Before he could conclude, all the throng present shouted aloud joyfully in praise and gratitude. And the princesses, descending the steps, gazed at the fearsome beast, and Libuše asked the young man how he had hunted him, and how he had caught him thus. Then there was silence. Kazi fixed her eyes upon the gallant huntsman, radiant with ardour, and listened breathlessly to all that Bivoj had to tell.

'It vexed and angered me that this beast should do us so much harm, and that everyone was afraid of him. No-one was even willing to go through the valley by the mountain of Kavka any longer. That was where he had his den, solitary as he was, there he lay in wait and stood against all comers, and there he's gored and torn men and horses and hounds without number. I tracked him out where he buried himself in his lair, and through a dark mud-hole under old beech-trees. He came there at noon to wade and roll. Then, when the gnats bit him badly, he scrubbed himself against the trunks of the oaks and went off to pasture in the fields boldly and openly. He never avoided any man, he attacked every one.

'So today I prepared for him. I intended to lie in wait until he returned from the pasture. But I'd no more than reached the edge of the valley when he burst out of a thicket opposite to me, suddenly and unexpectedly, and so quickly that I never had time to level my spear. It was in an open place; not a tree anywhere near. I couldn't jump aside in time, and I was loath to throw myself on the ground.

'In less time than it takes me to tell it, he was on me and had taken my legs from under me, and he immediately tossed his head round; but before he could

34

swing it back to rip me up with a long wound, I seized him by the ears. And I held him fast and wouldn't let him go. He grunted and jerked and struggled like a demon, and gnashed his teeth. But I hoisted him on my shoulders, and hurried back here with him.'

The shouts of joy and acclaim rang round the circle again; when it was quiet the young princess spoke graciously to Bivoj:

'The gods have blessed you and your strength. You have set our land free from a plague, and saved our fields from further damage. Accept my thanks, and the thanks of all. Now, brave huntsman, come and rest your weary limbs, take your ease and refresh yourself.'

37

She beckoned to the steward, and he took Bivoj and led him up the staircase into the great hall, and after them streamed the foremost of the men of the castle, and those from the village under the castle, and those who had encountered Bivoj on his way to Vyšehrad, and, unwilling to leave him, had accompanied him there with his strange, living burden.

The hall was not lofty, but very large. A single giant rafter stretched along the full length of the beamed ceiling, which was supported by great columns wonderfully carved and painted. On the columns hung here the antlers of an elk, or weapons and shields, there the horns of bison, or the unusually large pelt of a bear. The men sat down round heavy tables and logs hewn from centuries-old oaks, but first they led Bivoj to the foremost table in the right-hand corner of the hall.

On all the tables stood great jugs of mead, and they poured out from them the golden-yellow liquor into goblets and cups of earthenware and wood. The company drank and drank again to Bivoj and his strength. The young hero listened with pleasure to this chorus of praise; but secretly his gaze turned to the low, heavy door with the wooden lock, through which the Princess Libuše had left the hall with her sister. It was of Kazi that Bivoj was thinking, even in the flush and tumult of his triumph, and in his heart he was wondering whether he would be able to see her once again.

In the crowns of the trees, on the ramparts and the high towers, the glow of rose and gold had faded. Deep shadow shrouded the courtyard. But into the windows of the hall, which lay higher, the soft light of the long summer twilight fell through open shutters and shone upon the young princesses, as they entered again by the same door from the darkness beyond the columns. A maiden of their retinue carried in after them something wrapped in a dressed skin; and when at Libuše's command she unwrapped her bundle upon the table it was to reveal a beautiful, glittering belt. It was broad, with red straps, ornamented with embroidery and covered with small, hammered silver studs, embossed with bronze ornaments and decked with a shining chain, which jingled against the fine metalwork every time the belt moved.

The young princess offered it to Bivoj, bidding him take it as a reward. It came, she said, from her father's treasury, and her sister Kazi had herself chosen it for him.

'Sewn into this belt is a sprig of a powerful herb, and the tooth of a snake,' added Kazi graciously. 'If you walk in the forests in this belt you will never go astray, even in the darkest night, you will always escape the power of the wandering root, and be safe from witches and all the spectres of the night.'

The young hero bowed to the princesses; he bowed and gave thanks, and

38

all the men present hailed Libuše and Kazi for paying such just tribute to manly strength and courage. The princesses left the hall, and once again the joy and merriment of all broke forth, and they made merry until night came. Then, when the men dispersed after a rich feast of meat and drink, the steward of the castle led Bivoj to a quiet chamber and a bed laid with sheepskin. The young hero fell asleep, and slept soundly until morning.

When the next day dawned, Bivoj prepared to set out on his journey home to his own village, of which he was the thane. When the steward heard that he was preparing for departure, he told him that there was a horse waiting for him, saddled for him at the order of the princess, and that at the same time Kazi was also setting out on her journey back to her own castle. His hips girt with the shining belt he had received as a gift the previous evening, Bivoj made his reverence to the princess and thanked her. Then, all fresh and vigorous in his youth, he mounted a lively brown horse with a gleaming coat, and joined the retinue of her sister.

In the gateway he looked back once again, and he and all the company gazed up at the beam above the gate, from which jutted the vast severed head of the wild boar Bivoj had slain. There it hung black and bristling, the great muzzle glistening with the white tusks, to keep in mind the strength of Bivoj. Nor did Kazi leave the hero to ride among her train. For a great part of the journey he rode by her side, and when they came to the parting of their ways, without a thought for himself he abandoned his own way and continued in hers, until they came to her castle, its mighty ramparts mirrored in the river Mže.

Before the autumn was past Bivoj forsook his village and his clan to remain for ever at the castle of Kazín. For Kazi liked him so much that she took him as her husband.

Concerning Libuše

As once to her father Krok, so now the people from far and near came to Libuše when they had any disputes to be settled. They made haste to her wisdom to ask for judgement. And she in her wisdom judged impartially, holding a just balance between the opposing sides. At that time it happened that two neighbours, both headmen of clans, had a dispute about boundaries and fields. They quarrelled violently, hurling insults, until the goodwill due between neighbours died out between them and their clans, and hatred grew up in its place.

Neither of them wanted to give way in this dispute, each of them remained hard as flint, and when the time came for the princess to sit in judgement, both of them went hurrying off to Vyšehrad.

40

There Libuše, with a white wreath about her brow, sat in judgement beneath the spreading lime-tree, on a raised throne draped with a fine carpet. On her right hand and on her left were twelve jurors, husbandmen of the most powerful clans, distinguished men and already white-bearded. Before them all the open space around held a great throng of people, retainers of the household and men, women and children who had come there to seek justice, or to stand as witnesses for someone from their own clan.

Before the princess and the court arose the two quarrelsome neighbours. The younger complained bitterly that the elder wished to take possession of certain fields and boundaries without right. The elder, a man with a thick, full beard and a face lowering like a storm-cloud, interrupted his speech violently. Brusquely and sharply he desired and demanded that the matter should be decided according to his will, and he cared little whether it would injure his neighbour or no.

When Libuše had heard both of them and considered the case, she announced her finding to the chief of the jurymen; and when the jury had pondered among themselves both the dispute and the decision and agreed to her findings, the princess formally announced what she held to be the rights of the case: that an injury was being done to the younger man, that the fields with their headlands belonged by right to him.

Before she had finished speaking the elder, shaken by a gust of rage, struck the ground three times with his long staff and flushed dark red, and with flashing eyes shouted and cursed, bursting out like a sudden thunderstorm:

'So this is your law! But we know who did the judging —a woman! A woman with long hair but short wits. Women can spin and sew, that we grant, but not give judgements. Let her tend to her spinning and sewing, and leave the law alone. Shame on us men!' And he beat his head with his fists, and in the thick passion of his speech saliva ran down and stained his beard.

'Shame on us! Where else, look in what lands you will, where else does a woman rule over men? Only here, only us! We are a by-word for it, a jest. Better be dead than submit to such rule!'

Every man within hearing froze at such wild speech. The deep red of shame stained the princess's cheeks, and her heart was filled with bitter offence and grief over such ingratitude. But she suffered the attack patiently, and made no answer to her reviler. She fixed her distressed gaze upon the jurors, upon the assembly of the people, and when no-one cried out against the angry man, and no-one protested, she spoke to her people with dignity and nobility, though her voice shook with emotion:

'It is true. I am a woman, and I behave like a woman. Because I do not rule you with a rod of iron it seems to you that I have little understanding. It is

41

necessary that you should have a sovereign more stern than is any woman. You shall have him! Your wish shall be granted. Now go home quietly. Let the great council choose a chieftain. And the man they choose I will take as my husband.'

So saying, she left the courtyard and went into the castle, and at once sent messengers on horseback to the castles of Kazín and Tetín for her sisters. Then she went away alone into her enchanted garden, to the most remote corner, dark with thick bushes and spreading lime-trees, to a holy place where no-one but her sisters and herself dared enter.

There in the shadow of the lime-tree stood a pent-house roof of flat stones built upon wooden pillars, green with stone-crop and mosses. Beneath the roof shone the faint glimmer of a silver head with a gilded beard, the head of a wooden image which stood on a roughly hewn boulder. This image they reverenced as a god, and called it Perun.

Libuše knelt before it and bowed herself; then, seating herself beneath the boulder at the feet of the image, she remained there for the rest of the day and through the sunset, even when it grew dark beneath the trees, and the evening wind murmured through the bushes and groves. She sat deep in thought, motionless, herself like a statue, meditating the thing which had happened to her, and what was to follow, wondering what prince the people would choose, and what would be the minds of her sisters, whether they would be at one with her. Until suddenly she rose, as Kazi and Teta appeared before her in the darkening garden. The castellan, who had conducted the sisters from the gate to the garden as soon as they arrived, stood on guard at the entrance, and waited.

What Libuše said to her sisters, what the three of them together, caught up by the spirit of prophecy, talked about beside the image of Perun, and what advice they gave, no-one ever knew. The summer night was already drawing to its close, the sky was paling, and beyond the towers and ramparts of the castle and the tops of the trees stole out the pallid rays of the dawn.

At this hour, in the sighing cool of the early morning, the daughters of Krok returned from the garden. Between her sisters, whose heads were veiled, Libuše walked in her white wreath, tranquil now, and with her gaze fixed before her. They paced silently as shadows, and the steward gazed after them, amazed, as they passed him without a word and climbed the staircase to the great hall; until they vanished between the huge columns of the porch, still drowned in the shadows of the morning twilight.

Immediately it was full morning Libuše sent messengers to call on the great council to assemble the whole nation. And when the main harvest was over and the appointed day came, they rode and walked to the assembly, the men of all the race, elders of clans and many of their households, old, young, mounted, on foot, in caps, gowns and cloaks, and some also in arms, with helmets, swords and bows, for the way to the meeting-place led through the wilderness and the forests.

There were many present from far away, from the remote fringes of the land, the borders of Zličany and Pšovka, which lie in the direction of the rising sun; others from the point of midnight, where they rubbed shoulders with the proud Lukanian people and with Litoměřice, others from the noon, from the regions through which one passes to Netolice and Doudleby. Many came from the great forests beyond the castle of Krok and Stebno, beyond which the road passes on to Domažlice and into Germany, to the land of Bavaria.

In the many buildings of the large settlement below the castle, where they made ornamented saddles, reins, stirrups and spurs, arms and shields, firmly hammered at the edges and athwart the bosses with black iron and red-gleaming copper, there were not roofs enough to house all the guests who came. Their horses stood tethered to the fences or beneath the shade of the trees. There was a great bustle and din in the settlement and along the bank of the river. Friends and relations greeted one another gaily and talked of the fields and the hunting, of weapons and fights, but most of all of the quarrel of the two headmen, of Libuše's judgement and what was to follow it, and of whom they should choose as chieftain.

As the hour of the council approached and the trumpets sounded loudly from the ramparts and towers, the men hastened up the hill to Vyšehrad in a single great stream, which in a little while halted before the gateway of the castle, between the two towers. There every man raised his head and stared in wonder at the enormous boar's head nailed to the beam. They pointed it out to one another, and the name of Bivoj was on every man's lips, spoken in praise and admiration. Then the stream flowed on through the high gate, until it stopped in the great courtyard before the royal throne. Beside the throne were two seats of honour, one on the right, the other on the left, and on these sat Kazi and Teta beside their sister Libuše.

Everyone bowed low to the princess. Then she spoke, inclining her head gravely from her throne:

'Noblemen, thanes and men of all the nation, you have heard why I have called you here. You do not know how to value your freedom. I have seen it and experienced it. Inspired by the gods, I have proclaimed that I will rule you no longer, for in your hearts you demand that you shall be ruled by a man. You long for a chieftain, who will press your sons and your daughters into his service, and from your cattle and your horses take to himself the finest whenever he wills.

You want to serve, as you never have served, and pay taxes on your squirrel furs and horses and linen, until the burden will become heavy and bitter to you.

'Yet you will no longer bear this shame, to have a woman as ruler. I do not wish to frighten you, I say again what I said at the inspiration of the gods, and what the spirit of prophecy also revealed to my sisters. Choose a chieftain, but wisely and carefully, since it is easy to appoint a ruler, but hard to unseat him once he is appointed. If you are still of the same mind, everything shall be done as you wish. And if you ask it, I will advise you, and myself announce his name and habitation.'

'Tell us! Tell us!'

'Advise us! Advise us!' cried out all the assembly with one voice. The crowds which had formerly stood silent as a wall, attentively listening, now shook with excitement and rushed forward until they pressed at the foot of the throne, as ripples rush across a field of corn before a sudden wind.

Libuše rose in her white gown, with the wreath about her forehead, and towering over them, stretched out her hands towards them. Instantly a great silence fell, every man stood motionless, staring at the exalted princess. Raising her finger, she pointed to the mountains to the north, and said:

'Beyond those mountains, in Lemuze, is a modest river, the Bělina by name. Near to that river is a village where dwell the clan of Stadici. Not far from the village is a fallow field measuring in length and breadth a hundred and twenty paces, a strange fallow field, for it lies in the midst of so many tilled fields, and yet belongs to none of them. There your chieftain is ploughing with two pied oxen. One ox has a white head, the other is white from brow to back, and his hind legs are also white. Now take a gown and a coat and a purple cloak such as is fitting for a prince, go and carry to this man the summons from the nation and from me, and lead hither your prince and my husband. His name is Přemysl, and his descendants will rule over this whole land and all its seed to eternity.'

When therefore they had nominated the headmen of the most distinguished clans to announce to the man of Stadice the will of the people and the princess, Libuše spoke to them thus:

'You need not search for your way, nor ask. My horse will lead you, do not hesitate to follow him. He will lead you and bring you home again by the right path. When you see him halt before a man and neigh, then that is he of whom I have spoken. You will not believe me, until you see your chieftain sit at meat at an iron table.'

When Libuše beckoned, they led in her own riding horse, a white horse with a broad neck, from which flowed a long mane. He bore an ornamented saddle, under the saddle a furry hide, and his broad breast-harness shone with bronze discs and bosses.

As soon as they had laid over his saddle gown, coat and purple cloak, he paced forward, and the noble embassage set out on their journey after him.

It was the first day of autumn, a calm and sunny day. Libuše's horse paced quickly, with a confident step; none of the men led him, or directed him by so much as a word. He went with certainty, as though he were on the way to his stable, until the men marvelled, and the suspicion gained on them that the horse was not making this journey for the first time, that the princess had often ridden here in her spectral journeying in the evening twilight, and before cockcrow had again returned to her own court.

Not by a step did the white horse stray from his path. Nothing could decoy him from his course. More than once they passed a herd of horses grazing, and their merry neighing welcomed and lured him. But the white horse paced on, turning his eyes neither to left nor right. And when they sat down in the fields beneath a wild pear-tree or in the faint shadow of a red-barked pine to rest, the princess's horse stood quietly waiting, and was the first to set out again on his way.

46

So they crossed hills and plains, until in the morning of the third day they drew near to a village between two hill-slopes, at the edge of a narrow valley through which a river flowed. When they had reached the village a boy ran up to meet them. They asked him:

'Tell us, boy, is this the village of Stadice? And is there dwelling here a man named Přemysl?'

'Yes, this is Stadice,' the boy told them, 'and there is Přemysl in the field driving the oxen.'

They saw, at no great distance from them, a tall man who paced erect and noble behind the plough and urged his team of pied oxen with a goad. One of them had a white head, the second was white from brow to back, and his hind legs white also, white as snow. They were drawing the plough along a broad headland, and when they drew near to him the princess's horse halted, and for an instant turned sidelong and reared up, neighing for joy. Then he faced forward again, and bowed his head before the young ploughman, who halted the plough and let the oxen stand.

The ambassadors took from the white horse the prince's robes, a long gown hemmed with rare fur, a beautiful coat of fine cloth, and the cloak, and approaching Přemysl, bowed low before him and gave him greeting.

'Blessed among men, prince ordained for us by the gods, all hail to you! Leave your oxen, change your clothes, be pleased to mount this horse and ride with us. The Princess Libuše and all the Czech nation summon you to go with us, and take up the sovereignty ordained to you and to your heirs. We have chosen you to be our judge, protector and prince.'

Přemysl listened in silence, and silently he thrust into the soil the goad which he held in his hand, and loosed the oxen. Lifting off their yoke he said:

'Go back whence you came.'

He had scarcely said the words before they turned, and in a moment both had vanished. Below the village they disappeared into a great rock, which opened before them and closed again upon them, leaving not a hoof-print behind.

Then Přemysl addressed the ambassadors in these words:

'Alas that you came so early in the morning! If I could have finished ploughing this field there would have been abundance of bread for all time. But since you made such haste, and have interrupted me in my work, know that there will often be hunger in the land.'

It seemed that the earth had given to the dry goad instant sap and life. The hazel switch began to bud as in spring on the tree, and immediately put out three shoots, three wands on which burst forth the green of fresh leaves and young hazel-nuts.

47

The ambassadors gasped, beholding this wonder of wonders. But Přemysl asked them if they would sit down with him at table, and invited them to breakfast. He turned the plough, and taking from the headland a bast satchel, drew from it bread and cheese, and laid them on the clean ploughshare shining in the sun.

'This is that iron table of which Libuše spoke!' So said each messenger to himself, remembering and marvelling. As they breakfasted with Přemysl around the ploughshare and drank from his jug, two of the shoots on the hazel withered and fell; but the third grew rapidly and richly in length and leaves. At this the guests were moved almost to dread. They pointed out the wonder to one another, and asked Přemysl what it meant that two of the shoots had died and only one remained and grew.

'I will tell you,' said Přemysl. 'It means that of my descendants many will begin to rule, but one only will remain a lord and a sovereign.'

Then the messengers asked him why he ate from the iron, and not on the grass of the headland.

'I eat from an iron table,' replied their chosen prince, 'so that you may know that my race will wield an iron rule. But hold iron in esteem! In times of peace we plough the fields with it, and in evil times we protect ourselves against our enemies with it. As long as the Czechs have such a table they will overcome their enemies. But if ever a foreign race shall wrest this table from them, the Czechs will forfeit their liberty.'

So saying, he rose and went with the messengers into the village to take leave of his clan, now held in such high honour and esteem. Then robed in the gown of a prince, with a glistening belt, and shod in princely shoes, he mounted the white horse, which again neighed joyfully under him. On the way the ambassadors asked Přemysl why he took with him his bag and peasant shoes, and he replied:

'I give them to you and bid you keep them for ever, so that my descendants may know from what stock they are sprung, that they may go in awe, and not oppress the people entrusted to their care out of pride, for we are all equal.'

When the journey was over, and they were already drawing near to Vyšehrad, Libuše came out to meet them in a diadem of shining silver, with rare strings of amber about her throat. She walked in a white robe, beautiful and exalted, and her eyes shone with joyful emotion when they beheld Přemysl in the distance, riding her white horse at the head of his train. With the princess went her maidens, and the courtiers and the chief men of all the clans, who had been waiting here with the great council for the return of the ambassadors with their new prince.

And they all rejoiced when they beheld this comely and stalwart man. But most of all the young princess, who had known her bridegroom at Budeč. Now they joined their right hands, and went blissfully into the castle; and with them

went all the nation to a great feast, and with acclaim they installed Přemysl in the stone chair of the prince. Then they celebrated the coming of their new prince and his marriage to Libuše. They celebrated it in the settlement below the castle and in the castle itself, where the courtiers and the guests sat down to table in the great hall on the spacious courtyard, and there feasted together.

They ate plenteously, and drank great quantities of mead, they drank and sang, or listened to the musicians as they played on stringed instruments and sang the old songs of the heroes and wars of the olden days. They celebrated their choice and they celebrated the wedding, all through the day and far into the night by the light of fires and torches. And when the fires had burned out, and above the forests the morning light was already flushing into rose, Vyšehrad was still ringing, and the village below still rocked to the merry din, while the morning wind carried its echo across the river into the dark forests drowned in pale mists.

So Libuše led Přemysl to the prince's throne. And when the wedding was over, she descended with him into a hall deep beneath the earth, hewn out of the rock, sealed by a heavy trap-door strongly reinforced with metal. In this underground room the walls and the rough benches that ran along them glittered with various metals, iron and bronze, silver and gold; for there hung swords, belts ornamented with hammered studs, conical helmets, coats of chain-mail, beautifully decorated shields, and there lay bracelets, clasps, rings and diadems of silver filigree, strings of beads of amber, stone, glass and metal, ornaments of pure silver beside great wooden dishes full of gold.

All this great treasure she showed to him, for now it was also his. She led him into her garden also, to the holy place beneath the ancient trees, where gleamed the silver head of the frowning Perun. There in the spring and summer they would sit alone together in grave conversation. In the gloom of the sacred wood above Jezerka, too, they often wandered, where Libuše had loved to linger with her maidens before her marriage, where she used to bathe, and where her ladies had combed out her beautiful hair and sung to her their delightful songs.

Now she walked there with her husband, and pondered order and justice. For at that time Přemysl was formulating many laws by which he led his exuberant people into disciplined ways, and by which his descendants continued to regulate their lives for long ages afterwards. And at that time, too, Libuše was inspired by the spirit of prophecy, and spoke out that which she foresaw.

Once she stood with Přemysl and her retinue and the elders of the people on the rocky precipice high above the Vltava. Long shadows already lay across the richly blossoming meadows in the valley, through which the brook Botič rushed beneath its alders and maples, and the vault of the tall willows. The forest on the Wolf's Gate was flooded with light already growing yellow, and between the groves gleamed like gold the fields of grain on the valley slopes beneath, and higher on the broad upland on the right bank of the river.

All the company were gazing at the splendid harvest, yellowing acre beyond acre, and all marvelled at the richness of their blessing. Then an old thane of the retinue began to recall aloud the aspect of this same spot in the ancient days, when he had stood here with the messengers sent out by the late chieftain of blessed memory to seek out the site for his new castle.

'What a wilderness it was then! Forest beyond forest, as it is there!' And he pointed towards the west, to the wooded hills beyond the river, shining in the sunlight. From the gleaming surface of the water rose islands riotously overgrown with an abundance of trees and thick underbrush. Birds circled in great flocks above them, and from the black shadows under the trees along the shore, where the wild hops swung from trunk and branch and bush, loud through the reeds clamoured the mingled cries of water-fowl.

All those on the heights of Vyšehrad fixed their eyes where the old man pointed: beyond the islands, beyond the river, to the wide forests which rose from the shore to climb the slopes of the hills of Petřín and Strahov, and all the prolonged crest of the uplands that extended everywhere in that direction.

Those ancient groves were sinking already into blue dusk. Above their crest rose in the distance a tall, straight column of pale smoke, rendered translucent by the sun; doubtless some hunter had kindled a fire for his comfort in those forest solitudes.

'Those woods ought to come down!' said the old man. 'We shall be getting visits from hungry wolves from those parts for a long time yet. And those forests beyond, round Strahov, Šlachov and Malejov, and all those groves that stretch along there everywhere. Unless we burn them down—'

He never ended what he was about to say. No-one was listening to him any longer. But no-one else uttered a sound, either. Every man stood motionless, afraid to break the silence even by a footfall, and gazed at the young princess who stood at the head of their company. Her cheeks had flushed into clear radiance in sudden ecstasy, her eyes burned with rapture. Holy dread breathed through the retinue, and touched every heart.

Uplifted and transfigured, as though neither husband nor court nor retinue existed for her, Libuše stretched out her hands towards the blue hills beyond the river, and gazing at the forest that clothed them to the summit, gave voice to the spirit of prophecy:

'I see a great city, whose glory will touch the stars.

'There in the forest is the place, three short miles distant from here; the river Vltava encircles it.

'On the north side the brook Brusnice encloses it with its deep valley, and on the south the rocky hill beside the forest of Strahov.

'When you come there you will find a man in the midst of the forest, hewing the threshold of a house.

'And you will call the castle you will build there, Praha, that is, the threshold. And as princes and chieftains bow their heads before the threshold, so shall they bow their heads before my city.

'Honour and praise shall be given to it, and it shall be renowned throughout the world.'

She fell silent. She would have said more, but suddenly the blaze of ecstasy faded, for the spirit of prophecy had left her.

And at once they crossed the river and climbed to the hilltop in the ancient forest, and finding a man there at work, just as Libuše had foreseen and told them, they set to work to build a castle in that place. They built it, and built well, they fortified it strongly, especially to the west, towards the forest of Strahov, for on that side the castle was most approachable. They made there a deep ditch and a high earthwork, and on the earthwork a fortification of hewn beams, and in this and above the gate they built high towers. Into their walls they drove wooden nails, and then plastered them with clay mixed with straw. And so they made plastered towers, to render them safer against fire, and against burning darts.

So the castle of Prague became renowned for its strength, and side by side with Vyšchrad it held sway over all the Czech lands.

It happened on a day that there came to Vyšehrad the thanes of several clans and many of the elders, celebrated among all the people, and said to Přemysl:

'O Prince, of everything we have enough and to spare, cattle and grain, fish and game. All that we lack is sufficient metals. What we ourselves can dig out of the earth is not enough for our needs, and for what more we want we must pay dearly to the foreign traders in skins and honey and horses. You are wise, take counsel with the princess for us, that she may tell us by means of the prophecies in what secret places are laid away the metals of silver and gold and all the other ores.'

When Přemysl had heard their request he told them to disperse to their own villages, but to assemble again at the castle on the fifteenth day, and then they should have an answer. And when they returned on the day appointed they found Přemysl seated on his throne, and Libuše beside him on a wooden chair which was marked with her own sign.

'Listen, gallant thanes and men of the Czech lands,' said Přemysl. 'Listen to the words of your mother, for with these same words she will enrich you and your heirs.'

They all gazed upon the exalted princess as she rose, moved by the spirit of prophecy, and walked through the courtyard and on to the edge of the ramparts. Přemysl walked beside her, and the thanes and the princess's maidens followed at a little distance, until Libuše halted on the rock high above the river Vltava, and spoke:

> *'What is hidden in the rocks, in the depths of the earth,*
> *The voice of the gods reveals through my voice.'*

She turned to the west, and stretching out her hands she said:

> *'I see the hill of Březový, and in it veins of silver.*
> *He who seeks shall find wealth.*
> *But the neighbour from the west, invited or uninvited,*
> *Will covet the metals in which lies dominion.*
> *Beware, lest from the gifts of your own earth*
> *He should forge fetters to enslave you.'*

Then turning to the left, towards the south, she continued:

> *'I see the hill Jílový, it is full of gold.*
> *There is strength in gold, and the power of wonders.*
> *But strength fades, and you will grow faint and weary*
> *If the holy fire of love burns out in you.'*

Again turning to the left, towards the east, she prophesied thus:

> *'I see a mountain with three crests, in its womb it has hidden*
> *For ages the treasure of silver.*
> *But since there are three crests, three times shall its metal*
> *Decline, and three times rise again.*
> *It will be a lure to the stranger, as a lime-tree*
> *In flower lures many swarms of bees.*
> *Drones will not master them, only the industry of bees.*
> *Then gold will grow out of silver.'*

When she had spoken thus, she turned yet again to the left, towards the north, saying:

56

'I see the hill of Krupnatý, and in its depths
Lead, and the cloudy gleam of tin.
But it lies on the frontiers, keep guard there
Watchfully on every step.
Where you yourselves yield only one inch
There you will always lose the whole acre.'

When she had thus indicated the hitherto secret beds of the metals, she turned to the thanes and elders, who had listened to her silently and with bated breath, and addressed them in these words:

'The gleam of seven metals burns on your soil,
And the fields shine with the gold of grain.
Your race will dwell here to all ages
And grow strong and blessed,
So long as the land of their fathers remains sacred to them
For their blood and labour and language,
So long as they stand erect before the stranger, honour their ancient code,
And act as brothers to their brothers.'

Often Libuše would descend from her castle to the foot of the rock of Vyšehrad, to her solitary bath, where Vltava had carved out its deepest pool. One day at this spot, as she looked into the flood of the water on the threshold of the bath, in the eddies of its dark depths she saw into the future, for at that instant the spirit of prophecy caught her up into ecstasy.

The currents flowed by, and with them glimmered in their sombre depths vision after vision. They came with the stream, and with the stream they passed, and as they receded they grew ever more black and threatening, ever more sorrowful, until the mind failed and the heart ached to see them.

Pale and trembling, Libuše bent her head above the river, and with horrified eyes followed the dreadful revelations of the waters.

In wonder and fear her maidens looked at their princess, as she peered into the river in agonised agitation, sobbing; and heavily then she spoke, in a voice strangled with grief:

'I see the blaze of fires, flames slash through the darkness of the waters. In the flames villages, castles, great buildings, and all dying—dying!

'And in the blaze of the fires I see bloody wars, war upon war. And such wars! Pale bodies, full of wounds and blood. Brother killing brother, and the stranger trampling on their necks. I see misery, humiliation, a terrible penalty for all.'

Two of her maidens brought to her the golden cradle of her firstborn. The soft light of consolation touched Libuše's eyes and lit up her pale face. She kissed the cradle, and then plunged it into the bottomless depths of the pool, and bending above the water she said in a voice trembling with emotion:

'Rest there in the deep, cradle of my son, until time shall call you back again!

'You will not remain for ever in the dark depths of the waters, the night that is to cover your land will not be without end. A clear day will dawn, and happiness will again shine forth over my nation.

'Cleansed by suffering, strengthened by love and labour it will rise erect in its might, and fulfil all its aspirations, and enter again upon glory.

'And then you will shine again through the dark waters, you will arise into the light of day, and the saviour of the land, foretold long ages before, shall rest in you, being still a child.'

The years passed, and when the foreordained day came, Kazi, who had often restored life to the sick by the magic of her blessing, herself became the prey of death. In her memory the inhabitants of the land raised a great and tall burial mound near to her castle on the shore of the river Mže, beside the path that leads into the district of Bechyně, over the mountain of Osek.

Then the finger of death touched the forehead of the saintly Teta; and she too gave up the spirit. Through all the region of Tetín they mourned for her, for she had been like a mother to all. Her ashes they buried on the mountain of Pohled on the western side, near to her holy place by the ancient oaks, beneath which she had bowed herself before the gods and offered sacrifices.

There, too, after her death they kindled a great fire, and for nine days kept it burning and sacrificed in it to the gods. Then they rolled a great stone and set it up on Teta's grave.

So Libuše was left alone, having outlived her sisters. Until at last her days, too, were fulfilled. By the inspiration of the gods she knew that she was nearing the close of her life. And thinking on the distant pilgrimage into eternity, into paradise after her father and sisters, she asked Přemysl to call together the nobles and the headmen of the clans, for she wished to speak to them yet once more.

When they had assembled on Vyšehrad, Libuše had a sacrifice consecrated to the gods, and then entered with Přemysl among the nobles and thanes gathered in the great courtyard. The princess walked in grandeur, a holy calm in her pale face, her eyes already fixed on eternity.

She announced to them all that her fate was drawing to its completion, that this was the last time she would thus behold and address them. Then she begged them all to maintain their loyalty and obedience to Přemysl, their prince, and after him to her son. Every soul about her listened with emotion, and grief fell upon them all, so that tears stood in the eyes of even the bearded men, as Libuše begged her husband to be patient with them always, and then stretched out her hands over them and blessed them all.

Returning into her own chamber, she lay down upon the earth, the mother of all, and died. And her husband and her son wept for her, her maidens and all the people wept with great lamentation, and they bore her body forth and burned it, and buried the ashes, holding a great funeral ceremony over her grave.

But where that grave was dug no-one knows for certain. The old people say that it was at her castle of Libušín, but there is also an old legend that it was at the castle of Libice, not far from the mysterious hill of Oškobrh, full of rare herbs and roots.

Libuše's treasure remained even after her death in its rocky hiding-place, just as she had shown it to her husband. Přemysl did not touch it, for he knew for what it was intended. And there the treasure lies to this day, deep in the rock of Vyšehrad, from which it will shine forth in the time of the greatest poverty and scarcity. And as it opens and reveals itself, there will again be abundance of everything, and all want will come to an end.

Libuše's golden cradle rested for long, long ages at the bottom of the river Vltava beneath the rock of Vyšehrad. The tide of time flowed on, and with it suffering piled on suffering fell upon the Czech land. Villages died, whole regions died. Hamlets and well-built towns perished in flames. Battle after battle flooded their native land with blood. Brother destroyed brother, most terribly of all in the clan of Libuše, and the stranger trampled upon their necks.

But the night was not without end.

The golden cradle under the rock of Vyšehrad rose out of the dark waters, its pure metal shining in the light of day, and in it rested the saviour of the land, being still a child: the little son of the last branch of the stem of Přemysl.

And the golden cradle grew with the child, until it grew into a golden bed, as the infant it nursed grew into a man who became the father of his country. In holy Karlštejn he kept this enchanted bed, on which he lay in his hours of repose, wearied with labour and the cares of kingship. And when he died, the golden bed would bear no other and vanished.

It sank again as a cradle into the hiding-place from which it had risen, into the dark pool, deep beneath the rock of Vyšehrad; and there it lies waiting—waiting.

The Women's War

I

When Libuše had departed into paradise, the maidens of her retinue saw that they were no longer held in such esteem as they had been accustomed to during their mistress's life. They found this hard to bear, and bitterly recalled the times when their princess had been the sole ruler of the land and governed all the men; and anger quickened in them when more than one of the men said to them mockingly:

'You used to be the rulers here, we had to bow to you, and now you're like lost sheep!'

Until at last this secret anger burst forth like a sudden flame. In their longing after their lost dominion and their hunger for revenge, the girls seized sword and bow, and never calculating the odds, launched a bitter war against all men. The leader of them all was Vlasta, formerly the most influential of Libuše's suite. She was the first to call them to arms, the first to take up weapons, then she marshalled them all together and withdrew them into a strong castle.

This castle they built for themselves as their fortress beyond the river Vltava, on a summit which stood somewhat higher than was Vyšehrad on the opposite shore.

The maidens obeyed Vlasta in all things as their princess and their general. At her advice and direction many of them dispersed into the various districts to invite all women and girls to leave everything, and hurry to Děvín, as they had named their new castle, to join the war against men, in order that women might regain the dominion in the land, and the men might be reduced to the tasks of servitude, and put to the plough again.

And Vlasta's call did not fall on deaf ears; it was no empty voice blown by the wind, but ran like a flying spark to kindle flames in the hearts of many women. Like doves taking flight from their cotes, so the women and girls fled from their menfolk, fathers, brothers and all they had, to the castle of Děvín, until its halls and chambers, its open courtyard and high ramparts swarmed with them.

The men, not far away at Vyšehrad, looked on inactively at this and laughed and mocked when they saw the maidens exercising with arms and riding horses. Even the old and experienced looked on with disdain, and when there was talk before Prince Přemysl of the women in arms, the elders spoke of them contemptuously, and with jeering and laughter prepared to put the prowess of the women to the test.

Everyone in the prince's retinue laughed about it, certain that it would be like flushing game. Only Přemysl was downcast, and said with grave anxiety:

'Listen, and I'll tell you why I am not laughing with you. You would not be laughing, either, if you had had such a vision as I had in my dreams.'

And wishing to warn them, he told what he had seen:

'It was night, and the sky was filled with thick, stinking smoke. In the gleam of fires I saw a maiden in a helmet. From beneath the helm flowed down her long hair, in one hand she held a sword, and in the other a cup. On the earth slaughtered men lay in their blood and dust. The girl ran like one demented, trampling the corpses, she filled the cup with blood and gulped it like a wild beast in greedy rage. Hear the voice of the gods, you men, and read their sign. By this vision I warn you, take heed to my words and do not value them lightly!'

II

Meantime, the women in Děvín were preparing themselves for battle against the men. They smothered the voice of their blood, and heartlessly and stonily announced even to their brothers and fathers:

'We are nothing now to you, and never will be. Let every man look to himself.'

Then they promised loyalty and faith to their cause and to one another, and swore a great oath under penalty of dying on their own swords, not to commit or countenance any treason. So they swore at Děvín to their general Vlasta, who appointed to each one her place and her duty.

The wisest ones she kept as her counsellors, to the most thorough and cautious she committed the care of the castle, and the most bold and audacious she prepared for the field, training them to fight on horseback and beat the men like dogs. And those who were beautiful of face and form and delightful to look upon, she singled out to act as decoys for men, luring them to destruction by means of their beauty and charm. For she designed to work the destruction of men both by force and by trickery.

But the men continued in their error and ignored all advice from Přemysl their prince. They rode to the attack of Děvín as to a merry-making. Every one of them thought that as soon as they showed themselves and waved their swords the women would take fright and run away, like cats put to flight by the rattle of a bag of peas.

But wonder of wonders! The women certainly did not stay within their ramparts, but neither did they run away. They burst out directly from the gate, and before the castle Vlasta drew up their ranks for battle. Mounted on a black horse, in chain-mail and with a helmet on her head and a lance in her hand, she addressed her virgin army in fiery words, urging them not to take fright, but to fight gallantly.

'If we let ourselves be overcome,' she cried, 'the men will only make a mock of us. You will be put to menial labour, worse, you will be mere slaves! Better to die, if need be, than to hand ourselves over to their mercy. Therefore have at them! Let not one be spared, kill every one, every one, no matter who, be it brother or father—'

64

And with these words she shook out her rein and urged her horse to a gallop. She shrieked and waved her lance, and the wild cry trailed after her flight. The ranks of warlike women charged after her, eager for battle, and in the leading rank, on Vlasta's heels, rode Mlada, Svatava, Hodka, Radka and Častava.

The darts and arrows of the warrior women rained among the men like a sudden snowstorm. They laughed no longer. They fell in their blood, not by ones and twos but by whole ranks, and before they could recover their wits, the women's cavalry was on them, thrusting and hacking into their confused cohorts.

The battle did not last long. Three hundred men lay on the earth in their blood. The rest took to flight. A thick, dark forest nearby was their shelter and salvation; but for that they would all have died.

Děvín and all the country round rang with the women's shouts of triumph. They exulted over their victory, which inflamed still more their thirst for battle, and brought them strong reinforcements. The legend of their prowess ran through all the land, and set light to the ardour of even those women who had hesitated. It was an ill time in all the countryside. More than one man was found in the morning killed, stabbed with a knife, and many, feeling uneasy for their lives, went away at night from their homes and lay through the hours of darkness in the deep woods.

And it was an ill time, too, for the men in the region of Děvín. They could find no means of breaking into the castle, they could not take it either by force or by cunning. There was not a single man within the castle, and not one of the girls turned traitress. Moreover, the women had their allies in Vyšehrad, who were not openly on their side, but secretly sent them reports of everything that went on, what the men were discussing and preparing, where they went, and where it was possible to run them to earth and ambush them.

So the war continued for a long time, openly in the field and secretly by trickery. Thus one of the beautiful decoys induced a trusting young man to come to her rescue, telling him that she would be going with nine companions along the road to Děvín. And he came and waited for her in a solitary place with his comrades, as they had agreed. The girl for whom he was waiting also came, and with her nine companions, as she had said. But at that same moment a host of other women burst out of cover, and killed the young man and his comrades every single one.

By cunning died also a young man who was fooled into believing a lovely member of Vlasta's escort when she promised to betray Děvín. As they had both agreed, she let him into the castle secretly at night, with a numerous company at his back. But neither he nor any of his comrades-in-arms ever returned from Děvín.

Cunning also brought about the death of a young thane, the gallant Ctirad, whom Vlasta hated most of all, because it was he who, in skirmishes and battles, had slain with the sword the greatest number of her women warriors.

III

One day in the summer Ctirad rode with several men of his guard through the fields, travelling from his native village to the castle of Prague. The young thane and his escort had swords in their belts, bows and hairy hide quivers slung across their shoulders. More than one of them even carried a lance. At that time it was not wise to pass through the fields alone or unarmed, since at any moment the women might attack from cover.

The sun was burning hot, and it was close weather. Not an ear, not a leaf quivered in all the acres of grain and hemp. Even in the forest, when Ctirad reached it by the path along which he was riding, the air was just as sultry. The shade of the old trees and dark rocks which hung over the deep valley seemed to afford no coolness or relief. The wind did not stir, not a twig moved, and the brook in the thickets beneath the rocks flowed soundlessly. Everything was silent, water, trees and birds; only a human voice suddenly echoed through the dead stillness: a wild and desolate cry.

Ctirad halted, and they all listened in amazement. The cry rang out at no great distance, from behind a rock; then suddenly it was silenced. At that same moment there sailed above Ctirad's head a raven, and wheeling over him, screamed aloud in its raucous voice. But neither the thane nor any of his companions noticed the great black bird, a warning omen. They were off on the trail of the human outcry. As they rode round the rock, involuntarily they reined in their horses, for what they saw was matter for wonder.

Beside the rock, flowering with golden mullein, and overgrown at the foot with blackberries and raspberry canes bearing the white flowers and the reddening fruit together, was a green clearing in a flood of sunlight, carpeted with fine grass and blushing osiers. At the edge of the glade close to the rock stood an old oak-tree, and beneath the tree lay a girl, bound with a rope to the gnarled trunk. She had fallen silent, worn out with calling and with anguish, her head drooping. Her untidy hair flowed down over her shoulders, over which was slung on a thong a huntsman's horn. But as the hoofbeats of the horses reached her ears she raised her head and again began to call, imploring the men to unbind her and set her free, beseeching them to have mercy on her.

Ctirad, moved both by the entreaty and by the voice of this beautiful girl, forgot all caution, and his companions with him. Eagerly he leaped from his horse, and drawing his sword, cut through the ropes and freed the girl. He had no suspicion that Vlasta had received word the previous day by one of her spies of his intention to ride to the castle of Prague by this route, and had made due preparation to see that he should not return, nor did he guess that this lovely maiden was a part of Vlasta's plan. Freed of her bonds, she thanked Ctirad passionately, and told him that her name was Šárka, and she was the daughter of the thane of Okořín. She said that the women of Děvín had fallen upon her in the wood, and were dragging her in bonds to their castle, with the intention of recruiting her to their own malignant company; but when they had brought her thus far, they were suddenly disturbed by the thud of hoofs approaching through the forest.

'They forsook me, they left me here, but bound me so fast that I could not move. And in wicked jest, look, they hung this horn round my neck, so that I could sound a call for aid, bound thus as I was—and there, look, they left me a jar of mead, so that my thirst should be redoubled.'

And she pointed to a great jar of mead set in the grass at her feet. And again she burst into tears, begging anxiously that the thane would not leave her there, since he had delivered her, but would take her home to her father, before those demons of women and virgins came back.

Ctirad, sitting down beside her, told her comfortingly that he would do so, and offered her the bottle, so that she might refresh and calm herself after such terror and suffering. She drank, and also gave him to drink. His escort in the meantime had dismounted from their horses, tethered them close by, and themselves lay down beside their master in the shade to cool off. It was noon. The pungent scent of the pines and of wild thyme and meadow flowers lay heavy on the air, quivering with heat. Nothing moved, scarcely a butterfly stirred in the sunlit glade. The men of the escort closed their eyes, and sleep came stealthily upon them.

But their thane was listening alertly to the soft words and alluring voice of the lovely Šárka, and drank with a will when she again offered him the mead. He looked at the horn that hung about her neck, and when she wondered innocently what kind of sound it made, he put it to his lips and blew a blast with the full power of his lungs.

The call of the horn rang and re-echoed piercingly in the dead stillness. Against the rocks and through the groves its note pealed, slowly fading and dying away until it closed in a long echo in the depth of the forest.

Suddenly it was as if a storm had burst. There was an abrupt, wild cry, close to them and all about them, behind trees, in the hearts of thickets, from the gloom of the groves. Like a ferocious swarm of bees a host of armed women burst into the clearing. Before Ctirad's escort could come to their senses, before they could leap to their horses and draw their swords, the women warriors were on them, striking and thrusting like furies.

Ctirad tried to reach his comrades. But even as he snatched up his sword from the grass the women and girls were thronging round him, and before he could swing his weapon to fend them off, he was borne to the ground. There they bound him and he lay in fetters where only a little while before he had delivered from her bonds Vlasta's trusted confidante. In vain he raged, in vain he called down curses upon them, invoking demons to punish them for this evil trick. Šárka only laughed; they all laughed, and with wild rejoicing led away to Děvín their stalwart captive, who was forced to walk in bonds beside Šárka's horse. His companions remained in the green glade, in the trampled grass, dabbled with blood. They lay in the sun, hacked and dead; swarms of flies settled on them, and from the heights of air above them the raven called, the omen they had not heeded, summoning his fellows to a rich feast.

So died Ctirad's escort, and so their thane was brought to ruin. And the wild rocky valley where this ambush took place is still called by the name of the woman who destroyed them all.

IV

Next day the guards and other witnesses brought the terrible news to Vyšehrad that not far from Děvín a wheel had been set up on a pole, and in it was twined the broken body of the thane Ctirad; and it was the women of Děvín who had thus put him to the torture.

The report was borne abroad through all districts and all regions. And then from all directions the men came rushing to Vyšehrad in arms, enraged and embittered by the malignance of the women, and asked Přemysl to lead them, for this act must be avenged. They promised to obey him in all things; but many did not even wait for his orders, but set out themselves in a great host to Děvín, and killed such of the maidens as they met with on the way. And many others they captured and brought prisoners to Vyšehrad.

Vlasta, furious as an enraged she-bear and arrogant in her certainty of victory, led her women warriors to Vyšehrad to storm the castle and kill all the men who held it. But before they came to the ramparts the men rushed out to meet them in full battle array, thirsting for a bloody revenge.

They met in a cruel and ruthless battle. Vlasta on her horse burst at the head of her troops into the ranks of her enemies. Rage possessed her, and single-handed she drove in a path for her companions. She believed that they were in full array at her heels; but the women could not keep up her pace, nor thrust into the opposing ranks so far as she, and at last Vlasta realised that she had fallen among the men alone, in the most violent heart of the fighting. Men pressed thick around her, and for the fierceness of their attack and their cruel weight upon her, she could not lift her sword. They pulled her down and tore her from her horse, and hacked her to pieces on foot.

So died Vlasta.

Her companions also fought vainly. And when they saw their general unseated, sudden terror fell upon them, and they, before whom the men had once fled in fear, now themselves took to flight — a wild and disorderly flight to Děvín, where they looked to find salvation.

Many of them were left on the battlefield, many more fell on the journey, nor did those who reached Děvín escape the same fate.

The army of the men rode in on Děvín at the same time as the fleeing women, and with them burst over the bridge and into the castle. It was all over, the end

of the women's strength and audacity. They cast away their swords, they sobbed again like women, they recognised their brothers and relatives again and fell on their knees before them, pleading sorrowfully and abjectly, and wringing their hands.

But the men exacted their vengeance for Ctirad, and all who had fallen in battle or by treason. They avenged them cruelly, sparing not one of the warrior women. All those beautiful bodies they delivered over to death, hurling them down from the windows and the high ramparts. And when they had destroyed all that army of women, they burned their Děvín to the ground and scattered it to the winds.

So ended the women's war.

Then there was order and law as before, and Prince Přemysl ruled alone, no longer opposed by rebellious women.

When Přemysl was far advanced in years, he fell asleep in the dream of death, and his spirit departed to his fathers. After him the rule descended to Nezamysl.

When Nezamysl went the way of all flesh, Mnata succeeded to the princely throne.

And when the tale of his days, too, was completed, Vojen assumed the sovereignty. After his death Vnislav ruled, and when he closed his eyes for ever, Křesomysl was proclaimed prince beside sacred Jezerka, where he had come to the assembly with the great council. And when they had made a burnt offering beside this clear spring, the foremost of the nobles placed the cap of Přemysl on Křesomysl's head, and all those about him cried joyfully:

'Křesomysl is our lord! And he will be a benevolent lord to us.'

All present hailed him and did homage to him, and then they conducted him in a joyful procession to Vyšehrad. There he was solemnly installed in the chair from which his ancestress had once ruled, and the founder of his family.

During the reign of Křesomysl the people were seeking mountains rather than ploughland and flocks. Great numbers of them had taken up the search for metals in the depths of the earth, and beside the brooks they washed gold out of the sand, for there was abundance of it to be found everywhere, especially in the southern parts of the country. The prince himself paid more attention to the prophecies of his ancestress than to anything else. He sent many miners to the hills of Jílový and Březový, which yielded up more silver than any other mountains.

From all directions people flocked to those parts to dig out the ore; every man wanted to get rich quickly. They abandoned everything at home. No-one cultivated the fallow land, the fields were left to lie waste, and weeds and couch-grass overgrew where formerly there had been thick grain ripening, and the murmurous voice of the quail busy among the stalks.

The people grew rich in metals, but the bread grains lessened. Round the mines there was great shortage, and the gold-washers and miners sent to buy bread in the district of Prague. Many thanes and elders of the clans looked with disfavour on this change, and resisted it, complaining that the mines meant the death of the fields, that for the sake of precious metals the clan households were being torn apart, and the old order and discipline were dying. Several of them came to the prince at Vyšehrad, and at their head was Horymír, the thane of Neumětely. They pleaded with Křesomysl, reminding him that he ought to value bread above silver, and begged him to disband this underground race. But the prince, greedy for the gleam of rare metals, paid no attention to their arguments, and the thanes went away empty-handed, discontented and angry.

Soon word reached the ears of the miners of this attack on them, and all the things that had been said to their damage. They met together at the mines, among their huts and sheds. Their meeting was like a nest of wasps disturbed when a messenger told them how the thanes had spoken of them at Vyšehrad, and what they had urged against them; and especially Horymír of Neumětely.

They raged and shouted, threatening revenge, hottest of all against Horymír. They wanted his blood, immediately, without any delay. Then others in angry jest yelled that if he was afraid of a shortage of bread he could eat his fill of it, that they would cram it down his throat until he was choked by it.

That pleased them. Like a pack of excited hounds after a stag they rushed towards the village of Neumětely.

Through the autumn dusk the mob of miners ran through field and fallow, darkening in the swift twilight.

It was night when they sighted Neumětely; the straw roofs of the houses, the tall stacks by the barns, and the little castle of the village in its round earthwork were growing dark between the trees. Here they hushed their footsteps, and silently crept into the enclosure like stealthy and cunning beasts of prey. But a good man had run in before them to give warning of what was happening. He had barely wakened the thane when a wild shouting broke out in the darkness. There was no time for resistance. The throng of miners had already rushed into the castle, and their eerie howling was growing rapidly nearer. There was nothing left for it but flight.

With a leap Horymír was at his stable, where stood his most beloved horse Šemík. In an instant he led him out and saddled him, and whispering a quiet word to him, burst out of the gate into the fields. The miners caught sight of him and ran after him, bellowing. He heard the beat of hooves in pursuit. He urged Šemík onward, and the faithful horse stretched out to a wilder gallop, until his mane sailed behind him, and earth flew from his hooves, and sand and sparks hissed into the darkness.

Behind the rider his pale tunic billowed out like wings, and for a while made a target for the pursuers. But only for a while. They could not match Šemík, who bounded forward with mighty strides and vanished in the darkness of the autumn night; until, at the edge of the forest, on a dark moorland, his admirable rider reined him in.

They were saved. But as the thane looked back he was seized with rage and grief. He saw fire blazing; his village was in flames. The red glow spread through the dark sky, darkened to an ever more angry crimson, and broadened to fill the earthwork.

'Everything there is afire!' thought Horymír bitterly. 'Buildings, yards full of grain, the stacks, all the harvest, all our work.'

And shaking his clenched right fist in the direction of the blaze he swore:

'May I burn to a cinder, may I be hewn in pieces with my own sword, if I do not take revenge for all, if I do not pay them back everything! And more, and worse!'

II

The village of Neumětely was utterly destroyed.

What the fire had not consumed, the miners carried away with them. With a rich booty they returned; they drove away the cattle, on stolen carts drawn by stolen horses they dragged the grain from Horymír's barns, and in wild glee they shouted on the journey, and back at home shouted still:

'If he feared hunger, let him go hungry!'

So they exulted. But there was silence and desolation in the burned village. The site of the fire, long shrouded in smoke, burned out at last, and the autumn wind carried its acrid stench across the countryside.

Before two days had passed Horymír gathered all the men of his clan, together with many others, good neighbours enraged by the violence of the miners.

When it grew dark, they all armed themselves well and rode out, with Horymír at the head, on his faithful white horse Šemík.

At the mines of Březový no-one suspected any evil. The miners were convinced that the fugitive Horymír was wandering through the district homeless, and that he was powerless to venture any move against them. Contentedly they lay down, thinking themselves safe, and did not even mount a guard. But late in the night they were awakened by a suffocating smoke and a sudden blinding red glare,

blazing up redly. The roofs were afire above their heads. Confused and terrified they rushed out, carrying their property and collecting their children together.

Then Horymír's company burst in upon them, cutting and thrusting with sword and lance. The thane himself on Šemík flashed sword in hand between the cottages, and erupting at the mine-shafts and workings cried to his people to smash and destroy everything.

Like phantoms of the night his angry company swarmed into the settlement, tore down the buildings, destroyed the tools, rolled great boulders down to choke the shafts, ruining everything that had been achieved by the hard work of the miners.

Before the day dawned the enemy was gone, vanished in the misty half-light of the morning. At Neumětely Horymír's company dispersed, but the thane himself hurried on. Šemík, fresh in his enchanted strength, carried him like the wind straight to the prince's seat, and when the sun rose Horymír, himself unwearied on his tireless horse, arrived before the gate of Vyšehrad.

The next day reports came to the prince's castle of what had happened at the mountain of Březový. Many of the miners hurried to Vyšehrad; all with one voice told of the horrors of that dreadful night, and all in indignation accused Horymír of the crime.

He, however, denied it, and called in witness the fact that at dawn on the day following that night he had already been at Vyšehrad. But Křesomysl, grieving for his silver mines, had Horymír cast into prison. Thence they led him forth again only when the jurors and the thanes whom the prince had called to the court were already assembled.

Horymír stood alone before the court, and against him a crowd of excited miners, demanding forcibly that he should be burned alive. The prince took their part, the thanes took Horymír's. They pleaded for him, that his life should be spared. But the voice of the miners weighed more, and the prince condemned Horymír to death.

Only one concession he made to the thanes, in moderating the sentence; Horymír was not to be burned alive, but to be executed with his own sword.

When this sentence was announced, Horymír addressed the prince:

'Honoured prince, by your justice I am condemned to death; and since I cannot have my life, I ask at least this one favour. Grant that before I die I may mount my faithful horse but once again, and ride on him for a moment of time. Then do with me what you will.'

'Ride, then,' said the prince, 'but without wings Šemík will be little help to you.' And he laughed, and ordered that the gate should be closed.

But Horymír, paying no head to Křesomysl's mockery, hurried with pleasure into the stables to his Šemík. He ran to him and embraced him round the neck, pressed his face against the horse's head and fondled him. Then he spoke one quiet word to him, and Šemík, neighing, pawed joyfully with his forefeet until the floor-boards thundered.

Then all men, prince and jurors and thanes in their ranks, even the miners and the guards and the people below in the courtyard, looked on in wonder as Šemík burst out of the stables and into the open, Horymír leading him by the bridle. Everyone admired the beautiful, fiery horse. He was white, dappled with grey, with a broad neck, long mane and a thick, flowing tail, and he paced on slender legs with small hooves, like a stag. His eyes gleamed as he tossed his spirited head and dilated his rosy nostrils.

His legs flashed in a playful, dancing step, and as Horymír leaped on his back he began to turn and sidle. In his delight at sitting his beloved horse again Horymír uttered a shout of joy, and Šemík reared on his hind legs and neighed until his neighing filled all the wide courtyard. With long, light leaps he began to circle the space. Horymír shouted for the second time, and Šemík leaped from one gate to the other. Close to the rampart Horymír shouted for the third time, and cried:

'Now, Šemík, up!'

Gripping with his knees, he took fast hold of the flowing mane, and at that moment Šemík cried aloud:

'Hold fast, my lord!' And with a leap he was up over the rampart, and with a second and gigantic leap he cleared the beamed battlements.

Everyone in the courtyard stood frozen in amazement.

The white horse and his rider went flashing over the edge, glimmering through the air like a bird, the horse's mane and the rider's hair streaming; then, like an arrow's flight, in an instant they fell and vanished.

In the castle men shouted aloud in astonishment and horror, and many rushed to the parapet to see where the desperate rider had fallen, where he lay with his Šemík, shattered in his blood.

They gazed from the ramparts and towers and gasped in renewed and redoubled astonishment, shouting in anger or in joy, according to where the miners stood and where the yeomen and squires. They pointed in excitement into the valley of Radotín, where with long leaps Šemík and Horymír were bounding over the plain.

Before the rider was lost to sight the thanes renewed their urgent pleas for him; the courtiers, after such a miracle, were easily persuaded to agree, and Křesomysl did not deny them.

He sent at once to Neumětely for Horymír, bidding him return in safety, for all was forgiven him. And the next day he came, but on another horse, not on Šemík, and submitted himself to the prince. But when the prince asked where Šemík was, the thane sorrowfully replied:

'There at home he stands in great melancholy, for by that gigantic leap he has done himself irreparable harm.'

Horymír did not stay long at Vyšehrad. The favour of the prince himself, the favour of the court, could not hold him there. His mind was with his faithful Šemík. As soon as he could he made his reverence to the prince and the courtiers, took his leave and hastened without drawing breath or sparing his mount to his own village, which his household and clan had returned to rebuild after their dispersal.

On arrival at Neumětely he hastened first to his beloved steed. The white horse was lying in his stable, for he could no longer stand; he informed his lord that he must leave him, and begged him not to give him to the birds or the wild beasts for a feast when he was dead, but to have him buried before the gate of his own courtyard.

Horymír in deep sorrow promised all, and took a sad farewell of Šemík. And when the beloved horse had breathed his last, all that he had asked was faithfully fulfilled.

Horymír buried him in the village, and to this day they show there a place marked with a stone, where the faithful Šemík lies buried.

When Prince Křesomysl had gone to his eternal rest, Neklan was enthroned at Vyšehrad, and ruled all the Czech race wisely and peacefully. With Litoměřice and Lemuze he maintained peace and friendship, and his word and will carried weight with their chieftains. But to the north and west he had an evil neighbour, the Duke Vlastislav, who ruled in the lands of the proud Lukanians along the Oharka and the upper Mže. Neklan was peaceable and prudent, Vlastislav wild and passionate; Neklan of a timorous heart, Vlastislav bold and warlike. He cared nothing for good neighbourly relations, nothing for right or justice, and he shed blood without mercy. He oppressed his neighbours cruelly, and more than once swept through the lands of Lemuze and Litoměřice and the whole Czech land with his wild hordes, levying taxes on all the countryside.

He took squirrels and black horses from the plough as taxes, and if anyone resisted, they had to pay tax not only for themselves but even for their dead. He took tribute, and he took people, too, most of all women and children, and those he took he sold into slavery. He had so many of them that he let them go cheaply to the Frankish merchants and the bearded Jews who came to buy both male and female slaves.

When he swept down for the last time upon the Czech lands he maltreated the unhappy country worse than ever before. Where the Lukanians passed everything was ablaze. They burned houses, towers, barns, stables, there was not a village that escaped the fire. All that was burnable they burned, did great slaughter with the sword, and drove away whole herds of cattle. The people took flight from the villages into the castles, behind walls and ramparts, but even these could not save them.

The castle of Dřevíč on the frontier did not escape the hand of Vlastislav; then Slaný, too, was stormed, then Budeč lay in ashes, and thence the Lukanians swept like a flood through the wide plain to Levý Hradec near Žalov, a holy place where the frowning cliff of Řivnáč towers above the Vltava.

They surrounded Levý Hradec, from which they intended next to attack the castle of Prague itself, and let no-one go out from the walls, nor anyone enter with food. There was great hunger within the castle when the siege grew too long. They had already killed all the animals within the walls, and even a handful of flour was scarce, and every shinbone a coveted prize.

Longingly the besieged people looked out from the walls and towers, their eyes fixed constantly on the 'great road' which led from Levý Hradec through Únětice near to Lysolaj, through the village of Holíšovice to the plain of Letná and Prague castle, which was the best-loved residence of the prince. Anxiously they watched for his army, which would surely come to deliver them.

But in vain. No help came from Prague castle, the 'great road' remained empty and deserted. They began to despair in Levý Hradec, and faint with hunger. Their cheeks fallen and their eyes glittering with fever and sickness, they laid their arms on the ground and said:

'We shall surely die here of hunger, for there's no help coming. Let us rather surrender to the Lukanians, let them do with us now what they will, kill us or spare us.'

And they would have done so, but before they took action they perceived that the Lukanians were raising the siege, forsaking the castle and preparing for departure. A reliable report had reached them that the men of Lemuze and Litoměřice, and their neighbours of Děčín with them, were riding through the Czech lands to the relief of the castle, and would take the Lukanian forces in the rear and flank.

Vlastislav in a rage swore a great oath:

'May Perun never come to my aid, may I be a slave henceforth to the end of my life, if I give in to the armies of Děč and Lemuze and Litoměřice.' And he vowed that he would humble the Czech lands, and hang up his shield in the gate of Prague castle as a sign of victory.

Then he departed from Levý Hradec to escape being crushed like a grain of corn between two millstones.

But soon he avenged himself, and first of all on the people of Litoměřice, for he built on their land a strong castle between the two hills of Medvěz and Přípet. He called it by his own name of Vlastislav, and installed in it a garrison of strong and brutal soldiers to plot against the neighbours, because they had helped the Czechs.

The people of Lemuze and Děč took fright at this; they asked for peace, and promised to abandon the Czechs and pay regular taxes. When the prince at Prague heard of this he was very downcast. Being of small spirit, he dared not venture alone, without allies, and therefore he resolved to give ground rather than go to war.

He chose a delegation of several thanes to go and talk terms of peace and friendship with the chieftain of the Lukanians, and take him precious gifts: several dishes of pure gold, two finely wrought helmets, beautiful shields, and ten splendid horses of noble pace and carriage.

Vlastislav, seated on a high wooden throne, carved and painted, received them in a fine sable cap decked with a heron's feather, and a splendid cloak of foreign weaving that fell in stiff folds, with great clasps to fasten it. He looked down at the messengers from on high through half-closed eyelids. Proudly he received them, and when they had delivered their lord's message, haughtily he answered:

'I have heard what your prince asks of us. I have seen the gifts he has sent to me. He acted foolishly in sending them. He has surely not sent me all the gold he has, nor all the horses and other goods. What he has sent he has sent only to whet my appetite. Take it back again, and tell your prince that I send him my thanks for this foretaste, and let him hide from me all he has and take good care of it. I am coming to him to take all, and with the rest this which I now return. And you, get you hence, and quickly, if you would not leave your heads here in place of gifts!'

The thanes in dread immediately turned and made their way home as fast as they could, only too glad to put Luka behind them. When they told their story at Prague castle, Prince Neklan turned pale, and did not hide his fear on hearing that Vlastislav in his over-bearing pride had set his heart on ruling the whole Czech land as he ruled his own.

II

As soon as the Duke of the Lukanians had made his haughty speech to the ambassadors from Prague he sent out the order through all five regions of the Lukanian land that every man should rise and take arms and join his army.

The herald rode at the head of an escort, all mounted on swift horses. He rode with his sword by his side, but another sword, the chieftain's sword of iron in a scabbard covered with hide, was borne before him point upwards. By his side his assistant wore about his waist a cord of plaited hemp. They rode like the wind, the herald and his comrade and their armed escort, through plains and valleys, forest and field. It was the springtime, when the corn was just coming into ear. From village to village they rode, from clan to clan, all through the hours of daylight from before dawn, and often into the late twilight.

Bursting into the enclosure of the village green, they at once called the head-man and all the youths and men of the clan. As they ran to join the assembly, the herald drew from its scabbard the chieftain's sword, brandished it before him in the air, and proclaimed his lord's command that everyone whose height exceeded the length of this sword must join the army at once, without a day's delay, that he must take shield and weapons and hasten to the chieftain's castle, where was appointed the muster for the war against the Czechs.

On that his comrade, unbinding the hempen cord from about his waist, held it high above his head, while the herald, pointing at the noose, pronounced his lord's dreadful threat that every man who reported to the field later than the day appointed should be hanged in such a hempen noose; and he reminded every man that no excuse would be accepted.

The herald further proclaimed that whoever owned falcon or kestrel, sparrow-hawk or buzzard should take it with him to the field, and that no man should leave any such bird of prey at home. Whoever disobeyed this order should die, executed by this same sword.

Once again he brandished the chieftain's sword until it sent sharp lightnings flashing in the sunlight. Then they measured against the sword all the men and youths, every one, and wrote down the number of them, so that they might let their lord know how many soldiers each clan was sending armed into the field.

Then they mounted their horses again, drove home the spur and rode on to the neighbouring clan, and so on and on. Rumour fled before them, and everywhere the chieftain's war-sword was awaited with excitement. The shepherds in the pastures gazed with wonder at the wild riders; in the villages the men welcomed them with acclaim, but the women in anxiety. Everywhere they brought agitation and clamour in their train, and trouble and care enough to the women and girls.

From the chieftain's castle they rode thus round Luka, the first region of the land, beautiful to behold. Everywhere in the fruitful plain the land lay rich and blessed, field and meadow, seas of flowers, their coloured ribbons glowing gold and rose among the verdant green, then again field after field, meadow and orchard, all bathed in the radiance of the spring sun. Through this paradise they rode with the war-sword until they had encircled all the villages, and turned away to the south, to the second region, lying on the right and left banks of the torrent Brocnice. When those parts had been summoned to arms they turned north to the Oharka, where before them on the horizon stretched the blue wall of the Ore Mountains. There they passed through the third region, the region of the river Úzká, and on the right bank and the left they summoned men by the sword and measured them by the sword, keeping count of the numbers.

Thence they hastened to the fourth region, to westward, the land beside the flood of Hutná. The war call rang abroad along the riverside and into the narrow valley of the Oharka, it echoed and thundered through the stream's deep gorge between the sheer banks and the rocks, where the waves murmured and roared.

And thence onward still, hasty and violent as a spring storm, to the mountains, to the upper course of the Mže, where among the black forests and hills and the dark marshes and broad swamps lie hidden the villages of Chlumčansko, the fifth region of the Lukanian land. When the inhabitants of these parts heard the chieftain's command and saw the flash of the herald's sword, they rose eagerly in wild joy, to the last man. They cared nothing for the measure of the sword, they neither wanted nor needed it; for they said they would all go, every man among them who was not too old or too young.

This wild, sunburned folk of the primitive forest rose in readiness, left field and woodland at once, and stretched out their strong, work-hardened hands for their weapons, for heavy maces and great metal-reinforced shields, covered with stretched black hides. They took from the mews their falcons and sparrow-hawks and kestrels, and coupled on leashes their fierce dogs of wolfish breed, long used to blood and fighting from their war with the wild beasts of the deep forests.

III

In the most remote corner of Chlumčansko, among lime and maple-trees on a hilly site beyond a wide marsh full of timothy grass and reddish brown moss, lay a small village of black fences and dark log walls, close to a long belt of forest. On the stout straw roofs grew green moss, houseleek and weeds.

The dwindling clan of the Žalans had been settled here from of old, and Straba, a young and stalwart man, was its headman at that time. He had neither brothers nor sisters, and one wife, and she was of Czech race. Straba had taken her from her own country as a slave when the Lukanians were last in arms and encamped before Levý Hradec. The captured Czech woman pleased him so much and took such possession of his mind, perhaps by some enchantment, that he said to her:

'You are my lawful prize, my bondwoman. Nevertheless, be my wife.'

She did as he willed, and became his wife, but in her heart she was not content. Life was grievous and sad to her in this remote village, longing drew her to her own homeland, and in bitterness of heart she remembered the horror and ruin the Lukanians had wrought in her native land. But she hid her grief and hid her anger, and her husband could not see into her mind.

But his stepmother, his dead father's widow, saw clearly and well. She was a tall woman of grave face and stern grey gaze, not young, but not yet an old woman. She understood magic and spells and had the gift of prophecy.

As soon as the chieftain's command was brought into the solitude of Žalov, the headman prepared to go to the army. He took down from the wall his shield, his bull-hide helmet with its iron hoop, sharpened his sword, made ready his arrows and fitted a new string to his pliant bow. He hung his mace to a saddle, and chose from the stable his best horse. It was neither beautiful nor large, nor of smooth and glossy coat, being indeed a shaggy beast, but swift as a swallow and hardened to all weathers, heat and frost, hunger and thirst.

Straba's young wife helped silently with these preparations, she brought him blankets and cloak, hide leggings with flexible straps for his legs, and put food in a pouch for him, bread and cheese, so that he might be provided for on his journey until he reached the chieftain's castle.

On the day before his departure Straba's stepmother said secretly to him: 'Come to the valley this evening, but don't say a word to anyone about it.'

When dusk came, the young farmer went out, as his stepmother had bidden him. He went to the forest beside the wide marsh, which was already growing dark; here and there in the flats showed the dark shapes of stunted alders and bog pines, and between the black clumps of harsh grass the pools reflected the gleam of the rosy sky. It was sunset, and windy, so that the turbulent rustling of the forest was borne distantly across the darkening swamp, and quivered still more loudly through the twilit valley. In its flanks rocks jutted, scattered here and there in the sparse grass, and above them and between them loomed an occasional tall tree, lime or oak or an ancient ash. Their tangled crowns were full of mistletoe, and in autumn and winter their bare branches were black.

In this gloomy valley beside a fire kindled upon a rock under an oak-tree, sat Straba's stepmother. Her hair hung loose, except where the pale band of a veil was drawn over her brow and ears and tied under her chin.

As soon as she saw her stepson she threw a strange root into the fire, and uttering the words of a powerful spell, she then said:

'Mist before me, mist behind me. Let no-one see us but the demons themselves!'

As she spoke, immediately the valley began to fill with white vapour. It spread through the valley, drifted up in wavering coils along the slope, above the vale, into the threshing tops of the rustling trees; and as Straba approached the fire the pale mist shrouded the whole hollow so thickly that the trees showed only as shadows. The flames burned clearly, and in their full blaze stood his stepmother, gazing with fixed grey eyes at Straba. She said to him:

'You are not my son, but your father was my husband. For that reason I have called you, to give you good advice; and here, for no-one but you must hear it.

'Know that I have cast my spells for you in vain. The Czech witches have more powerful enchantments. By means of their powers they overcome our charms. And as they overcome us, so you too will be overcome. I see clearly the misery to which you go. Alas, alas for our unhappy people! The gods lead you into battle, but they will turn to your enemies with their help.

'You will go into the field, but you will not return from it. The Lukanians are given into the hands of the Czechs. Even your duke will remain there, and all his men with him. Only you will escape death, if you do as I advise. Listen! When the battle begins, stand to arms against the first one who attacks you: Pierce him with your lance, but don't kill him. Cut off both his ears, hide and keep them, and mounting your horse, turn your back on the field. Pay no heed to the clamour and shouting behind you, don't look back, only flee. So shall you save yourself, but yourself alone.'

88

The red glow in the sky faded, the broad marsh grew black, and the stunted alders jutted from it like blacker shadows. Only the rotten tinder of a hollow willow-bole gleamed on the shore with a silent, secret light.

Straba passed by, going homeward from the valley. Deep in foreboding thought he walked, with rapid, uneasy steps. Before him his own yard was utterly dark among its great trees. The fire had long burned out, not even the gleam of a torch reddened there. Darkness and stillness; but as he entered the gate he heard a voice singing.

The singer was his wife and the song was a strange one, unknown to him. But she hushed suddenly when he walked in out of the darkness, and she made no answer when he asked her what she had been singing, and why just at that hour.

IV

Terror fell upon the prince at Prague, when he heard what was going on in Luka, and how Vlastislav was gathering together a great army. Neklan was afraid, and did not take heart even when they brought him the news that all the clans from every village of his race were hot with indignation at the insolence of the Lukanians, and all the country was up in arms and preparing for war.

Weapons were already clashing in the castle and on the plain of Letná around it. From all quarters clamoured the neighing of war horses, and the shouting and songs of the soldiers. But Prince Neklan crouched in the castle in the most remote chamber, and started at every sound. He could not master himself, he did not believe that he could win a victory over Vlastislav. In vain his friends encouraged him. He excused himself as a sick man, he complained that demons had weakened his body and softened his bones. His kinsman Čestmír, a youth beautiful to look upon and of handsome stature, bitterly reproached him for his unmanly behaviour, when all men were standing by in arms and waited only for him, and without him would lose heart. Neklan said at last:

'I won't go, I can't. But you go in my place. Take my arms and armour, and my horse, and you lead them. Let them think it's the prince who rides at their head.'

Then Čestmír took the prince's harness, the hauberk of chain-mail and the metal helmet of foreign workmanship, with the fine curtain of chain-mail to cover ears and cheeks, chin and throat, and the great shield shining with metalwork; he put on the prince's cloak, mounted Neklan's fiery black horse and went out to the plain of Letná with the foremost of the nobles in his escort, to where the army was assembled.

All the troops shouted with exultation and clashed their arms when they beheld their prince. Immediately they began to muster in battle array, foot soldiers and cavalry, in helmets of bulls-hide or shaggy hair-caps, with spears in hand, with slings and bows, and quivers full of well-flighted arrows.

Through the shining air flashed the lightnings of unsheathed swords, their points glittering; and in their ears many of the warriors also wore ear-rings that shimmered in the sun with a quivering brilliance. Čestmír on his black horse reviewed the army, having first made sacrifice to the gods on behalf of all.

He waved them forward with his sword, and shouted aloud in his youthful, vibrant voice, and they marched. The earth shook and thundered to the tramp of feet and the stamping of horses, and the air rang with songs and battle-cries. Company after company marched before Čestmír, the men of all the race, according to their clans and their degree and their strength in arms.

And there were hordes of them, when the men of so many clans were mustered all together, and hordes even from one clan, mighty in arms and even mightier in its teeming numbers, which marched in a separate company under the pennant of the tribe.

So passed the men of Netvořice and Tuře, the clans of Čjaradice and Drahelčice, nicknamed the Barefooted, the men of Běchovice, Úhonice, of Buděhostice and Nahoruby, of Žíň and Bozkovice, and the most audacious and the foremost in goods and gear, the men of Vršovice and Munice and the clan of old Těpta.

By the 'great road' the army marched to Lysolaj and on over the Goat's Back with its dark rocks, and leaving Levý Hradec on the right, hastened eagerly to meet the Lukanians and halt their violence and ravages.

But when they came to Tursko, in the wide plain, Čestmír halted his troops, for he could hear the Lukanians already drawing near. In good time he drew up his array on a low hill from which they could see the enemy army approaching like a black cloud, enormous, strong, outnumbering the army of Prague. But the general of the Czech forces was not dismayed by their numbers. Standing on an elevated spot near to an old oak-tree which grew solitary on the hill, he addressed his army. And the army listened to him reverently, believing that they were listening to the voice of their prince.

'Behold the proud sons of Luka!' said Čestmír. 'How many of our men have they killed already, how many villages burned, how many women and children led away into captivity! Now they come to burn again and kill again. They want to exterminate us and make slaves of us all. We must resist them, whether we will or no, to protect our families and save the Czech land from shame. We

are fighting for liberty, for our last salvation. Rather let us leave our bones here than bear the disgrace of fleeing before them.

'We will not fly! We'll stand our ground, and I will go before you. If my head falls, do not you take fright, but press on against them until you triumph. And in your triumph, if I should fall, bury me here in this spot.'

The army shouted its ardour, and cried through all the assembled companies: 'Where your head falls, there we'll leave ours also!'

'We shall triumph!'

'We'll slaughter the Lukanians!'

By this time the army of the Lukanians had flowed into the plain of Tursko, horse and foot, all well armed, with shields stoutly reinforced, many in coats of mail or at the least in wadded linen armour, all the race born men of war, especially the clan of the Trnovanians, and those from Žlutice and Radonice, with the men of Úhošť, Chraberec and Třebčice, and wildest of all the warriors from the regions of Chlumčansko beyond the forest, in their blankets and furs and skin caps, armed with great spears and heavy maces. They led packs of hounds on coupled leads, large, fierce wolf-dogs and ferocious shepherd dogs. Others bore on their wrists and shoulders birds of prey, hawks and falcons and sparrow-hawks and white buzzards. So they drew up their battle array across the wide plain facing south, opposite the Czechs, who with their left wing occupied a hillock to the west, and leaned their right wing upon a wooded rise above the village of Chejnov.

There arose a gigantic clamour from all the host of the Lukanians, like thunder rolling out of the clouds; the conflicting cries of ferocious beasts, the barking of dogs and yelling of human creatures, the neighing of horses and bellowing of horns, so that the uproar was borne afar across the field of Tursko.

At the head of all his host rode the proud Vlastislav in his metal helmet and plate-armour, with a naked sword in his hand. As soon as he saw the ranks of Prague, and saw that they did not flee but stood their ground, he halted his army and addressed them from the stirrups in a ringing voice:

'See these timorous cowards! See how they seize on the hills. But it will do them no good, for they're feeble, feebler far than we, and fearful of spirit. See how they dread us! They don't stand to meet us here in the plain, they're afraid to face us so. They'll take to their heels as soon as you attack. Up and at them, then, swiftly, violently, crush them under your feet like young corn crushed by hailstones. Loose your dogs upon them, and launch your hawks at them and scatter them like pigeons!'

Like shot arrows the hounds burst from their couplings, and in a frenzy of baying they flew forward in a many-coloured stream. At the same moment there gathered above the Lukanians a rustling cloud of wild birds. Loosed from their jesses they

took wing, and confusedly mingling they soared upward like snowflakes in a storm, the air vibrating with the humming of their wings and their screaming and mewing.

A shadow fell upon the Lukanian host from the living cloud, but in an instant it swept forward across the plain, as the vast darkness hurtled through the air towards where the army of Prague stood waiting.

On the earth beneath, fierce barking and howling, a demoniac baying of hounds in full cry; in the air, rustling and humming, and the clamour of countless voices, all mingling in a fearful pandemonium that deafened the ears. And after the hounds and the cloud of hawks went the war-cry of the Lukanians and the blaring of trumpets, until the torrent of voices and sounds rolled far and wide across Tursko.

The Lukanians in wild enthusiasm swept forward over the plain, thirsty for blood, and at their head Duke Vlastislav, on a horse with a streaming mane, shouting and brandishing his sword. About him and behind him came the companies of his soldiers, flushed and glaring in the fury of the attack and hoarsely screaming.

Then Čestmír, like a boulder torn from a mountain by lightning and rolled down to crush and destroy everything in its path, launched himself down the hill to meet the Lukanians. After him came his army. Clan vied with clan to overtake him, but always at the head flew Čestmír alone, in the armour of the prince. And now they clashed, and now they fought, striking, thrusting, hewing, Čestmír always in the thickest of the press. He hacked and hacked, and the heads of the Lukanians fell like poppyheads.

Vlastislav burst out of the throng suddenly as a lightning-flash, and rushed straight at the leader of the Czechs. Their struggle was like the frenzy of a storm, cruel and long. Blow upon blow, until the sparks rained down, until the rein fell from the Lukanian duke's one hand, and his sword from the other. He swayed sidelong from his horse, and down he crashed, dead and covered with blood, among the fallen and the wounded, trampled under the hooves of the horses.

A shriek of rage and horror, a cry of wild joy echoed through the tumult. The Praguers struck out about them with new strength, forcing their way forward, the Lukanians were already giving ground and cowering before them. At that moment Čestmír's horse fell. But the rider himself, leaping clear on nimble feet, still hacked and thrust his way forward, warding off his foes with his shield.

More than one arrow stuck fast now in his chain-mail, more than one lance jutted from the hide of the black shield. And always the arrows and the spears flew and struck quivering in the shield with violent blows, their shafts vibrating, until even the strong arm of the hero shook, exhausted with the weight. Čestmír cried to his soldiers to bring him another shield, and would have cast his own away, but in that instant a heavy lance pierced his body, and the general fell to the earth with his shield on his arm and his sword in his hand, full of arrows and murderous lances in the midst of his terrible reaping.

So it happened as he had foretold before the battle. His head fell, but his soldiers, raging at this loss, pressed forward ever more furiously and slaughtered all before them, sparing not one man, until they had slain the Lukanians to the last man. The birds of prey had scattered and flown away, the fierce dogs were slain or fled, but of the Lukanians every man remained on that battle-field, even the duke, excepting only Straba, as his stepmother had prophesied in the valley.

The insolence of the Lukanians was crushed, their strength shattered. The army of Prague shouted with exultation, but their rejoicing was silenced when they beheld their dead leader. They bore him in his harness, his shield full of lances, they bore him to the hillock where he had desired to be buried. And there, when they had disarmed him of helmet and armour, they burst into loud and bitter lamentations, recognising the bold Čestmír, and realising how he had sacrificed himself.

Then they prepared a grave for him at once on the hillock, beneath the ancient oak, and when they had burned and buried the body on the night following the battle, they raised a great mound over the tomb, and the whole army took part in the solemn rites for their fallen general.

They made ready great quantities of honey, and brewed mead from it, and then they sat down to drink, and all together they drank to his memory. And Neklan came from Prague castle and wept over the grave of Čestmír. And when they had completed the ceremonies and finished their drinking the entire army rose and pressed on farther into the lands of the Lukanians.

V

On his fleet but unlovely horse Straba rushed away from the terrible battle. The point of his spear was still wet with blood, for at the beginning of the fight he had pierced the first Czech warrior who rushed at him. Straba went no farther into the engagement. Hacking off the ears of the fallen soldier, he mounted his horse again, and paying no heed to the uproar, the screams and the trumpets, he rode headlong away as though there were phantoms hard on his heels.

So he fled until evening; and in the night he hardly gave his horse time to breathe before he was galloping on again, through the fields and fallows of the lands of Chlumčansko. Villages and settlements he avoided, so that he need not confess how he had fled from the battle. The day passed, and a second night after it, and at dawn after this second night he rode, weary man on weary horse, into the remote solitude of his clan.

The village still slept in twilight, and darkness still clung in the old lime-trees, beyond which gleamed the first faint streak of the east. As Straba rode into the courtyard he met certain women coming out of his house. They started in dismay when they saw him, and sorrowfully they said:

'At an unhappy moment you are come.'

He leaped from his horse and rushed into the room, still dim in the dawn twilight. On the bed beside the window lay something beneath a white cloth, and by its outline he knew it to be a human corpse. The shutters were open to give free flight to the soul. Straba strode to the bed and whipped off the cloth. In the pale ray of the dawn, trembling through the open window, he beheld the ashen face of his young wife. Her eyes were closed, her hair streamed loose about her, and on her breast — clotted blood, a deep wound.

He stiffened, unable to believe what he saw; and at that moment his step-mother stood behind him like an apparition, motionless in her white robe, her grey eyes gazing sternly at the dead woman.

'Draw back her hair,' she said darkly.

He drew back the thick, beautiful hair from his young wife's right temple, possessed by a frightful suspicion. He drew back the heavy hair and gazed at the wound it had covered. In trembling haste now he drew aside the hair from the left temple. And there again the same bleeding wound.

Dumb with amazement and agitation, he hastily opened his pouch and drew from it the ears with their bloodstained ear-rings. They belonged to a woman, he recognised it now; then he knew that it was she who had attacked him in the battle, that she had wanted to kill him, and that he had killed her instead. And it flashed through his mind how she had behaved before his departure, and how in the late evening she had sung to herself that strange song.

'You knew this!' he shrieked at his stepmother.

'But you would not have believed it. You were under her spell. She was a Czech woman, and she hated us. Come and make sacrifice to the gods in the valley.'

And Straba, giving orders that the corpse should be carried away out of the village, went out to the sombre valley after his stepmother, frowning and dazed as though in a frightful dream.

Durynk and Neklan

I

Grief had fallen upon the land of Luka, and lay over it like a dark and heavy shadow. There was not a clan, not a village which did not have many dead to mourn. Everywhere in bitterness and tears they spoke the name of the field of Tursko, where the strongest and bravest of the men of Luka had perished. Everywhere they lamented them, not only their deaths, but also that their bodies lay in the field at the mercy of the birds of prey.

Terror contended with grief. The news had flown through the land that the Czechs were marching on from Tursko, and had already crossed the frontier. Horror rushed before them into every region. People fled from the frontiers into the interior, to the shelter of forests and castles, and brought terrified accounts of how the Czechs were now taking their revenge upon every village.

The rumour was no empty one, nor did it spring only from their fears. By day the clouds and columns of black ascending smoke from fires bore witness to that, and by night the ill-omened glow that reddened the sky. Villages were burning, and many a field of rich grain withered in a sea of flames, while the wind carried its smoke and stench far across the countryside.

And there was no defence. The strong men had remained at Tursko. The enemy advanced rapidly, overwhelming region after region. Everywhere they begged for mercy, and with desolate entreaties surrendered themselves to the prince of Prague, who was destroying and burning their castles on all sides, first Vlastislav's castle, then his remaining strong fortresses on the Oharka in Luka. But they did not capture the son of Vlastislav there. Certain of the people came and betrayed where he was, hidden in the hut of an old woman, in the rocks beside the river. Neklan sent his guards there at once, and before two days had passed he beheld before him the young orphan, Vlastislav's only son.

He was five years old, a lovely child, a little boy with soft golden curls already waiting for the ceremony of their first cutting. He stood before his father's enemy, never dreaming of his misfortune and his danger, and fixing him innocently with his clear eyes, made his bow as he had been taught.

And Neklan was moved with pity towards him, for his tender age and his hard fate, and for his charming appearance. He did not harm a hair of his head, nor did he even take him away with him into captivity. He left him in his own country, in the region of Luka itself, and had a castle built for him there, so that the duke's son should have a seat worthy of his dignity. This castle was called Dragúš. But it was not a fortress, for Neklan took the precaution of having it built in an approachable and vulnerable spot, so that it should not afford support to the Lukanians if they should ever conspire together and start a rebellion.

Then Neklan returned into Bohemia, and with all his great booty made a ceremonial entry into Prague castle. There he made plentiful sacrifices, glorifying the gods who had given him the victory, praising them and giving thanks that the dreadful enemy was wiped out who had haunted his mind with fears from his awakening at daybreak to his lying down at evening, spoiling his rest and sleep like a nightmare.

The proud race of the Lukanians was humbled, and he who should some day have ruled over them, Zbislav, Vlastislav's little son, lived quietly in retirement at his castle of Dragúš. And with him lived his tutor, a man of foreign birth, a Serb named Durynk, in whom Vlastislav had placed complete trust.

Neklan, too, had confidence in him, and confided Zbislav once again to his care, and with him the castle of Dragúš. Summer passed, and autumn, and winter came on, the first winter after the battle of Tursko and the death of Vlastislav. The days shortened and grew ever more mournful and sad. And so did the mind of Durynk. He paced uneasily through the castle, as though he could find no rest anywhere.

An evil thought was with him wherever he went, like a shadow, and gave him no peace. Ambition and greed put it into his mind. Endlessly an inner voice was whispering to him:

'Get rid of this boy, get rid of him! Neklan surely can have no peace as long as the son of Vlastislav lives. Do away with this son, and you'll relieve the prince of his load, and the prince will reward you — and richly, richly! This castle you hold in stewardship for the boy will be your own, and all the district round it. You'll be lord and master, and not merely a steward and a servant. You'll be putting the prince of Prague under an obligation if you rid him of this child once and for all —'

Thus the demon whispered to him, and so this cruel thought tormented him without ceasing and he could not drive it away. It returned to him again and again, and most of all when in solitude. Until at length the sudden dreadful thought would seize him even when he sat with Zbislav by the blazing hearth in the winter twilight. Then the boy would wonder uneasily what was happening, that Durynk should stare at him so strangely with his greenish eyes beneath their thick brows.

But the child would be reassured at once when his tutor, rousing himself out of his dark thoughts, stroked his pupil's golden hair and spoke tenderly and affectionately to him once again.

Thus gently one day he invited Zbislav to go down with him to the river to catch fish. The charming little boy jumped for joy, and put on his cap and fur coat and ran out eagerly. Durynk, with an evil intent in his heart, took with him a broad axe, and said that they would use it to hack out a hole in the ice to get at the fish. Zbislav danced along beside him delightedly. They approached the riverside by a path which lay deep in snow. It was late afternoon, and a clear and frosty day.

The landscape was deserted, and silence hung over the river. Motionless along the shore stood the old willow trees, vaulted and dark, and the tangled alders with their bare branches. Only little cones showed black upon the trees, or lay dark in the snow, which shimmered with a glittering light, as though full of crystals. Even the tall, withered grass along the shore, and the thickets of bushes, were white and sparkling with sharp needles of snow. The river lay silent. On the gleaming, greenish ice that covered it little clusters of frozen snow shone like white water-lilies. Zbislav ran gaily on to the ice, and would have crossed to the farther shore, but his tutor called to him:

'Wait now, and watch, when I cut a hole.'

And he began to cut. The boy watched every stroke curiously, marking how the ice splintered, split and shattered until the water glinted through, and he could see deep into it through the wide opening. Durynk invited him coaxingly:

'See, my lord, look closely, see how the fish are swimming under the water. See how many of them, how they swarm there.'

The boy, with perfect trust and suspecting nothing, went down on his knees and stared down eagerly into the water, looking for the fish. And as he knelt and bent his curly head low, the axe struck deep into his slender neck.

Blood gushed over the pure ice and the white snow. Durynk threw aside the axe, drew out a sharp knife from the pouch at his belt and completed his abominable work. Then he fled in haste from the spot.

In the alders and the tree-tops it was already growing dark, but between the trunks gleamed the last red streak of the departing day, crimson along the horizon. In that hour of deep dusk the people found on the ice the headless body of a little boy. By the cap which had fallen from his curls and by his fur coat they recognised the poor body as that of their prince's son. Aghast, they grieved and lamented, pitying the poor child, and they carried his body to the castle.

But there they hunted in vain for Durynk. They were told that only a little while earlier he had had a horse saddled, and had ridden away from the castle on it. Where, no-one said, for no-one knew.

II

Durynk set his course straight for Prague castle. When he arrived there, Prince Neklan was just in counsel with his nobles. Durynk, wishing to announce his deed before them all, did not wait, but entered the council hall. He gave them greeting, and when the prince, astonished by his coming, beckoned him forward, he spoke out aloud before the assembled council:

'I was a faithful servant to the Duke of Luka, but to you, O Prince, I want to be even more faithful. Believe this, and know that with one stroke of this axe I have made it possible for you, Prince, and for all of you, my lords, to sleep safely in your beds, no longer forever with one ear open. I bore in mind that he who'd keep his house and thrive leaves no spark of fire alive. This last little spark I have quenched and put out, to save you from future ruin.'

Unwrapping the bundle he carried under his arm, he drew out from a white cloth the severed head of a golden-haired little boy. It still looked just as in life. Durynk laid it upon the table before the prince and his nobles, and cried, pointing at the head:

'Behold, the avenger of his father's blood, who would some day have destroyed you, lies defeated at no cost in your blood. Trust me, this child, had he reached manhood, would have removed the bloodstained heads from many of you and yours.'

Prince and nobles stood sick with horror, and Neklan turned his face away. Voices of rage and revulsion and disgust rang through the hall. Then the prince rose from his place flushed with anger, his eyes flashing, and cried vehemently to Durynk:

'Ignoble man, take away your gift out of our sight! Whom did you wish to serve? Me? And do you think I could not have done what you have done? And I should have been destroying my enemy, but you have killed your own lord. The son of your benefactor, ungrateful man! I never bade you kill him, but ordered you to use him honourably. You should have guarded and protected him, and is this how you have dealt with him? And you expected a reward? Well, I will give you your reward, and indeed it is a great gift I offer you. Hear it! Of three deaths you may choose whichever you will. You may leap to your end from a high

rock, hang yourself on whatever tree you choose, or fall upon your own sword.'

Pale as snow Durynk heard the verdict of the angry prince; then, with head and eyes lowered, he crept from the hall, trembling and breathing to himself:

'Alas for me, this I never expected. Alas, alas for me!'

But no-one pitied him. And Durynk went away from the castle and hanged himself on a certain tall alder which stood beside the road. From that day until it was destroyed, this tree went by the name of Durynk's alder.

III

At that period there extended over Skalky, opposite Vyšehrad, an ancient and holy wood. In the dim depths of the grove, under the shelter of huge trees, there stood on a mossy boulder a frowning image of Morana, the terrible goddess

who conducted human souls to the threshold of eternity. In the sombre shades of the wood and in the open highlands round about it stretched the fields of her pitiless dominion, and here numerous mounds heaved their rounded green shapes out of the grass over the ashes of the dead.

Lower down the slope, near the brook Botič, above which the branches of close-growing trees intertwined, there was a smaller graveyard; but it enshrined more distinguished ashes.

Here in the shadow of the murmuring boughs, in tombs lined with stones and covered by tall barrows, the chieftains and princes of the land lie at rest. The wise Přemysl, who gave law and order to the land, was the first to be buried here, and all those who ruled from the princely throne after him followed him to this resting-place: Nezamysl, Mnata, Vojen, Vnislav, Křesomysl. And here, when his heart stilled in death, they laid Prince Neklan also.

Then the nobles and elders of the clans met in the grove by Jezerka and chose Hostivít to be their prince. They led their choice in a clamorous procession to Vyšehrad, and there seated him upon the princely throne, and invested him with the princely cap which had once adorned the head of Přemysl.

And after long years, when he too went down to death, they laid him in the lower burial place beside his ancestors.

Legends of Christian Times

I HAVE SEEN THE SHADOWS OF PAST AGES...

Vrchlický

A new age began, and with it new and strange events worthy of remembrance. *A* new age began, as the forerunners of Christianity came to the land. They came like the first gleam of daylight before the dawn, and after them it was light, for they brought the knowledge of the only God.

107

A song rang out from the depths of a dark wood on the Moravian border, and resounded from the cloudy dimness of the forests in the Slav tongue:

'Let us call upon our God and our Redeemer, let us go before His face and declare His praise.

'Oh sing unto the Lord a new song, O sing unto the Lord, sound forth His glory among the nations—'

And behold, from the frontier wood in the gateway of the land, by which travellers enter Moravia by way of the castles of Litomyšl and Hrutov, along the road to Trstenice came forth the priests of the one God, Bishop Methodius with his companions and his pupils. He was the first, together with his brother Cyril, that holy man, to sow the grain of the holy learning and of good works in the pagan hearts in the lands of Moravia and Slovakia.

Archbishop Methodius, having come from glorious Velehrad, stood on the threshold of Bohemia and blessed it, and began the work of God at once in these border regions of the land, at the castle and settlement of Litomyšl. From there he pressed on deeper into the country with his priests; and everywhere he proclaimed his message, teaching and preaching the word of the holy books and their wisdom.

The Czechs rejoiced to hear the wonderful works of God in their own language, and flocked to hear the preachers and to listen to Methodius, in whom burned the true love of Christ and pure compassion. They listened devoutly as he proclaimed:

'I sprinkle you with pure water, and you are cleansed of your idols and of your sins. The only God will have mercy on you and cast out your offences.'

His speech and his teaching and the singing of his priests found favour with them, and they came willingly to be baptised, as their prince Bořivoj had already been, and with him his wife Ludmila, the daughter of Slavibor, chieftain of Pšovka. The people gathered together in crowds when the priests conducted their services to God in the Slav tongue, for they possessed in the Slav language the Gospel and the psalter and other books.

Soon the people lifted penitent prayers, and in sincere devotion sang as the priests taught them: 'Lord, have mercy upon us!' and other sacred hymns.

Wherever the holy apostle lingered for a longer time in his preaching, he founded churches to the glory of God, in memory of Saint Clement. The first of these he founded in Litomyšl at the prince's castle, and this was the first of the churches he dedicated to Saint Clement. The second consecrated in this name was at Hradec on the Elbe, the third at Sadská, the fourth at Vyšehrad, and the fifth at Levý Hradec.

The light of grace penetrated the thick border forests and, shining through all the land, pierced the gloom of the secret pagan groves. And they perished. The people of the new faith came and destroyed them, overturning the idols, felling the sacred trees in the fields and the valleys and burning them.

When all these had been swept away, they ordered that never again should anyone lift up new-born children over the flames and dedicate them to the spirits of the fire, nor should anyone plead that this rite would be beneficial to the child all the days of his life. They ordered that no-one should offer sacrifices to demons and evil spirits, or bury their dead in woods and fields, or hold ceremonies at crossroads and places where three tracks met for the repose of their souls, or dress up actors in masks over the dead and invoke empty shadows.

Perun's image was thrown down from Vyšehrad, the worship of the terrible Morana ceased. Her frowning statue in the grove at Skalky was shattered, and many other idols also were cast down and broken.

The gods of forests, waters, winds and darkness vanished. Many grieved for them, and had no wish to renounce them in the waters of baptism, and in particular witches, sooth-sayers and magicians. They fled deeper into the forests, into secret valleys under the mountains. There they carried away with them their ancestors and their idols, and there continued to prostrate themselves before them and offer sacrifices, cursing the new God.

But the new God was strong.

The clamour of the bells rang out over the wide countryside with power, the hymns swelled ever louder and more commandingly in the sacred, moving dimness of the holy chapels and the round churches, under the blue clouds of fragrant incense, before the altars splendidly adorned with paintings on a gold ground, and with rich carving bright in the gleam of the candles.

A new world began, and with it new and wonderful events worthy of remembrance.

King Svatopluk

In the church of Velehrad the people had finished the hymn after the sermon; the last echoes of the sacred song had died away, and the eyes of all present turned to the altar. The hour of Holy Mass had come, and Archbishop Methodius himself was to conduct it; a solemn service, for it was a great feast day, the day dedicated to the holy apostles Peter and Paul.

The candles were already alight on the altar. They had been burning for a little while, but Methodius did not come. In the church the people waited, quietly praying. Moment after moment passed. The sun was already high, its rays fingered their way in at the windows of the cupola, and filtered downwards in a golden stream into the nave of the church. Suddenly everything blazed into brightness and clarity, the walls, the pictures of the saints on their golden ground, the heads of the believers, women and grown men and elders, and the fair locks of young girls and children.

In this bright radiance the reddish flames of the candles paled, for they were already burning down. A whisper passed through the church, carried in hushed voices, and people looked round, bending their heads together, speaking together quietly and questioning what had happened to cause this delay. Softly the question passed, and softly came back the answer, borne to every corner of the holy place: that the archbishop was waiting for the king, that the king had given orders that High Mass should not be celebrated without him, that they must wait for him, that he would surely come.

'Where is he? Where is the king?'

'Why doesn't he come?'

Everywhere they were asking, and everywhere they gasped and started when someone replied that he was out hunting. This morning early, before dawn, the king had gone out hunting with a numerous retinue and a crowd of retainers. Hunting, on such a holy day!

Then suddenly they fell silent as the revered Methodius appeared. The hour of noon was already at hand, it was impossible to postpone Holy Mass any longer. The archbishop was followed to the altar by priests and deacons, all in rich vestments. He began the holy service; deacons and priests assisted him, burned incense, intoned and sang the sacred music.

The people, kneeling or standing with folded hands, gazed upon the beauty of the altar in the full gleam of the candles, that shimmered over the priestly robes and the carvings and pictures. They listened to the prayers, and to the songs of the priests, as their voices echoed under the vault. And they all understood the reading of the Word, the prayers and psalms; they understood every word, and filled with ardent and heartfelt piety they lifted up their minds in rapture to God. They had forgotten the King.

At that moment there pealed into the church the sound of a wild, dark tumult, a confused mingling of sounds and voices, drawing near in great haste, and mounting like the thunder of a storm. Rushing and wild shouting, the sound of horns, the barking of dogs and neighing of horses. The din was close at the very church doors now, loud on the threshold; now it echoed beneath the vault itself; and now the author of the storm strode up the nave of the church, straight to the altar. At the head of his wild retinue came King Svatopluk with his cap on his head and his sword in his hand, and after him his huntsmen with their hounds.

The priests fell silent, the people drew back aghast, shrinking into the shelter of the walls and columns. But the king, paying no attention to anyone and brandish-

111

ing his naked sword, strode to the altar and burst out in wild anger at the archbishop. Why had he not waited? Why had he gone to the altar, why had he not waited? But at the steps of the altar he checked his rash advance and stood staring with blazing eyes, face to face with the man of God.

Confronting him, the archbishop stretched out his right hand.

'Not a step farther!' he cried in righteous anger, 'lest God strike you on the spot! You are possessed with devilish pride. I am to obey your whim rather than the spiritual law. And you do not respect the church of the Lord! For that offence you are accursed, and God will humble you.'

The king crimsoned from neck to brow, blind and mad with rage; yet this speech halted him like a blow. His gaze sank, overborne by the nobility of his adversary; he drew back, lowering his sword, and hesitated; then, turning, he rushed out of the church, and after him his yelling huntsmen and his train.

But when he reached his castle he was possessed once again with pride and defiance. He would not acknowledge his fault, and he was filled with shame and rage to think that he had let himself be defeated by the word and the glance of the bishop. He sent to him at once, and ordered him never again to come into his sight and presence. The holy man did as he was bidden, and immediately set out on an apostolic journey from Velehrad through the regions of which he was the spiritual guardian and leader; and everywhere he preached the word and confirmed the Christian faith. And so he did until the day of his death.

But all this time the king remained adamant against him, ungratefully forgetting what this saintly man had done for the Moravian empire, how he had brought there the light of the true Gospel, and dedicated to its people all his labour and his life. Still he persecuted him, and interfered with his Slav order on the advice of his enemies from Germany.

But Svatopluk did not remain unpunished; the word of Methodius was fulfilled. Fortune forsook the mighty king who lay under a curse. He was attacked in arms from all sides, he and his people: the Poles, the Hungarians, the Germans, even the Czechs, were in ferment and would not submit to his rule. All men shamefully looted and harried his Moravian kingdom.

The king gathered all his strength to defend himself against so many enemies and repel these troubles from his empire. But storm followed storm and blow followed blow, and ruin dogged him constantly.

Then the king pondered, and realised that God had sent this trouble upon him, that all this misfortune had fallen upon his realm by reason of his pride and insolence. And often now he remembered Bishop Methodius, against whom he had sinned so grievously. The saint was ever in his mind, and remorse possessed his heart.

He grieved deeply in the spirit when he heard that the number of his enemies was increasing, that the kingdom suffered ever worse deprivation, and the lament of the oppressed was uplifted now from all sides and wrung his heart. So he called together his nobles and the foremost of his squires and counsellors, and asked them what he must do. But none of them was able to give him any advice against the dispensation of God.

When this council, which he had called in his military camp, ended with the evening he withdrew alone, saddened and grieving, into his tent. And none among his courtiers and his subjects ever saw him again. The guard did see him when at about midnight he again emerged from his tent, mounted the horse which was tethered beside it, and rode quietly through the sleeping camp. No-one noticed him, and the guards who stood at the edge of the camp recognised him and did not challenge him; respectfully they let him pass, although it seemed strange to them that he should ride out so late at night.

No-one guessed that for a long time he had found no peace or contentment in all his glory and power, so grievously did it burden his conscience that he had used so harshly the noble benefactor of the Moravian land, and troubled his order and his rites. In his sleepless nights he had meditated contritely how he could atone, until in this hour he had resolved that he would give up everything that had led him into such arrogance and insolence, all his royal might and splendour. He would leave everything, his army, his court and his servants, his treasures and his fine arms, all the power that had led him into sin. He would forsake everything, in order that the Moravian kingdom might be relieved of the misfortune and suffering it endured for his sake.

He left the camp and rode through the solitary night, until he came to a certain spot on the slopes of the mountain of Zábor, dark on all sides with extensive and impenetrable woods. Here in time past three hermits, with his support, had built a church.

In this black forest, in this remote place among the trees and thickets, he pierced his horse's breast with his sword, and then buried in the ground the blade reddened with the blood of the faithful beast. Unarmed he walked on through the gloomy groves, unwearying, and prayed as he went, until with the dawn he came to the place where the hermits dwelt.

At this time they did not know who he was, nor did they suspect, for until this hour they had never seen him, and he himself did not disclose his identity. He said only that he was a penitent who wished to devote himself to the service of God, to fasting and piety. So they received him among them, and Svatopluk, sometime king of the Moravian empire, became the humble and obedient servant of the simple hermits. In a poor wooden hut, in a rough monkish gown, lived the lord who had formerly clothed himself in sables and precious robes, and inhabited the spacious and splendid halls of royal Velehrad.

As long as he lived he remained unknown among them. Only when he felt that his hour was close upon him did he make himself known to the monks, and tell them who he was and why he had come there. And having spoken, he died.

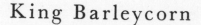

King Barleycorn

I

When King Svatopluk vanished thus without trace, the people of Moravia took thought to choose another lord for themselves. They looked about them to see who would be the most worthy and suitable person to ascend the royal throne.

At this time there lived in the district of Přerov at the castle of Chropín a squire, the lord of wide estates, a rich man, esteemed by lords and squires alike, and beloved by his subjects. He ruled them humanely and, having the gift of the spirit, he judged wisely and justly. And so lords and yeomen said to one another:

'Why should we look elsewhere for a ruler, when we have him here among us?' And they chose the lord of Chropín with one voice, without any disputes or arguments, and everywhere their choice was praised, and the people rejoiced over their new king.

In order to get to know every corner of his Moravian empire, the king made a great journey through his realm; everywhere he was greeted with great acclaim and much glory, whether he rode south to the regions where the grapes ripen, or through rich and happy Haná, or north or east or west through the valleys between the forested hills. Everywhere they wished to do him honour; lords and yeomen outdid each other to gain his favour, they flattered and praised him, brought him gifts, and lavished upon him extravagant feasts and rich banquets. When he returned to his castle of Chropín he was oppressed and discontented. It seemed to him too quiet and deserted there, nothing at home gave him pleasure, not even the devoted affection of his lovely and gentle wife. He longed for loud and lavish entertainment. So he ordered his courtiers to arrange feasts and invite to them many and distinguished guests.

Lords and squires in rich robes hemmed with fur, with shining sabres and swords at their splendid belts, in expensive caps trimmed with heron's plumes, rode into Chropín on fine horses with embroidered saddle-cloths. They came riding from all quarters of the realm, so that the castle could hardly hold them, and the little town was full of their servants and their horses. There were feasts in the castle, and great celebrations, and that not once nor twice. During this time the nobles fell in with their lord's will, and celebrated with luxurious feasts and entertainments, at which the guests sat long and drank deeply.

When the labouring men returned from the fields at evening, the babel of merriment rang loud from the castle of Chropín; cups clinked, stringed instruments and songs echoed in the glow of torches and candles. And when the people, having slept briefly after their heavy labour, rose early in the morning to go to the fields again, in the castle the clamour and gaiety still continued.

Then they gazed gravely at their lord's palace, wondering aloud anxiously what manner of government this could be, and what would come of it. And everyone remembered their most kind and gentle lady, the queen. They pitied her from their souls, saying to one another what she must be enduring, and how hard this must be for that good lady to bear, for she held aloof from festivities and banquets, which gave her no pleasure.

They were not anxious without reason. Neither his own nor the royal income could any longer pay for the king's hospitality. So he began to levy oppressive taxes, ever more and more of them, and greater and greater; and he ordered his tax-collectors to bring pressure to bear at need if his subjects tried to avoid payment.

The people now looked towards the castle of Chropín with anger and hatred, and they complained bitterly against the king, and cursed him. Only when they spoke of the queen was their speech unchanged. Indeed they regarded her and spoke of her now with even deeper sympathy, saying how she pleaded and entreated for them to the king, begging him not to grieve and oppress them so cruelly.

And what they said was true; but not one of them saw the tears which the queen wept in solitude and secret. No-one heard how gently and sincerely she reproached the king, out of her anxiety and love for him, nor how the king flared into anger against her and roughly repelled her, sending her away trembling and with drooping head, her eyes so darkened by tears and shame that it was wonder she did not stumble. Until one day the king, when he had again levied new taxes and the queen had once again interceded for her people, flew into a rage and drew his sword on her, flying at her so fiercely that she barely managed to escape from the room.

In his frenzy the king gave orders that she should be driven away out of the castle that very instant, for he never wished to set eyes on her again. And when he looked out from the window towards the gate, to see that his order was being carried out, the very sight of the poor lady sent him into such a renewed fury that he rushed out of the room and flew after his wife with drawn sword. But the queen caught sight of him in time.

Now she had no resting-place and no refuge anywhere. In deathly fear she looked round, but there was nowhere she could shelter. Only a field of ripening barley stood beside the road, a broad, rich field, that shone white and fair in the sunlight with its harvest of rich ears, shimmering with innumerable silvery beards.

She fled through the barley, until in a moment she vanished in it as though she had fallen into a golden pool. And immediately the waves that convulsed the field were stilled again, and the surface of the barley closed and stood motionless and silent as though no breath of air stirred. The king came running, only to search in vain for the place where his lady had disappeared.

The village women found her later, and by her side a child to whom she had given birth there. They carried them into the village and there cared for them tenderly, and to the queen's son they gave the name of Barleycorn, because he had been born in the field of barley. But the king got to know about his lady's place of refuge, and having no pity even on his own child, he had both wife and son removed away from that place. Soldiers came and took them away to some far region, and no-one knew where. But what had happened did not fade from the king's mind. Often he saw again the tormented face of his lovely wife, and

often thought of his only son. And most frequently of all when he wearied of his guests, of his feasts and empty delights, and sought solitude.

Then he was possessed with such a fever of longing that at last he sent messengers to his wife and child, to bring them back to him at the castle of Chropín. The envoys returned, but empty-handed and terrified, and the king was filled with dread when he heard that the queen and the little prince had vanished from their place of exile, and that no-one knew where they had gone.

He gave orders immediately that search should be made for the lost pair, and the first to set out in obedience to the order were the people of Chropín and the district of Přerov; and that willingly and gladly, for they were setting out to find their beloved queen. The king himself took horse and went out with his companions to look for his family. He rode and rode, not leaving out of consideration any corner of his realm; he searched the plains and he searched the mountains, he hunted through villages and castles, forests and caverns, until he came to a large, dark wood on the mountain of Zábor.

There in his search he entered the dark cavern of an old hermit with a long, white beard; and he asked the pious old man if he had any news of the queen, and of her son Barleycorn. The hermit rose, and standing face to face with the lord of Chropín, gazed at him with the stern regard of a judge, and spoke to him with the voice of prophecy:

'For your sins and your offences you are not worthy of your noble wife and of your son. He will heal what you have injured. As you are the ruin of the Moravian land, so he will be its blessing and salvation. As they curse you, so they will bless him. Know that you will never find him, nor even see him. He will reveal himself and appear when things are at their worst with the Moravian nation, when their enemies afflict them most sorely. When it seems that the final destruction of his people is approaching, then Barleycorn will come with great might, drive away the enemy and set Moravia free from the foreign yoke. But as for you, go and do penance!'

Broken in mind the king returned to his castle. He acknowledged his sin, his conscience tormented him, and longing for his wife and child gave him no rest. Like a black cloud he wandered through the castle of Chropín. He avoided people and sought solitude, until suddenly he mustered his courtiers again, filled the castle with guests and held high revel. But the gay voices of strangers gave him no comfort. Abruptly he left the table, left his guests, and paced without rest all night through the halls and courtyards, until despair overwhelmed him, and he leaped into the bottomless well of the castle.

II

The hermit's prophecy about the son of the lord of Chropín flew like wildfire through the Moravian land, and the people unceasingly expected the coming of King Barleycorn. In the castle of Chropín they kept the table constantly laid for him and a chamber made ready, as though he might come at any moment.

They waited for King Barleycorn, they waited and looked for him, the people of Chropín itself, the cities of Přerov and Žalkov, and all the other inhabitants of the province of Přerov. Every year they gathered in the towns and villages, and groups of them even went out, sword in hand, to roam the countryside, through village and field and woodland, looking for the desired and longed-for King Barleycorn, their hope of a better future.

And when things grew worse and worse, when the serfs of later ages groaned under forced labour, they took comfort in the name of King Barleycorn and the prophecy of a brighter day to come. And when under the Emperor Josef the bonds of serfdom were greatly eased, everywhere in the country districts people began to believe that the promised King Barleycorn had come, that the longed-for time was near when feudal labour would be utterly abolished and full freedom given to all men. And for that reason the people could not and would not believe it when the news came that the Emperor Josef was dead.

He still lived, the country folk were absolutely convinced of it, he had only hidden himself from the lords who were bitterly opposed to the liberation of the peasants. Somewhere, they said confidently, the emperor was wandering in disguise among his people, going from village to village. And again they called him by the name of Barleycorn.

But this was a new King Barleycorn.

The nobility did not like him. The lords feared him, and had their suspicions that in his name malcontents were roaming through the villages, stirring up the people to rebellion. Therefore they, too, hunted him; in ancient times search was made for the secret king in every village of every lordship, by night, and everywhere at the same hour.

All those who were in the lord's service, gamekeepers, foresters, wardens and apprentices, chancellery clerks, porters, musketeers, all set out in arms through the villages and searched house after house. Mayors and councillors had to give them full assistance. And when they had thoroughly searched every building, bedrooms, living rooms, cellars and attics, and patrolled the whole village, they made a halt at the inn to fortify themselves at their lord's expense.

But their quarry, King Barleycorn, never fell into their hands. He went on walking secretly among his people and comforting them with the assurance that feudal labour would pass away, that all would be well for all men. In every village he had his known acquaintance, or more than one, and he came to visit them, but always in the night, when the household was asleep. He came unexpectedly (he was of middle age and of a tall figure) in a cloak of blue cloth, cap on head, and wearing a long coat and blue breeches tucked into his boots. These boots always shone like a mirror, even if there had been heavy rain or storms, and he himself was also dry even in the rain, his cloak, his cap innocent of any drop of water. His cloak saved him from getting wet, and also served him in other ways: he needed no sleep, he knew neither hunger nor thirst and took no food or drink, and no man could see him unless he so willed.

In the darkness he revealed himself, he came in through closed doors, sat down at the table and talked with his own, asking his neighbour about various matters, but chiefly about the burdens of forced labour that were being laid upon the people. He told them that still more cruel taxes would be extorted from the peasants, that they would have to pay dues on all they had, even on brooms. But this would be the last; after it these un-Christian extortions would cease, and even feudal labour would be swept away.

So he sat and talked, but he never broke bread; and suddenly he rose and departed again as he had come, through closed doors, and never said where he was going. Nor did he ever stay in any man's house through the night. Again he took up his solitary pilgrimage through the dark night, wrapped in his enchanted cloak, the comforter of the people; through rain and mire he went, road or no road, calm and sure, without fear of his pursuers.

More than once he has met them when they marched out in arms to seize and bind him. And he walked beside them part of the way, King Barleycorn, the living consolation of all the oppressed, to all the faithful the embodied hope and faith of a better future for the Moravian land; a faith and hope which have out-lasted the storms of the ages, which cannot be quenched, know no waning, and please God will never fail us!

The Banner
of Saint Wenceslas

I

It was winter in summer.

In that year one thousand one hundred and twenty-five after the birth of the Son of God, in the month of June after the festival of the Holy Spirit, snow fell in Bohemia, and hard frosts came, so that in many places trees died, and in the mountains the brooks froze, and that not thinly, but with layers of thick ice. And a thing stranger yet: when the true winter came after it, when everything lay deep in snow, the violent storms of summer terrified the people. At the end of the same year, it is said, many people heard heavy thunder and saw lightning before Christmas Day, during Advent, while others heard and saw the same on Christmas Eve. And there was fierce lightning in the night after the festival of Saint Stephen, first of the martyrs.

Then the sky grew dark again, and hung heavy and low and full of snow over the wintry landscape, only to blaze once again with blinding lightnings; and this was on the second day of the New Year, just before daybreak. The heavens opened again, and lightnings both livid and red mingled flash upon flash, blinding the eyes that beheld them.

People crossed themselves and talked of evil omens and of war which would surely follow. How could it be otherwise, bearing in mind the fierce disputes which had broken out again in the prince's clan? The word passed through the snow-laden countryside, through castles and fortresses and villages and cloisters, that the Prince of Olomouc, Otík, called the Black, had fled to Regensburg in Bavaria, to the German emperor, contesting the right of his cousin Soběslav to the princely throne, though Soběslav had been raised to his sovereign place by the loving acclaim of the nation.

Everywhere the charge was being repeated with bitter reproach that Otík, himself born a Czech, had committed gross treason against his own race, that he was courting the emperor and begging help from him and from the German princes, and promising them everything they asked for if only these foreigners would attack Soběslav and Bohemia. And everywhere they expected the attack, for they knew that the Germans would need little urging; they would willingly march upon Bohemia for money, and to avail themselves of Otík's promises, as well as to enrich themselves with other booty. And bitter rage filled every heart when they heard that the Emperor Lothar, in an insolent speech, had summoned Prince Soběslav to judgement, bidding him render account by what right he had accepted the sovereignty over Bohemia, which, said Lothar, only he, the emperor, had the right to confer. Let him come and answer for himself before a German court, said Lothar, or he should feel the power and the sword of the Holy Roman Emperor.

But their eyes sparkled and they shouted their joyful approval when they heard what reply their Prince Soběslav had sent back into Germany: that he placed his sure hope in a merciful God and in the help of Saint Wenceslas and Saint Vojtěch that Bohemia should not be given over to the power of foreigners.

'It shall not be! God grant it never shall!' the cry went up resolutely everywhere; and in good heart they made ready for war. They thought that it would come in the spring, when the snows had melted and the roads were clear and drying.

But the sign of the lightning had not flashed for nothing. And suddenly in the clear frosty nights there appeared in the sky an evil omen, a comet trailing its long hair. Silently, ominously it blazed among the inconstant, flickering light of the minor stars. All eyes turned to gaze at it, and everywhere men were asking anxiously what this new omen could be bringing, what it signified. The next day came news from the Ore Mountains that struck like thunder out of a clear sky: the Germans were already preparing for the battle. The emperor did not intend to wait for spring, he was already setting forth into Bohemia.

From the Ore Mountains to Šumava in the south and as far as Vitoraz, eastward to the Polish frontier, guarded by the castle of Kladsko, north to the forested rampart of the Giant Mountains and on to Žitavsko and beyond Kámen on the Elbe, through all the Czech lands and into Moravia there arose a feverish activity, the warlike commotion of sudden and urgent preparations. No-one paid any attention to the frost, or cared that snowstorms howled along the roads. The enemy was gathering for an attack on the country, and they must defend it. The prince called to war, their good Prince Soběslav! He had already ridden in from Moravia, where he had taken possession of Otík's portion, and was summoning men to arms everywhere.

They heard that from the gate of the land at Litomyšl, under the forest, in Chrudim, in Sadská and elsewhere, whether the roads were open or no, everywhere he entered the churches to pray with his people, and having prayed with them addressed them, bidding them have no fear but acquit themselves like men, for God would not suffer a just cause to be crushed. He also said that he, their prince, could not yield to the emperor, for the honour of the country and for his own honour; and everywhere they repeated ardently what he had said to the nobles and squires of all the regions of his princedom at Prague castle:

'Rather would I see the ruin of my whole house than the shame and disgrace of my country.'

Gladly and readily, therefore, they took down from the walls their arms and harness, swords, lances, maces, bows and quivers and shields, their good helmets with nosepieces, coats of mail and hide tunics sewn with metal plates, and hastened every man to the castle of his district beneath the standard of his clan. From every region far and near great companies flocked to Prague, on horseback, on foot, in helmets and furs and fur-lined cloaks, in caps of lambskin, wolf-hide, lynx-hide and other furs; various in their dress they came, but all at one in the valour of their hearts and their eagerness for battle. When the Czech army was thus gathered in full muster, Prince Soběslav ordered the priests to make ready the lance of Saint Wenceslas, which was kept in the church of Saint Vitus, so that on the morrow when they marched they might take it with them into the field as their shield and protection against their enemies. But when the day dawned, and priests and lords and squires and all the people flocked into the church at the castle, where Holy Mass was to be celebrated before the army marched, only the prince himself was missing.

He had lingered at that hour in his chamber with his chaplain Vít, whom he had called in to him unexpectedly. This Vít was a true man, a passionate patriot for his nation and his tongue, pious and brave and dear to the prince. Agitated and moved, the prince now confided to him in the early morning a strange thing.

'Hear,' said he, 'what manner of dream has visited me this night. I dreamed that Saint Vojtěch drew near to my bed and ordered me to take with me to the battle the banner of his father, which he said is hidden in the church at Vrbčany. It was a wonderful vision, and I want to obey his command. But there can be no delaying now, for everyone waits only for me, and it is time that we set out. We'll go forth at once, as soon as Mass is finished. But you, my dear chaplain, fulfil my wish for me. Mount and ride in haste to Vrbčany to confirm this dream. Go in arms, and with an escort, not alone. If you find there the banner of Slavník, take it in my name, and ride quickly after us, and you may yet overtake us in time.'

The gallant chaplain, comforted and encouraged by this strange vision and rejoicing in the hope of help from above, willingly and gladly did as his prince desired, and made no delay. Before Mass ended, before the prince made ready for the field to the song of his whole army, the chaplain was out of Prague castle. Two squires of the court and several men-at-arms rode with him; on swift horses they hurried to Český Brod, and thence onward, passing by Chotouň, the native village of Saint Prokop, and leaving it on their left as they rode on to the village of Vrbčany. This had formerly belonged to the great lordship of the powerful Slavník. Before the winter day darkened to twilight they entered the quiet village, deep in snow.

Above it on a slight prominence the round church rose towards the flushed sky, fortified with a high earthwork and a wall. In the foreground jutted a tower, protecting the single gate in the sheltering wall. There the priest of the village led the prince's envoys within to look for the hiding-place of the banner of Saint Vojtěch and his family. The daylight had burned out, and deep twilight filled all the hushed holy place.

The priest Vít, with his companions and the parish priest, knelt before the altar and prayed silently that their journey might not prove in vain.

Then they lit wax candles and began their search, until behind the altar in the wall they came upon a secret recess, and in the recess they found an ancient cloth, a strip of silk of no great width, and for half its length forking into two narrower strips, with the embroidered symbol of a star.

Then they all rejoiced, and knelt down behind the priest Vít, who had fallen on his knees before the altar, to offer praises to God aloud for His goodness in granting to them this sign and hope of victory in their grave and difficult war.

Scarcely pausing to give themselves or their horses time to breathe, they

mounted once again and hastened back. They paid no heed to the night, but hurried with their treasure to overtake the army in time. They galloped soundlessly through the silent, frosty night in the loose snow, like apparitions; they galloped beneath the clear sky, in which the comet glowed still with its mute and menacing light, in the fitful glimmering radiance of innumerable stars.

I I

So they hastened tirelessly, night and day, galloping in the track of the Czech army, a track plain to be seen, recognisable even in the distance; broad was that road through the snow, stamped hard and full of thousands of footprints, the hoof-marks of horses, and the smooth tracks of heavy sleighs gleaming in the sun.

By that road they hurried steadily northwards without difficulty. Before them floated a cloud of white vapours, blown gustily from the dilated nostrils of their galloping horses. It was hard frost, their faces were scorched red with it; it gilded with silver the moustaches and beards of the armed riders, and whitened the hides and manes and the shells of the ears of their much-enduring chargers.

And now the ridge of the Ore Mountains rose along the horizon before the riders, robed in white, and now they had passed Teplice; and beyond this town they overtook their army. The chaplain Vít leaped from his horse and strode straight to the prince's tent. Prince Soběslav was overjoyed and gave thanks to God when he heard all their story, and immediately had it proclaimed through the entire army.

The joyful news swept through the camp like the wind, and as many as could came flocking from all sides to the open space before the prince's tent, to behold this miracle. There stood the prince himself, a splendid figure of a man in his great cloak edged with rare fur; he stood on a great sleigh, so that he might be seen by all, and with him was the priest Vít. Without helmet, his head uncovered like that of his chaplain, the prince held the banner high, crying aloud ardently and in a voice that carried far through the camp:

'Behold this sign of the grace of God! Here is the lance of Saint Wenceslas, and on it, look, this standard which Saint Vojtěch has revealed to us.'

And all men, young and old, gentlemen and commoners, doffed their caps and knelt, reverently making the sign of the cross; and murmurs of wonder and joy and fervour and thanks to God mingled aloud round the sleigh and the prince's tent.

The joyful word was passed on through the camp, to the log ramparts where they lay keeping guard in the snow over the passes and hollow ways among the hills, and on to the furthest outposts. And on the morrow these advance guards sent back word of the German army approaching.

In great force the assembled might of the German peoples drew near; the greatest number of them were Saxons and Thuringians, with a great host also of Flemings, Frisians and Brabanters, and also many from the Rhineland and Schwabia and Bavaria. The interminable ranks showed black along the road between the snow-covered hills, winding like a gigantic snake uphill and down and uphill again. Laboriously and heavily they came, for the way was almost impassable for horses and men alike. They waded through the snow, plunging into drifts, slipping and falling. For all the frost they were running with sweat, and steam rose cloudily from their horses. And on the mountain paths their heavy arms were doubly burdensome.

More than one knight, flinging off his harness, marched on foot beside his horse. And the foot soldiers reeled fainting, with many pauses. But the knight who rode in the foremost ranks in a chain-mail coat, the gallant Margrave Albrecht, called the Bear, still waved and urged them onward. So did the lord who rode beside him in arms, with brown, weathered cheeks and black hair, Otík the Black himself.

Thus they had passed the heights, and were already wending their way downwards by the sinuous, impassable track, until the vanguard and a great part of the main body of the army had reached the valley. There in the vale of Chlumec stood the Czech army already drawn up in battle array. Above the companies quivered their standards, gleaming in the frosty air, and above them, highest of all, the banner of Saint Wenceslas, the standard of the whole army. The chaplain Vít, armed and wearing helmet, carried it. With him around the standard stood a round hundred of the Czech lords with naked swords, and the provosts and chaplains, all forming a watchful guard for the most holy symbol.

The eyes of all the Czechs were fixed before them, where the innumerable host of their enemies confronted them. They could see no end to it, all the valley teemed with the Germans, and above the vast black cloud of their array flashed the myriad lightnings of their arms and armour. The moment of decision was upon them; the hearts of all beat tumultuously at the thought of this hard and unequal battle.

At that instant someone raised a shout and pointed upwards, and everyone gazed up into the sky, where a great eagle sailed through the shining air. On powerful, spread wings he hovered above the Czech army, and then flew forward, straight at the ranks of the Germans. Every voice, every sound was hushed in wonder, so that every man heard the eagle scream. He flew at the Germans with a great cry, as though he had sighted and sensed his prey.

Before this good omen had passed — ah, hush! a great noise burst over the Czech army. The vast peal of a bell, and after it the splendid chiming clamour of many bells rang through the air above the heads of the soldiers.

Everyone trembled and wondered, moved by the secret flood of sound, and every spirit was uplifted. Their faces brightened, their eyes shone, many quivered with ardour. With rapture the priest Vít grew pale, and tears welled from his eyes. Carried away by emotion he looked up to heaven, and cried into the hush of holy dread:

'Oh, brothers, the Lord God is with us. Be constant! Constant ever! Look there! See how Saint Wenceslas shines in the heavens on his white horse, robed in white and bearing his lance with this banner! He is fighting for us! See how he soars above us in splendour of light—Saint Wenceslas, patron of the Czech lands!'

They turned their eyes to heaven, they lifted their hands, many of them weeping for joy and wonder, and all together, moved with one inspiration, burst into song from their hearts: 'Lord, have mercy upon us!' Far through the valley to the slopes of the snow-laden hills echoed the sacred melody, the legacy of their forefathers. And as the song swelled in triumph, Prince Soběslav from his horse waved them forward with drawn sword, and the whole host, singing, exalted, thirsting for battle, swept forward against the enemy.

The song died in the tumult of battle. The storm swept through the valley where the armies clashed. The Germans fought bravely, but they did not hold fast. They could not. Like a torrent the Czechs hurled themselves upon them, the main body from the front, the reserves on the flanks. They hacked and thrust, slaughtering their enemies, streaking their surcoats with red, pressing them back into the passes. There brought to bay, the Germans stood like a wall and could go neither forward nor back. They fell in a ferocious struggle. The snow ran red round them, and the spilled blood hardened in the frost, froze on their clothes, on the snow, on their weapons and their very wounds.

Then the Germans began to run, and to throw away their shields. He who could flee, fled, or if he could not he tossed away his sword in the snow and begged for mercy, for his life, surrendering himself to captivity. Thus were taken the bishops of Middelburg and Halberstadt, the Count of Lara, and even the Margrave, Albrecht the Bear himself. But the man who had been the source and cause of the war, Otík the Black, lay among the slain. Their number was great. The Czechs had slaughtered some five hundred noblemen, not counting those of lesser rank.

The Emperor Lothar gazed down from a hillock in horror on the frightful slaughter wrought among his men, and could give them no help. He himself was already in danger, and had to consider taking to flight with those who remained to him. But it was already late. The Czechs stopped up his every way of escape, and he could not fight them, he had not the strength. Without the consent of the Czechs he could not stir a foot. The emperor was surrounded, imprisoned with all his remaining forces.

No course remained but to ask for peace. Count Heinrich Grojský had to beg the Czech prince to come to the emperor; which Prince Soběslav did, and spoke and acted fairly. When the emperor acknowledged him as prince, and recognised the Czech right of free election, he was allowed to go free, and sadly he returned to Germany with the remains of his army. Grief came with him into the land, and particularly into Saxony, which on Czech soil had lost the greatest number of dead, and from so many noble families.

But merrily the victorious army returned from Chlumec into Bohemia with its vast booty. The joyful news flew before them; everywhere people listened in amazement to the story of the miraculous help of God, of the omens on the battle-field, and of Saint Wenceslas and his banner. Not their fathers nor their grand-fathers, they said, had ever covered themselves with such honour as the Czechs had won in this battle at Chlumec. Inexpressible joy filled all the land, and with great honour and glory the citizens of Prague welcomed their gallant Prince Soběslav and his army.

And this battle of Chlumec was fought to its glorious end on the eighteenth day of the month of February, in the year of Our Lord one thousand one hundred and twenty-six, in which year also our most enlightened Prince Soběslav rebuilt on the mountain of Říp the chapel of Saint George. And this chapel was then consecrated by Zdík, Bishop of Olomouc, son of the worthy chronicler Kosmas.

III

And hear the story of yet one more glorious victory, of the miraculous help given them in that battle, and of the strange vision of John, the son of Svojslav.

It was in the year 1260, when the Czech king Přemysl II was at war with Hungary, with King Béla and the younger Stepán. For a long time both armies lay confronting each other on the Moravian plain, down in the Austrian border-lands on the banks of the river Morava. On the right bank lay the Czechs, and on left the Hungarians and their allies, Poles, Russians, Croats and Serbs, other Serbs also from Bosnia, Wallachians, Magyars, Tartars and wild Kumans, who are also called the 'Sailors', and Khwariznian Turks. In all there were a hundred and forty thousand and more, a great force, especially strong in cavalry.

The Czech king had only a hundred thousand men. Of these seven thousand were Czech cavalry, armed from head to foot in chain-mail or plate-armour, and riding chargers also well armoured. And there were in Přemysl's army Czechs, Moravians, Silesians, a few Germans from Austria in reserve, and Brandenburgers, Germans and Slovenes from Carinthia. With the king were many renowned Czech and Moravian lords. And with them also were the bishops of Prague and Olomouc, and certain German knights and princes from the empire. So the two armies lay confronting each other, and the river flowed between them.

Neither was willing to ford the flood to the opposite shore before the eyes of the other, to lay itself open to injury. So day followed day, and when a week had passed the two kings made a compact by mutual agreement, and confirmed it on oath: that on an agreed day, the eleventh of July, the Czechs would withdraw farther from the river, and on the following day, the twelfth, the Hungarians would freely and without hindrance ford the river to the same shore. On the third day, the thirteenth of the month, which was the day of Saint Margaret, their decisive battle was to be fought.

So it was agreed, and the Hungarian king and his magnates swore to it with a solemn oath. But they did not keep their oath; against the agreement, as soon as they found the fords duly unguarded and the hour favourable to themselves, the Hungarians crossed in the night to the opposite shore, and with all their incalculable forces struck at the Czechs on the twelfth and thirteenth days of the month.

The Czechs, relying on their opponents' word and oath, expected no such dealings, and were still unprepared for battle. Their army was not even fully mustered, for many companies had ridden out foraging for their beasts and themselves. So when the Hungarians launched their attack the Czechs were immediately in great danger. The Hungarians had encircled them in a crescent formation, and were the stronger force of the two.

At first panic seized the Czechs, when through the glowing air bellowed the demoniacal shrieks of the Kumans, hurtling forward crouched on their horses like an immense stampede of wild mares, so that the earth shook. But the soldiers burst into their hymn: 'Lord, have mercy on us', and terror fell away from them all, and manfully they stood to arms and began to fight.

And wherever the Lord Jaroš of Poděhus turned with the standard, the enemy gave back before him, shrank away and turned to flee, and the iron-armed guard that kept it received no injury, nor even their mounts.

When this fierce battle began, it was afternoon, and sultry almost to swooning; and those troops who were held in reserve behind the main body of the army beheld a marvel.

Above the squadrons of the Czech army, horse and foot, above the field of helmets and the pennants of the clans appeared suddenly a great bird, soaring on outspread wings. It was an eagle, but white in colour, whiter than snow; its head and throat glittered with gold, and there was a halo of light about it.

It soared above the Czech ranks, hovering over the banner of Saint Wenceslas. Wherever the banner gleamed and waved in the convulsions of the bitter battle, there the eagle hung bright above it.

And the white and glowing bird began to grow, and grew and grew, its wings widening their vast span until they covered all the iron-clad guard. Beneath the gigantic pinions a great shadow fell upon them as from a cloud, and veiled men and horses. Only the banner of Saint Wenceslas remained clear and radiant, and its golden point blazed and shone out of the dimness of the shade, a single star, burning with a mysterious brightness like a sunbeam above the press of the battle.

Then suddenly it faded, the white eagle in the sky vanished, and the burning sun shone again upon all the host. This was late in the afternoon, when the Moravian plain echoed to the triumphant cries of the Czech soldiers, and in clouds of dust the Hungarians had taken to panic flight, galloping in confusion back to the river. In frenzied flight they leaped madly into the Morava to reach its further bank. But they died in the flood, horses and men, in such numbers that they stopped the course of the river, and over the ramparts of their dead the Czechs rode dry-shod to the opposite bank to take possession of the lavish camp and the rich booty the Hungarians had left behind them.

When this Hungarian war was beginning, in the spring, among those who prepared to join the army was a certain gallant squire, John, the son of Svojslav. But when he had horse and arms and harness all ready for the field he fell dangerously ill.

So he could not ride with them, but was forced to lie in his bed, and there he remained for some weeks. But what troubled him most and made him deeply sorrowful was that he could not go with his king to the battle, and even worse, that no-one brought to his door the news for which he was impatient.

One day, when all the courtyard was still dim with the morning twilight, he fell into so grave an attack that the friends who kept watch by his bed thought his last hour had come. His face was lividly pale, his half-closed eyes grew dulled, and his breast heaved with harsh and painful breaths.

Then the fit eased, and he lay still, and presently his face began to change, the cheeks flushing to their normal colour, the lips smiling. Then he opened his eyes fully, and they shone clear and bright; briskly he raised himself, and sitting on his bed he said in a voice brimming with joy:

'Give thanks to God! Praise Him, as I praise Him! Give thanks, and hear what I have seen in this hour. I was away from here, on the battlefield. I saw our Czech people there, but badly up against the Hungarians, who had attacked them unexpectedly and brought them into great peril. My heart trembled with fear for them. But at that moment I beheld—oh, listen!—the patron saints of our land shining in glory. First of all Saint Wenceslas in a shining coat of mail and helmet. By his side was a sword in a golden scabbard set with pearls, and in his right hand he bore his standard. And after him came Saint Vojtěch in his bishop's robes, then Saint Prokop the abbot with his crozier in his hand, and last walked the five martyred brothers in their monkish gowns.

'Saint Wenceslas looked round at Saint Vojtěch and Saint Prokop and all of them, and said—I heard him clearly:

' "Our army faints, come, let us go to their help." And as he said it he levelled his standard against the enemy, who all turned and fled, while our men fought and pursued them gallantly, singing that sweet hymn: "Lord, have mercy—" '

Then John, the son of Svojslav, folded his hands, and all those about his bed marvelled and said:

'Surely the Lord God has given the victory to our king this day.'

Later, when news came from the battlefield and the army returned from the war, it was clearly shown that John, the son of Svojslav, had this vision in an ecstasy at dawn of the very day when the Czechs in the Moravian plain won a glorious victory over the Magyars, and that was on the twelfth day of the month of July in the year of Our Lord 1260.

IV

The banner of Saint Wenceslas vanished during the storms that convulsed the land, and there is no memory or record of how or when it disappeared. There is only a comforting legend that it was not destroyed by a sacrilegious hand, nor did it become the prey of foreigners, but it is still in our own country, and again restored to that place from which it was taken ages ago at a time of terrible danger, to be the shield and inspiration of the Czech army: in the fortified church of Vrbčany.

But it does not lie in its former hiding-place now, but in a safer, though also more unapproachable, place: in the hill beneath the church it lies on a marble

137

table in a vaulted strong-room. It is silent there; the clash of arms and the voices of heroes alike are stilled. But in the half-light of the cell, through which the golden point of the standard gleams like hope in the dark night of adversity, faintly from above comes the echo of war songs: 'Lord, have mercy upon us' and 'Saint Wenceslas, lord of the Czech lands', to bear witness that their descendants have not forgotten, that courage still quickens their hearts, and that they have not ceased to fight for the rights of their land and the tongue of their forefathers.

The Story of Bruncvík

I

When Prince Žibřid died, his son Bruncvík ruled over the Czech land. The young prince was noble by nature, and just to all men, but he did not remain long in his empire. He had always in mind the heroic deeds of his late father, the honour he had won and the glory that made his name illustrious, and in the third year of his reign he resolved that he would go out into the world to win honour for his country in his turn.

'My father won for himself the sign of an eagle, but I want to win the sign of a lion,' he said to his wife, when he told her what was in his mind. The young princess was very sorrowful at this news, and begged him not to go, not to expose himself to such perils.

When Bruncvík did not wish to listen to her she burst into tears and embraced him, weeping and again begging him not to leave her in solitude and sadness. But Bruncvík comforted her tenderly, saying that she would not be left alone and forsaken, for he would bid her father remain here with her and stand by her in the task of governing. And taking a ring from his finger, he said:

'Here I give my ring into your keeping, and take your ring from your finger. Whatsoever you may hear, never believe unless you yourself behold this ring. But if you do not see me again within seven years, you will know that I am no longer living.'

So when the princess's father had come, Bruncvík had thirty horses saddled, and gathering his chosen companions about him, made his farewells to his wife Neomenia and her father, and set out into the world to seek adventures, like a true and gallant knight.

And they rode and rode through many and varied lands, ever on and on, he and his knights and his men-at-arms, until they could ride no farther, for they had reached the shore of a wide sea. But even here they would neither stay nor turn back. Bruncvík provided himself with a ship and boarded it with his companions, taking even the horses aboard with him, and so they set sail across the vast sea into unknown regions.

When they cast off from the shore there was a favourable wind blowing, and so it continued to blow for a long time. Until one night, when they had been at sea for a quarter of a year, it suddenly veered. In the dark night the sea grew rough. Bruncvík's ship rocked in the storm, and the wild waves tossed it now high into the sky and now deep into the abyss of waters. The sailors were in great terror, but their panic increased when they suddenly sighted through the darkness a distant yellowish glow, and were aware of a strong and penetrating fragrance.

Only then did they begin to lament and bemoan their fate, for they knew that the light and the scent came from the Amber Mountain, which had the power by virtue of its radiance shining through the night to attract everything, be it man or beast or boat, everything within fifty miles of it on all sides, directly to itself, and draw it close by its living force. And whoever touched on that shore, there on the Amber Mountain he must remain, and never, never would he get away from it again.

So the sailors lamented in terror when they saw how the wind had driven them. In vain they offered prayers and made fervent vows trying to change the wind. But it drove them on, and as soon as it had brought them within fifty miles of the mountain, the ship flew like an arrow straight for the Amber Mountain, speeding through its yellow glare, which towered high into the darkness and spread far across the stormy waves.

Suddenly the ship struck against the shore of the island in the centre of which the Amber Mountain soared. On this island Bruncvík disembarked with his companions, and they led the horses ashore as soon as the sea had grown calm, which it did very suddenly. It was then already dawn, and in the light of the sun they realised that the island was barren and deserted, empty of people, and that it bore nothing on which they could live.

As they walked round it they saw on the shores many rotting and shattered ships and many human bones, whitening in the sand under the burning sun. And Bruncvík and all those with him were exceedingly depressed at this. They saw that these were men who had died miserably here, and dreaded what wretched fate awaited them, also. Sorrowfully they looked all round them, and gazed across the limitless sea, whose green waves stretched away into infinite distance.

When they had somewhat regained their senses and rested a little after the storm, they made strenuous efforts to get away from that place. They re-embarked in their ship, pushed off strongly from the shore and hoisted the sails, then they seized the oars and rowed strongly and untiringly. And the boat moved. It moved away from the island, and they began to take comfort and believe that they had mastered the magic power of the Amber Mountain. As this hope began to quicken in them they leaned still more vigorously into their oars and toiled until their faces crimsoned and their bodies ran with sweat.

And the ship moved quickly, until suddenly it stopped and lay as still and quiet as though at anchor—back at the shore of the island beneath the Amber Mountain.

Bruncvík was cast down into despair, and they were all sick with disappointment, seeing that they were indeed condemned to remain on this inhospitable island. As long as they still had food on board their ship they did well enough; and during the time that they stayed there they made two more attempts to get the ship out to sea. But every time it turned in its course and went back to the shore as on the first occasion.

When all the supplies from the ship were gone, they killed their horses and lived on their meat. But when they had eaten the last of them, Bruncvík's own horse, cruel hunger took hold of them and tormented them. Desperately they searched for any means of satisfying their hunger; but in all the island they found not a single grain of corn, not a single bird, nothing which could provide them with food. But still they looked hopefully for God's mercy.

When at last they grasped the certainty that their hope was vain, despair took possession of them, and they resigned themselves dully to their fate, sat or lay down on the shore beside their ship and waited for death. And one after another death took them.

At last only Bruncvík himself and a certain old knight, Balád by name, remained out of all that company beneath the Amber Mountain. Then the old knight, as he sat beside Bruncvík staring out over the wide sea, said suddenly to the young prince:

'My dear lord! If only your lady and your squires knew of your present misfortune!'

Bruncvík was deeply sorrowful at this. And Balád said to him:

'Don't grieve, my dear lord. If you'll do as I tell you, you may yet find a safe way of escape from here. Only I don't know to what place you may come.'

'But what of you?' said Bruncvík.

'Trouble not about me. I am old, and I no longer care. It is my lot now to stay here. But if you succeed in saving yourself and at some future time come to good fortune, remember my faithful service.'

'And what is it that you advise me to do?' asked Bruncvík.

'My lord and prince, you have seen how, the first year after our coming here, a great gryphon bird flew to this island, and the second year also it came, once only. And this year it will certainly come again, for it seems that it must be its custom to visit this place once a year. This bird must carry you away, if you please to attempt it.'

'And how could he carry me away?' asked Bruncvík in astonishment.

The old knight pointed to a horse's hide that lay beside the ship, and counselled his master to lie down in it, but to take his sword with him. And when he had done so, the knight took a thong of leather and sewed him in, and laid him thus in the horse's skin on the Amber Mountain.

Not long afterwards there was a vast humming in the air, and the vibration of violent gusts of wind as before a storm. And this convulsion came from the flight of the gryphon, approaching the Amber Mountain on its gigantic wings. When it appeared above the mountain it was as though an immeasurable cloud had gathered and hung there. For a moment the gryphon hovered high in the air on spread wings, then suddenly it plunged downwards, and seizing Bruncvík as though he had been no more than a grain of wheat, soared again into the air and flew away.

On the island beneath the Amber Mountain it was again silent and deserted. Mournfully stood the rotting, disintegrating ships, their shadows motionless on the sandy shore, where the bones of the dead bleached in the sun.

Only one living creature remained here: the old, faithful knight Balád, who sat in the sand exhausted and wasted with hunger, leaning against the wreckage of a dead ship, and staring upwards anxiously with his dulled eyes after the monstrous gryphon, which was already dwindling in the distance, carrying his young prince to some unknown land.

II

The gryphon flew with Bruncvík over the broad sea, in rapid flight it sped for three days and three nights, and in that time covered hundreds and hundreds of miles from the Amber Mountain, until it drew far into a range of desolate mountains, and cast Bruncvík into the nest among its young. As soon as it had dropped him there it soared into the sky again and flew away after other prey. The young gryphons hurled themselves on this handsome morsel, screeching angrily, and tore with their talons at the skin about Bruncvík. As soon as he was free, the prince drew his sword, leaped to his feet and slew all the young gryphons.

When he had thus delivered himself he fled from that place, never pausing to take breath. Up hill and down dale he ran through those inhospitable mountains, over lonely bare hillsides and through forested valleys, until he came to the rim of a deep ravine.

Hardly had he reached this spot when a wild roaring and bellowing burst on his ears. He listened for a moment, not knowing what to do. But now he could not turn back. He had to go forward, and so, trusting only God, he set forth into the ravine, and pressed on until he came to a high rock. And there he halted, beholding a most strange and terrifying sight, a battle to the death between a ferocious dragon and a lion.

Frenziedly they fought for their lives, and their roaring and clamour filled the valley so that the trees and the rocks trembled.

'Now, dear God, which of the two should I help?' thought Bruncvík, standing at no great distance and looking on at this struggle. 'It was for a lion I came journeying, and for the symbol of the lion I have already endured so much; I can do nothing else but help the lion, come what may.'

So he resolved, and drawing his sword, he struck out at the green, gleaming dragon that shone like metal, and had nine heads. As he began to hack at it and cut off its heads, the lion, all dabbled with blood and exhausted and breathless from the ferocious fight, withdrew from the battle and lay down to rest.

So Bruncvík maintained the battle alone. He fought manfully, the blows of his sword raining upon the monster's scales. But the dragon was invincible. Bruncvík was beginning to grow weary; he was no longer attacking, but only

143

defending himself. On that the lion, who had now regained his breath, made a lightning leap, closed his jaws on the dragon and tore him in two. The peril was gone.

But Bruncvík was afraid of a new danger, for now he had the lion to fear. The lion, however, did not leap upon him, but lay down at his feet. Bruncvík desired to leave that place, but as soon as he took a step the lion rose and went after him. So he did constantly as Bruncvík passed through the valley, keeping close on his heels at every step. The young prince was not pleased by this; he did not trust the lion, and would have been glad to get rid of him.

He gathered acorns and beech-nuts to eat, and then climbed up into a tall oak-tree. There he sat in the crotch of a great branch, hid himself among the thick foliage of the old tree, and waited for the lion to go away. He waited and waited, an hour, half a day, and always the lion sat beneath the oak-tree and looked up into the thick boughs. Night came; Bruncvík spent it slumbering in his tree. When the morning chill awoke him, the first thing he did as he opened his eyes was to look for the lion. And there was the lion, still beneath the tree. There he sat like a faithful dog, and remained sitting all the next day, gazing up sadly into the branches; and the second night the same, and never moved from the spot.

But the third day, when Bruncvík still did not descend from the tree, the grieving lion roared so loudly that the oak-tree shook violently, and Bruncvík, startled by the sudden terrible sound, let go of the branch and fell to the ground. There he lay half-stunned, and could not even get up. He was very weak, as he had nothing to eat; but he was not left without help. The lion, which had bounded away from him, returned in a short time carrying a doe he had hunted and killed, and laid it at Bruncvík's feet.

The young prince saw now that he had been wronging the lion, and that there was no need to fear him. And when the lion, leaning against him, laid his head in his lap, Bruncvík stroked his thick mane as he would have fondled a faithful dog. From that moment he began to love him, and the lion remained devoted to him all the time that they wandered in those desolate mountains. For three years Bruncvík roamed the wilderness among the forests; and the lion was always with him wherever he went, and always he hunted wild animals and brought them to his master.

Once in these wanderings Bruncvík reached the summit of a high mountain, from which he could see before him a vast expanse of sea, and very far away across the waters the towers of a castle. He rejoiced to see a human dwelling again, for until that moment he had neither found nor glimpsed any. He hastened in the direction of the sea, praying to God that he would grant him the mercy of reaching this castle.

Fifteen days had passed before he burst out of the desolation of the mountains and reached the sea-shore. The beach was deserted, sandy and stony. Bruncvík, full of hope and longing to get to the castle, immediately began to fell trees with his sword and cut pliable wands, and carrying all to the sea-shore, set to work to make a great raft, and launched it into the water when it was done. He set it afloat at a time when the lion had left him to hunt for food; and this Bruncvík had done purposely, for he did not wish to take him with him for fear he would be a hindrance to him.

Just as the young prince had pushed off from the shore the lion returned, carrying his kill in his jaws. But at once he dropped it and with a roar leaped into the sea after his lord. He made a gigantic leap, and his fore-legs reached the raft. Thus clinging with his claws, he swam for a long while, until Bruncvík, moved by such devotion, helped him out of his precarious position on to the raft. And so they sailed off together on the poor boat, at one end of it Bruncvík, at the other the lion.

For nine days and nights they sailed on their raft. Often the sea made sport with them, and more than once Bruncvík was in the water to his waist, even to his throat. The sky over them darkened, all the heavens grew dark, until they sailed constantly through thick twilight, not knowing where they drifted. Bruncvík, anxious and uneasy in this darkness, could see only that they were no longer on the open sea, but on the right hand and on the left the outlines of mountains showed black through the dimness.

It grew bright and clear again when they sailed beneath the Carbuncle Mountain. This mountain shone upon them with a brilliant red glow, until at last they emerged from the darkness. And there before them they beheld a castle towering over its islet in the full sunlight. It was the same one which Bruncvík had seen from the summit of the high mountain. He disembarked on the shore, and accompanied by his comrade the lion, went into the castle. Its lord was King Olibrius, and he was a strange person, not like other men. He had two pairs of eyes, one pair in his face, the other at the back of his head. But more extraordinary still were the creatures of his court; many had one eye, many one leg, many were horned. Others had two heads, or even had the heads of dogs, some of them like red foxes, others half grey and half white. Many were big as giants, while others were dwarfs, and ran about between the legs of their larger fellows.

Bruncvík was wretched and uneasy in this place, and wished to go back whence he had come. But King Olibrius detained him, asking how he had come there, whether of his own will or of necessity.

'I set out from my native land of my own will, but I came here of necessity. I beg you, help me to go back to my home,' Bruncvík requested.

'You can leave here only by way of the iron gate,' replied the king. 'But I won't open it to you and let you out by it until you have rescued my daughter, who has been carried off by the dragon Basilisk.'

There was no help for it; Bruncvík saw that he must either remain among these royal phantoms or rescue the king's daughter, so he resolved that he would brave the dragon Basilisk. King Olibrius had a boat made ready for him, and in it Bruncvík with his faithful lion sailed away to the island and castle of the all-powerful dragon.

III

They came to the island without any difficulty; but it was almost impossible to get into the castle, for this castle had a three-fold gate, and at every gate fierce monsters on guard. Bruncvík had to fight his way past them, and the struggle was hard and unrelenting, from gate to gate ever more terrible, so that Bruncvík would never have won his way into the castle if it had not been for his faithful lion.

As often as his lord weakened and faltered in the battle, the lion leaped to his aid and fought off the monsters until Bruncvík had gathered his strength again. So they forced their way at last into the palace of the castle, and into a splendid hall, where Bruncvík found the daughter of King Olibrius, a lovely maiden, but wound about by serpents from heels to waist.

She was filled with astonishment when she beheld the knight. She could not believe that he had won his way into the castle by force; she thought that the dreadful guards at the gates must have fallen asleep. But then she begged Bruncvík not to venture into still greater danger, but to turn back while there was time, for even if he had killed the guards at the gates he would never overcome the dragon Basilisk and his company. She urged him to make haste away, for it was high time; at that very moment Basilisk, now her dreadful lord, was approaching the hall.

But Bruncvík stood his ground unafraid, though in a moment Basilisk's company began to pour into the hall, squealing and hissing: glistening serpents of all kinds, lizards, serpent-like she-monsters and many and various apparitions. They came singly, in clusters, in coils, all bursting in upon him together in such a torrent that in an instant all the vast hall was full of them.

Bruncvík gave battle at once and with zest, strengthened by a ring which the maiden had given to him, and by virtue of which he gained the strength of twenty men, and still further fortified by his longing and determination to deliver the unhappy lady. And the lion helped him gallantly. He slashed at the monsters with his tail, crunched them in his jaws, tore them with his teeth, clawed them to pieces; and so all that shrieking, hissing crew was destroyed by his strength and Bruncvík's sword. The young knight had already won the victory; but at that moment a dreadful noise like thunder shook the hall, and Basilisk himself, a dragon with eighteen tails, glittering in changing metallic colours and breathing fire from his jaws, burst into the room and rushed at his opponent.

Now for the first time things went ill with Bruncvík. He defended himself, fighting bravely and hacking at the dragon; several times he wounded him, but he himself was also bleeding from his injuries. He suffered many wounds, and several times was felled to the ground. But each time the lion came to his aid. And when in turn the lion was weak and faint, Bruncvík gathered his strength and launched anew into the battle. This lasted until twilight, through the whole night, and until noon of the next day. Then at last Basilisk fell, stretched out his limbs and died. The lion roared loudly, but Bruncvík, covered with wounds, lay on the ground like one dead.

Then the daughter of King Olibrius came to the poor prince's help. She washed Bruncvík's wounds, and bound them up and healed them, taking such good care of him that on the ninth day he rose again from his bed. And taking the rescued maiden, he led her to his boat, and returned with the lady and the lion to her father's castle, eagerly expecting that now the iron gate would be opened for him, and he would be able to return to his own country. King Olibrius welcomed him joyfully, but he made no mention of the iron gate. Nor did he want to hear a word about it, saying that Bruncvík must stay with them, for his daughter Afrika had fallen so deeply in love with her gallant deliverer that she wished him to become her husband.

Bruncvík burned with anger against the king and his daughter, and in his heart he bitterly reproached her for her ingratitude. But since there was no way out of it and no help for him, he was forced to submit, and he took the king's daughter to wife. But his mind was eternally elsewhere, far away in his own land with his true wife, Neomenia, and ever as time passed he grieved and longed for her more and more.

Sorrowfully he sat on the shore and stared far across the sea, hoping that some ship would appear there to deliver him from this prison. But nowhere in all the broad expanse did the white of a sail appear, not a ship stirred on the green waves which played in the sunlight, echoing with their murmurings the heavy sighs of the young knight. Often also when he was solitary he would wander through the castle, cursing it in his soul, and with it the king and his daughter and all their monstrous court.

Once he was drifting thus through the castle, deep in mournful thought, when he came into a cellar which until that moment he had never seen. There lying on a stone table in the cellar, he saw an old sword without a hilt. Without thinking he drew it from the scabbard, and as he gazed upon it he realised that it was made of choice steel and wonderfully sharp. He liked it so much that he twisted the hilt from his own sword and set it on the old sword, which he thrust into his own scabbard. And his own sword, now bereft of its hilt, he laid in the ancient scabbard on the stone table, and so went away and left it there.

When he met with Afrika he did not tell her what he had done, but he asked her what sword that was that lay in the cellar. The king's daughter was startled, and immediately went and locked up the cellar with nine locks. Seeing this, Bruncvík asked her all the more eagerly what sword this could be, and why they hid it away so carefully.

'If you knew what great power that sword has!'

She said no more. But Bruncvík pressed her, and did not cease to beg her to tell him, saying that surely she could do so, since she held the key to this sword, and he could not touch it. So at last she gave in.

'If you want to know, then, listen. The sword has these powers: if you should draw it from the sheath and say, off with a head—or twenty, or thirty, or a hundred thousand heads—immediately those heads would fall.'

Bruncvík laughed at this, as though he did not believe it; but her speech remained quivering in his mind, and already he was considering how he could put it to the test. So one day when several of the grotesque courtiers, red and grey, hump-backed, and with two heads or the heads of dogs, came to him in his room, he drew his sword and cried: 'Now, my sword, off with the heads of the foremost of these monsters!'

Immediately the heads of all those who were present leaped from their shoulders, and he gathered them up and flung them into the sea. And shortly afterwards, when King Olibrius with his daughter and all his courtiers sat at table, Bruncvík drew his sword suddenly and cried:

'Now, my dear sword! Off with the heads of all these phantoms, and the king and his daughter, too!'

And so it happened. Bruncvík, having revenged himself for their ingratitude, left the dead and went out quickly and prepared at once for his journey. The boat sailed with good fortune, and Bruncvík set his course for home and his native land.

148

IV

The wind blew favourably, and the boat sailed happily over a calm ocean. Bruncvík met no-one on the way, saw neither boat nor island. On the seventh day it happened that at last he sailed close to an island, and even from the distance it was comfort to him to see it. It was green and fertile, tall, rich trees grew along the shore, towering into a blue sky, and buildings more beautiful and wonderful than he had ever seen gleamed between the branches.

From this island the wind carried to his ears delightful sounds. Charming music pealed from it, with gay fanfares of trumpets and rattling of drums; then lovely songs in both men's and women's voices drifted to him enchantingly over the waves, borne on the shining air. And Bruncvík longed for people, and the urging of his heart and the sweet sound of this music drew him to the island.

When he landed there he saw that there was a great festival taking place, with much merry-making and many people, on horseback and afoot, all in rich dresses of velvet and silk in bright colours; and in particular he beheld many graceful ladies and maidens with faces and eyes and hair of great beauty. Here young men rode on horseback, splendidly armed, running courses in a tiltyard, there in a great open space they were dancing, singing and playing. As soon as Bruncvík approached and began to watch them they flocked round him, young men and maidens together, crying:

'How did you come here? But however you may have come, you shall dance.'

'And you shall stay with us!'

'We won't let you go! You must stay with us for ever.'

Lovely maidens and women held out their arms to him, men surrounded him. Then Bruncvík recovered his senses, and realised that this was but a sweeter and more tempting peril, that in this consoling beauty lay his ruin. Starting out of his inaction he plucked out his sword and cried:

'Off with the heads of those nearest!'

And immediately the heads of the nearest fell. But the others were not frightened, they cried aloud:

'You won't escape our hands like that. You'll still have to dance with us, and ride with us. We are the children of Asmodeus, devils damned to this place, and here we have power—'

Hearing this, Bruncvík again drew his sword and shouted:

'Off with the heads of all these demons!'

And all their heads jumped from their shoulders, and Bruncvík, hastening away, boarded his ship and sailed on. He sailed and sailed, and went astray also for several weeks, until at last he saw a most beautiful city shining in the distance.

Anchoring at this coast, he went towards the city, and the lion with him. He saw not a soul about the town, and it was silent at the open gate and in the streets and the square. It was as if this beautiful city had died. But all the houses were open and richly furnished; everywhere he found the tables laid with an abundance of food and plenty of good wine.

As Bruncvík went from house to house, he heard suddenly the sound of trumpets and drums, and they blared and drummed very loudly. An army was entering the city; these were the troops of the Astriolians, and at their head on a black horse rode their king, Astriolus.

Bruncvík, sensing that he would not fare well with them, turned away and would have left the town; but on that they caught sight of him, and hemming him in, asked him how he had come there.

'Howsoever I may have come here,' replied Bruncvík, 'know this, that I am not afraid of you.'

Then they laid hands on him and led him before King Astriolus, who said to him:

'Give us your word that you will stay here with us for ever, or I'll have you mounted on the burning horse.'

'Your threats do not frighten me. I place my hope in God, since He has already helped me out of great terrors and dangers, and He will also help me out of your hands.'

Astriolus ordered that the burning horse should be led forth. Four men laid hold of Bruncvík and began to drag him forward to mount him upon this monstrous beast, but he drew out his sword and said:

'Off with the heads of these four!'

And the four heads fell at once, and the lion suddenly leaped upon them and tore them to pieces. Astriolus, enraged at this, ordered forward a company of his army. They advanced with a great blaring of trumpets, several thousand of them, and surrounded Bruncvík, but the prince, undismayed and without a tremor, stood in the middle of them brandishing his sword, and cried:

'Off with the heads of twenty men, thirty, a hundred—off with a thousand heads!'

And immediately heads rolled and bodies dropped in such numbers that the earth shook. Horror fell on all those round about, and on the king himself; they shrieked in terror until the king cried:

'Hold your hand, Bruncvík! Hold your hand for God's sake, and cover your sword. I promise you that I'll have you conducted to your own country, only kill no more of us!'

At Bruncvík's request he swore this with a sacred oath, vowing that he would

fulfil all, that he would conduct Bruncvík with all he had, and his lion also, without any hindrance or injury into Bohemia. Then Bruncvík sheathed his sword. And as Astriolus promised, so he did. It was on a Thursday at early twilight that he led Bruncvík to the frontiers of his empire; and thence Bruncvík passed on without difficulty into his own realm.

V

When he drew near to Prague, he dressed himself in a hermit's gown and went with the lion to his castle. There he found great bustle and merriment, for just at that time Neomenia, his wife, was about to be married. It was now more than seven years since Bruncvík had left Prague and gone away into the world. In all this time Neomenia had seen nothing of his ring, and at last she yielded to the advice of her father and accepted the suit of a distinguished prince who wished to take her as his wife. When Bruncvík in his hermit's robe came to the castle and heard what was happening, he was very sorrowful.

But he said nothing to anyone, nor did he reveal himself. He approached the cup-bearer who was carrying to the festal table cups of silver and gold, and dropped into the cup from which Neomenia drank the ring which he had worn on his finger until that moment. Then he turned at once and left the castle; but as he came to the gate he wrote upon the door there:

'He who went away seven years ago is here.'

At this there arose not a little alarm and consternation. And in the meantime Neomenia had emptied her golden cup and seen in the bottom of it Bruncvík's ring, and immediately she recognised it. In her sincere emotion she did not conceal whose it was, but said that Bruncvík was surely returned. Her bridegroom was aghast at this. He leaped up and ordered his horse to be saddled at once, to ride after his rival and kill him. With thirty horsemen he rode hard after him until they overtook and seized him.

Bruncvík, seeing that they meant to take his life, unsheathed his sword and cried:

'Off with the heads of this bridegroom and his servants!'

Down fell the heads, the headless bodies crashed from their horses, and the horses trotted quietly back into the town.

Bruncvík betook himself to one of his princely castles, and called together his lords and squires there, and they greeted him with great joy and rode with him to Prague. As they drew near to the city they met Neomenia, with her father and a great escort, who had all come out to seek for Bruncvík. They were all overjoyed at this meeting, and most of all Neomenia, who wept tears of bliss.

Then they all returned to Prague, and there all the citizens, old and young, welcomed Bruncvík with great delight and acclaim. They were happy that their prince had returned to them and brought them a lion; it was a joy to all the land when the prince had it proclaimed in all the towns that a lion should be painted on the gates, and also on the national standard, which is a white lion on a red ground.

From that time Bruncvík lived contentedly with Neomenia, and ruled happily for more than forty years longer. The faithful lion was always with him and close beside him. And when Bruncvík died at a great age, leaving an only son, Ladislav, the lion no longer wished to live without his lord. He pined and languished until, roaring for the last time in his grief, he expired on Bruncvík's grave.

And Bruncvík's miraculous sword?

That is walled up firmly and deeply in a pillar of Charles Bridge, where the statue of Bruncvík stands with the likeness of a lion at his feet. There Bruncvík secretly had the sword concealed before his death, and there the magic weapon has lain for centuries. It will reappear only when things are at their worst with the Czech land. When the country is most sorely oppressed, then the knights of Saint Wenceslas will burst out of Blaník to the country's aid, and the patron saint of Bohemia himself will lead the Czech people.

And as he rides over Charles Bridge, his white horse will kick and tear out Bruncvík's sword from the stone with his hooves. Saint Wenceslas will seize it, and whirl it above his head in a terrible stroke, and cry:

'Off with the heads of all the enemies of the Czech lands!'

And so it will happen, and there will be holy peace in the land.

I

A young clerk of the order and rule of St Benedict in the monastery of Opatovice came to his abbot just before the hour of noon, to announce that an unexpected guest had arrived at that very moment, some lord, evidently of high birth, with two mounted attendants. They had dismounted at the gate in the first courtyard, and the lord had gone straight into the church.

The abbot, a grave and reverend priest, asked whence the rider had come.

'From Hradec.'

'What did he say?'

'Nothing. And neither did his attendants.'

'What does he look like?'

'He is of medium height, perhaps forty years old, with a black beard. A grave gentleman, finely dressed, but his gown is dark and without ornaments.'

The abbot considered for a moment, then rose, and leaving his apartment, passed through a long corridor of the building, and down the staircase, into the ambulatory which enclosed the quiet 'paradise court' of the cloister. The court at that hour was bathed in the flood of sunbeams which had just begun to fall there. Their golden radiance penetrated even into the ambulatory, painting upon the paving and the walls the shadows of the romanesque columns. The heat of the August day could not yet be felt here, for from dawn almost until this hour cooling shadow lay over all.

It was silent and empty among the ancient buildings. At this hour all the monks lingered in their cells. The abbot moved through light and shade, and emerged from the coolness into the flood of heat and light in the second, main court, a spacious place, where the surrounding buildings stood out clearly in the shining air from the blue, cloudless sky that framed them, and particularly the two church towers and the great body of the churchit self, all constructed in Romanesque style.

The abbot advanced to the portal, with its magnificent courses of masonry ornamented with rich carving of petals and leaves and strange beasts. But at that moment, out of the pleasant coolness of the church door walked the strange gentleman. He had his cap still doffed in his hand; he was sunburned, black-haired and going bald at the brow, with a broad face, and he stooped a little as he walked. As the abbot looked into his large dark eyes, and as the stranger spoke, he realised that this was no ordinary nobleman. Graciously the visitor thanked him for his welcome, and gladly accepted his invitation to dinner. They went back together into the ambulatory, and round the paradise court straight to the refectory, for the note of the monastery bell echoed through the deep noonday hush, announcing to the village and the people in the fields the hour of the midday rest.

Down the centre of the long, vaulted hall stretched a row of oak tables, shining with the dim lustre of pewter dishes, and ranks of chairs and stools. The monks were already waiting, old and young together. When the customary grace had been said, they sat down to meat, at the highest table the abbot with his guest, in carved oakwood armchairs.

Throughout the meal the guest talked graciously of the monastery and of the church, which he praised as a beautiful piece of work, strongly suggesting Italian workmanship, especially the portal. But the abbot told him that in fact it was the work of Czech artists, for the church had been rebuilt from the original smaller one, though the first monks, immediately after the house was founded, had indeed been Italians from Monte Cassino. Then the strange lord began to speak of the maternal monastery, for it seemed that he knew it well. He talked of Monte Cassino, of the Italians, even of Rome, so eloquently that all those who sat near him forgot their food.

And the more his guest talked, the more uneasy the abbot grew. From the moment when he had heard that the stranger had ridden in from Hradec he had entertained the thought that this might be someone from court, for only that morning he had heard that on the previous day the emperor had arrived at Hradec with his household. And when the clerk had told him that this gentleman had gone first into the church, the abbot had recalled what he had heard about the Emperor Charles: that whenever he came to some new place, he always went first of all into the church.

And now all this accomplished conversation and knowledge of the world, and every act of the stranger designed to awaken respect and admiration... As soon as the guest had laid down his knife and washed his hands in the shining copper water-bowl, the abbot drew him aside with him into the window embrasure, and begged him not to take it amiss if he asked him his name.

The guest promised that he should know it presently, but asked him first to go into the church with him, and to take with them the two oldest monks in the monastery. The abbot willingly complied, and led his guest by way of a passage straight into the church. It was lofty and vaulted, with three aisles separated by round columns supporting enormous round arches. The misty light of a dim and secret dusk filtered in by the few windows to fill the whole noble space, and the rich wall-paintings were lost in its gloom.

They all kneeled together before the high altar; and when the stranger rose from his knees he said:

'My lord abbot, you wished to know my name. I tell you therefore, and these brethren here, that I am Charles, Emperor of Rome and King of Bohemia, and your lord.'

The abbot made haste to offer apologies for having received him with so little ceremony, although, as he admitted, he had had his suspicions of the honour that was being done to his house; but indeed he had not been able to believe in it. But the emperor smiled graciously, and said that all had been very well done, that he had not wished to be recognised by anyone, and that was the reason he had left his court behind in Hradec, and told no-one where he was going.

'And this I did,' he continued, 'so that I could speak more freely with you. Father abbot, these two brothers are the oldest and the most trustworthy in your house?'

'They are.'

'Dear fathers,' said the emperor then, 'here in this house of God let me tell you why I came to visit you. I have heard that in this monastery you have a great treasure. If it is indeed so, I hope you will not conceal the fact from me. And I, for my part, promise you that I have no wish to take from you any part of it, either by my own hand or through any other man. I should like only to look upon this treasure, nothing more.'

The abbot and the brothers stood silent in consternation, until the abbot requested that they might have a moment for consultation. The emperor consented, and when the monks had conferred together the abbot said:

'Be pleased to know, your Majesty, that this treasure does exist. But not one of the brothers of the order—and there are five and fifty of them in the household at this moment—has any knowledge of it. Only I and these two brothers know about it, not a soul besides. If the Lord God should suffer one of us to be taken, then we should confide the secret to one other, so that there may be always three, the abbot and the two senior brethren. Be pleased to know also that we are bound by a grave obligation, and may not tell anything about this treasure, either by word or sign. And moreover, the approach to it is very difficult, and no fit road for your Grace to go.'

But the emperor still pressed them to tell him, vowing that he too would keep silence, and say no word of the treasure to any other. The monks again took counsel together, and the abbot then avowed that it was not proper for them to speak, but neither was it proper for them to refuse the request of their king.

'Therefore,' said the abbot, 'we can do one of two things. Either we will tell your Majesty about the hiding-place, but not show you the treasure, or we will show you the treasure without revealing where it is hidden.'

'Rather, then, let me see this treasure,' the emperor decided.

Then they requested him to do as they should bid; and he promised. They led him from the church into the sacristy, thence they descended into a cellar paved with tiles, where it was very dark. One of the monks took flint and steel and lighted two wax candles. But as soon as their flames lit up the darkness, the second monk approached and drew a cowl over the emperor's head, turning it back to front so that the emperor could see nothing. He could only hear how they were raising and lifting aside the tiles.

Then they guided him into some kind of hole, and begged him to take care in the descent, for they must creep down a ladder. He went down after them deeper and deeper into the darkness for a long time, and when at last they reached the foot of the ladder they turned the emperor about and led him, changing course several times so that he should not be able to remember his way or have any sense of direction left to him. They had now to walk along a long, dark passage, where he was aware of the marked dampness of the air. All the gallery had a musty smell, and their footsteps rang hollowly. It seemed to the emperor that the road would never end; but suddenly they halted him, and as soon as they lifted the cowl from his head he saw that he was in a close, airless cellar, dimly illuminated by the gleam of the wax candles. By their small light he saw, as the abbot lifted the lids of certain iron chests, the glimmer of silver, hoard upon hoard of silver everywhere, some cast into rings, some in whole bars.

Thence the monks led their emperor into the next cellar, and there he beheld a great quantity of rings and thick bars of pure gold, of great weight and unworked.

The emperor marvelled; but in the third cellar he was dumb with amazement. Here was the greatest treasure of all; an enormous hoard of both precious metals, gold and silver, but all fashioned into wonderful works of art. Beautiful chains, cups and chalices, crosses and reliquaries, all glittering with gold, and with the still more brilliant and scintillating radiance of precious stones, blinding the eyes with their brightness.

As the emperor stood gazing at all this beauty, and all this immeasurable wealth, the abbot said to him:

'My lord, these treasures are conserved for you and for those who come after you. Therefore take whatever best pleases you.'

But the emperor would not. So the abbot, saying that it was not seemly that he should go from thence and take nothing with him in memory of his visit, proffered to him a splendid ring, set with a wonderful diamond of great size and value. The emperor accepted it with thanks.

Then they returned, and as they passed again through the three cellars they covered the emperor's head with the cowl as before, and led him here and there, but brought him at last to the ladder, and so they mounted again into the cellar. When they had covered the opening from sight they put out the candles, and took the cowl from the emperor's head; and all together they passed into the sacristy, and thence to the church, and prayed together before the high altar.

The emperor thanked the monks, and begged them: 'Good fathers, let me know one thing more. May I mention to my friends—but to a few only—that I have seen in my kingdom such a wonderful and rare treasure hidden beneath the earth? I promise I will never say where, or in what region.'

The abbot and the monks consented. The emperor looked at his ring as he prepared to depart.

'This gift of yours will be held by me in such esteem that it shall never leave my finger, and shall go with me into the grave.'

It was already late afternoon when they came out of the church. The emperor

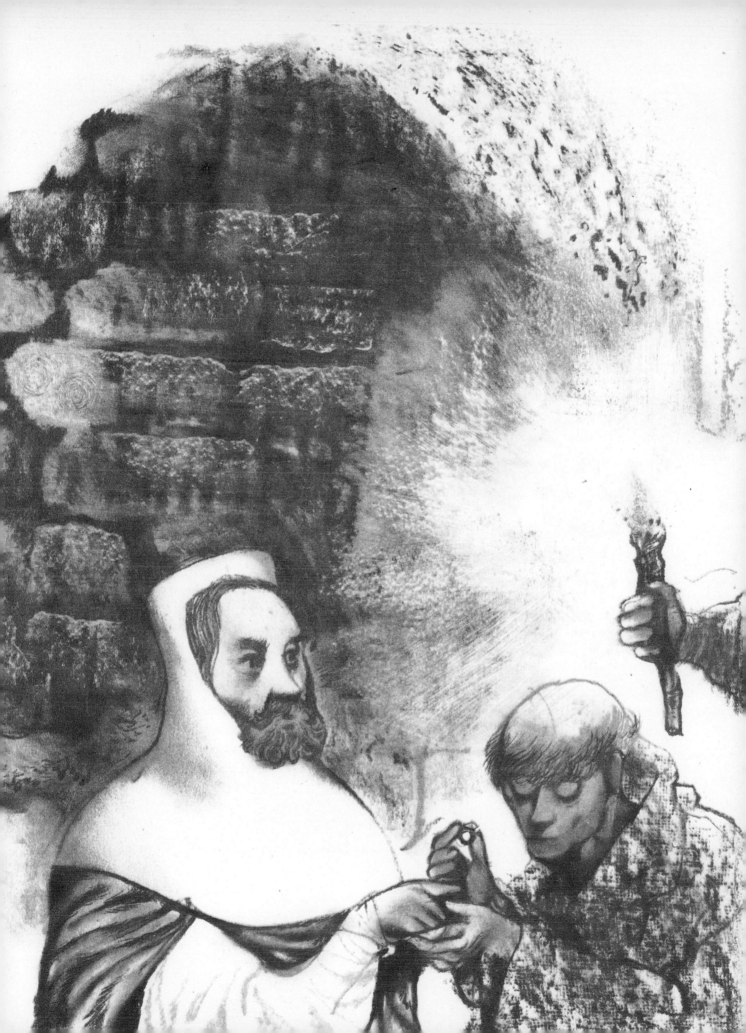

lingered no longer. He took his leave of the abbot and the brothers, mounted his horse, and escorted by his two chamberlains rode back along the Elbe, upstream through the meadows towards Hradec.

There the courtiers were curious to know from the chamberlains where he had been; and when they heard, they wanted to know what the emperor had been doing at the monastery.

'He took his dinner there, and after dinner he went into the church with the abbot and two old monks, and prayed there with them for a long time.'

They told no more, for they knew no more. Indeed no-one did, for the emperor kept the secret. Only shortly before his death he told a few of his counsellors that they must leave his ring on his finger after his death, and let it be buried with him, for it was a memento of the treasure of the monastery of Opatovice, which the brothers had showed to him many years before.

And it was done as he requested.

II

Years had passed since the death of Charles the Fourth of blessed memory. At the end of the reign of his son Wenceslas the Fourth, in the year 1415, an unexpected visitor arrived at the monastery of Opatovice, the lord John Městecký of Opočno, with two mounted grooms. It was in November, just at the feast of All Saints, late in the afternoon when it was already growing dark, and the deserted meadows round about and the bare trees along the Elbe were black shadows in the early dusk. And a freezing wind was blowing.

It was no wonder that the knight rode into the monastery and asked for a night's lodging, saying that he had intended to go as far as Hradec, but it was such bitter bad weather outside, the wind cut like a knife even through his cloak, and it bade fair to be a very dark night.

The Abbot Peter Lazur, that old and worthy priest, received the knight kindly, and ordered that a good meal should be given also to his two grooms as likewise to their three companions, who, as the lord Městecký said, had been delayed along the way, but would presently follow them there. These three duly arrived when it was already fully evening, flushed with the wind and cold. At that hour their lord was sitting with the abbot and the brothers in the refectory, in the light of the wax candles on the tables and close beside a vast green stove, which gave an agreeable warmth.

The knight was full of news. He told them of the Council of Constance and of

Master John Huss of Husinec, but most of all he talked of Prague, saying that it was laid under a ban for the sake of Master John of Jesenice, a disciple of Huss, and that all religious services in Prague were stopped. And he bitterly attacked the new learning and the people of Prague for rebelling against the priests, and the king for enduring all this.

Just then a new guest arrived, the lord Otto of Bergov. He said that the impassable roads and the terrible weather had compelled him to take refuge beneath the hospitable roof of the old monastery, and asked for a night's lodging for himself and his five mounted grooms. He was astonished to see the lord Městecký there, but rejoiced that he would have a companion on the morrow on the road to Hradec.

The abbot greeted the lord of Bergov no less kindly, and continued sitting with the knights even when the brothers had dispersed to their cells after supper. The lords sat at their wine near to the stove, the warmth of which was all the more pleasant to them as the wind roared through the dark night outside, until the shutters shuddered and rattled. The lord Městecký went on with his reports, and the lord of Bergov also had news to tell. And both of them drank mightily, pouring out beaker after beaker of the red-gold wine, until their faces grew ruddy and their eyes shone.

But suddenly both of them fell silent and rose from their places, as the note of a war-trumpet blared abruptly through the darkness outside, a sharp and piercing sound, penetrating even the roar of the wind. On that signal the two knights seized the abbot by the arms, and the lord Městecký said sharply and sternly:

'My lord abbot, you hear that trumpet. That's a signal to us that our men-at-arms already have the gate in their hands, and have let in their fellows, thirty of them—you hear? They're lying in wait there in the dark. By this time they're all within the monastery. You and all here are in our power.'

The abbot, stunned with shock and dread, forced out with an effort: 'What do you want?'

'The treasure, your monastery treasure. No harm will come to you if you tell us where it is. We know you have it somewhere here underground. Tell us where it is!' stormed the lord of Bergov.

'I do not know.'

In the corridor there burst out a sudden clamour, cries of alarm and the clash of arms.

'Look for no help,' threatened the lord Městecký. 'You hear, those are our men. Speak, where is the treasure?'

'I will not tell you,' replied the old abbot, trembling but resolute.

'We shall torture you!'

'Do as God wills. But I must not, I will not tell.'

The lord of Bergov burst out of the refectory, and at once in came four grooms armed to the teeth. To them the lord Městecký handed over the old abbot. Through the dark of the November night came the clang of a bell ringing the alarm, for one of the monks had run to it and begun a peal to call the nearby village to their aid. But hardly had he set the bell swinging when the soldiers burst in upon him, and paid him for his boldness with a mortal wound.

Red lights flashed through the monastery, the windows of the church were aglow; even through the cells and the dark ambulatory and courts, everywhere the torches and the blazing pine-flares gleamed, everywhere glimmered the figures of fleeing monks, and the plundering soldiers who pursued them, beating and killing and carrying off whatever booty they could find. Only the abbot was left in the cloister, but bound, in a cellar of the courtyard, where the grooms of the lord Městecký stretched him on a ladder and beat him by the light of pitch-flares, and ever and again the lord Městecký or the lord of Bergov would thunder at him:

'Where is the treasure? Where is it? Speak, or you shall die!'

But the abbot endured all this torment manfully and remained silent, vouch-safing them no answer, even when they burned his side with torches.

When the bleak and misty day broke, all was silent and deserted in the monastery of Opatovice. The house had been completely sacked. All the shining dishes, the money, all the jewels, even those of the church, the lords Městecký and Otto of Bergov had carried away. When the villagers came to the monastery they found many of the monks lying wounded, and the abbot tortured almost to death.

The damage to the whole monastery was immense, but the enormous underground treasure was saved by the abbot's suffering and death. For the abbot, Peter Lazur, died soon afterwards.

Five years later the lord Městecký of Opočno, who in the universal turmoil and confusion of the times had escaped the punishment due for the crime he had committed with his accomplice, came once again to the monastery of Opatovice, but this time not as a robber, rather as its protector. He brought there a garrison, a war company of soldiers of the Emperor Zikmund, into whose service he had entered against his own countrymen.

With this company he garrisoned the monastery against the Hussite citizens of Hradec and the brethren of Oreb. This time he made no search for the great treasure hidden in the earth. Soon he had to leave to join the army in the field,

but the garrison remained, and twice fought victorious battles with the people of Hradec, the first in December of this same year 1420 at the monastery itself, and the second in March of the following year not far away, at the village of Podolšany, where Luke, the general of the Hradec forces, himself fell in battle. But in April the soldiers of the emperor retired from Opatovice in terror before the great army of Prague, Oreb and Hradec, which had stormed Kutná Hora.

As soon as Zikmund's forces had withdrawn came the lord Diviš Bořek of Miletín, with the brethren of Oreb and the men of Hradec, and took a bitter revenge on Opatovice for their two defeats and their many losses. The old and splendid monastery was set on fire.

The convent with all its buildings burned. In the level meadows by the Elbe, above whose blossoming green turf the gilded crosses of the towers and the noble church had shone, blackened ruins stood, the shattered cloisters round the paradise court desolate and overgrown with weeds; and there was the silence of death where once the monks had sung the hours.

The monastery remained thus deserted. And deep beneath its ruins remained also the vast treasure of rare metals, precious stones and goldsmiths' work; it lay untouched, there where already it had lain for centuries. And the place remained a mystery. Only the legend of it was handed on through many generations, and persisted even when the ruins of the ancient biulding mouldered and fell to pieces.

III

They crumbled and vanished when the water reached them. Long, long ago, in a time of great flood, the waters of the Elbe washed over them and drowned them; and as with the passage of time the course of the river in these parts changed, a part of the ruins lay below its level, at the bottom of the river-bed. Thus the Elbe, which formerly flowed beside the monastery, now flowed over it, and when the water was low and clear, people used to come to look at the crumbling fragments of the ruins beneath its surface.

But a part of the site remained on dry land. On this spot, beside the river, they built a mill; and it is said that where the high altar used to be there grew a lime-tree that lived through long ages. Often in the summer evenings the miller's apprentices and customers would sit in front of the mill and talk about the Emperor Charles and the treasure, speculating in which spot it could be, and whether it would be possible to get at it under the water, and what they would do for themselves if they could find it.

And often they raised their eyes to the old lime-tree, the gigantic crown of which towered black and tall in the dusk. The breeze carried to them the rustle of leaves and the strong and heady sweetness of its blossoms like the murmur of prayers and the scent of incense from the altar of God. And at the hour of midnight the bushy branches of the old tree began to gleam as though the light of the rising moon shone through them. Then lights gathered and glowed in the crown, shimmering along all the boughs and illuminating the night sky. Whoever witnessed this miracle crossed himself in amazement and dread. The local people fell on their knees and prayed as though before an altar. More than one of them, at such a time, heard the strains of sacred singing, distant and faint as though borne from a distance, ascending about the lime-tree and drifting on the wind down to the river, where it faded and died away into silence.

At last this mysterious place filled men with wonder even in broad daylight, and especially the miller and his journeymen and customers. Once in the reign of King Maximilian, the father of Rudolf the Second, the wheels of the mill of Opatovice stopped suddenly of themselves, just at midday.

Everyone ran out to the river, and there, wonder of wonders! The wheels had ceased to turn because no water was reaching them; for higher up the course of the river, above the mill, the flood vanished in the middle of its bed, falling there in a roaring, thundering torrent into some cavity or abyss.

So it continued falling for a good half-hour, and during that time not a drop flowed to the wheels, so that the mill stood as if enchanted. But after half an hour the water flowed in its course again, and rushed on as before to the mill, and turned its wheels. At the spot where the river had thus disappeared the miller, his journeymen, his customers and the people of the village stood talking of the wonderful occurrence, until they hit on it that there must be some cloister cellar beneath the place, that its vaulting had collapsed, and the river had gushed into the cellars and along the network of passages, and certainly drowned also the gallery leading to the treasure. It was all over now, they said; it was hopeless now for anyone to attempt to reach it.

And yet they did attempt it. Not local people, but foreigners.

It was in the sorrowful period after the battle of the White Mountain, when four Italians came to Opatovice. They said that they were divers from Venice, in Italy, and that the Emperor Ferdinand himself had sent them here to find that sunken treasure.

Nobody hindered them, and so, having made their preparations, they plunged into the Elbe at the spot where the monastery ruins were to be seen. There they

165

intended first of all to survey the foundations and the remains of the buildings. But they did not stay there long. Two of them came to the surface again almost at once. Two remained below the water longer. Their companions waited for them, but in vain, for those two never returned. Perhaps the current swept them away, perhaps they lost themselves beneath the water in the ruins of the old monastery. Not even their bodies were ever found.

Their fellows never ventured into the river after the treasure again. They mounted their horses and rode away empty-handed.

And so the treasure of Opatovice lies to this day deep in the earth, and the Elbe, flowing over it, guards it well.

O PRAGUE!
THE NAME ITSELF A SONG, WHOSE VERY SOUND
PLUCKS AT THE STRINGS OF EVERY TRUE CZECH SPIRIT
AND SETS THE HEART VIBRATING

Svatopluk Čech

About Old Prague

I

Once Charles the Fourth invited to his castle of Prague Archbishop Arnošt of Pardubice, the high Chancellor, the burgrave of the Czech kingdom and other distinguished Czech lords and courtiers, together with certain masters renowned for their arts, among them his astronomer. He sat down with them in a splendid hall, the wooden ceiling of which was ornamented with carvings, painting and gilding, and its walls covered with rare French tapestries. They sat at a table gleaming with wax candles and shining with gold and silver dishes, plates, goblets and jugs of beautiful form and rich ornamentation.

167

When they had supped, and it was beginning to be close and sultry in the hall, the emperor rose and invited his guests to go out with him and cool themselves in the fresh air. He went before with the archbishop, leading the way on to a balcony to which their dining room gave immediate access, and after them went the lords and the scholars in lively conversation.

But as they emerged on the spacious balcony the emperor and his counsellor fell silent, and all the others hushed their talk. They stood mute with astonishment at the beauty of the royal city below them.

Prague slumbered in the summer night, in the flooding light of the full moon and in deep shadows. In this enchanted light the gables and roofs of the tall houses, the churches, the towers soared in beauty, the windows of the buildings and the great oriels glittered, and the bushy crowns of the trees in the many gardens and on the islands mingled in the gleaming radiance with soft, cloudy outlines.

And all in deep stillness. Only the weirs below hummed and murmured. King and courtiers, charmed by all this loveliness, stood gazing through light and dark; their eyes wandered along the slopes of Petřín in the blue dimness, over the Little Quarter immediately beneath them; they beheld its illuminated spaces, the archbishop's palace by the river, where the gilded roof of its fortified tower burned; they looked across the modest bridge, along the river, shimmering like spilled silver, and beyond to the rest of Prague, the Jewish Town, the Old Town enclosed in its ramparts and bastions, above which towers and churches soared towards the night sky. There the streets and arcades had grown dark, there all things were drowned in light and shadow and deep twilight.

And they looked beyond the Old Town, along the plateau with its wide spaces, where the church of Saint Lazarus showed white and pale, and the church of Saint Peter on the hill of Zderaz stood freely, not hemmed in by a crowd of houses; where the village of Opatovice drowsed and the church of Saint Stephen in the village of Rybník towered high in the pallid moonlight, and beyond it the church of Saint John on the Battlefield. There the sheen of the moonlight flowed freely over gardens, orchards and fields of ripe grain, far to the horizon, to the heights planted with vineyards, misty with white vapours.

Silent every one, they gazed on this enchanting picture outspread before them, until the king, moved by so much beauty, said:

'Beautiful is this land of mine, and in it I find my greatest delight. I hold it as a chosen and more precious orchard among my other fields. But in this orchard the place of the greatest consolation and joy—behold, Prague! Is there anything more beautiful?'

The king's eyes were shining.

168

'A most beautiful city,' said Arnošt of Pardubice, 'and most happy, as the chronicler calls it, because it was exalted by a sainted prince. And now it is and will still be adorned by your love. The prophecy of your Majesty's first ancestress is already fulfilled. Prague grows in greatness and glory. Princes bow to her, she enjoys honour and praise throughout the world. And she will be yet more glorious.'

'With the help of God I will gladly adorn her,' said the king sincerely. 'And indeed I hope—' But suddenly he turned to the old astronomer, who was gazing gravely before him.

'Surely, master astronomer, there is a beautiful and great future before this city? You are frowning? Speak!'

'Your Majesty, do not ask me at this moment to proclaim what the heavenly songs foretell.'

'Speak!' commanded the king. 'I want to hear what you have read in the stars.'

'It is sorrowful hearing, my gracious lord.'

'Yet I will hear it. Speak!'

Then the disconsolate master announced to the king and his retinue, who drew near to listen to him anxiously:

'I have come to know from the heavenly signs that the Little Quarter will be destroyed by fire, in a great holocaust, and there—the Old Town will perish in a terrible flood. All will be ruined, all—there will not remain one stone upon another.'

All who heard him stood aghast, gazing at the king, who listened in evident grief and dismay. But in an instant he turned again to the city, and waving his hand towards it he cried:

'But Prague shall not perish! It shall remain, it shall continue! And even if the Little Quarter and the Old Town are destroyed some day, others shall arise here. There I will build a new city, there, look, there shall be a new and great Prague!'

He pointed beyond the Old Town, up towards the broad plateau, to the fields and orchards and the villages of Opatovice and Rybník. They breathed again, their faces cleared, and the wise archbishop expressed what the Czech lords and courtiers were feeling at that moment, and wishing to their king with all their souls:

'God bless your Majesty!'

As Charles the Fourth had resolved, so he did. At once he set to work to make all the preparations for the founding of the new town. He himself defined its extent and the line of its ramparts, and himself laid the foundation for them. He was present at the measuring out of the streets, he decided the site of the market and the square. Often he talked and took counsel with the builder, and often came to see how the work was progressing, and on every occasion he spoke to a mason here or a day-labourer there, questioned them and made them gifts, pleased that the work was continuing successfully.

Only once he grew angry, and that was when he came to look at the New Town on returning from a journey into the German empire, and saw that the surveyors had added a new street in his absence. It led to the church of Saint Henry, and already they were building the houses along it.

As the emperor saw it he stood in amazement and displeasure, and asked sharply who had ordered this street to be founded and laid out there.

'No-one ordered it, your gracious Majesty,' said the builder, dismayed. 'We thought that it would be suitable. But if you wish it to be halted—'

'Let it remain,' decided the emperor, 'but let it be named for all time Unauthorised, since I gave no order for its establishment.'

So the New Town grew. The buildings increased like mushrooms after rain. But it was not only the citizens of the new city who were building, for the lord of the Czech lands himself built, also. And that most lavishly: monasteries, and towered churches. Thus he founded also the church of Saint Jerome, and beside it the monastery of the Benedictine monks in that region of Skalky, where ages before had flourished the grove of the goddess Morana. He raised this church at great expense. It is said that special tiles were fired for this building, identical with those in the castle of Karlštejn, of grey clay and glazed on the upper surface, and the church roof was designed so thoroughly and artistically that they used for it the tree-trunks from a whole forest.

The church and the monastery were twenty years in the building, and it was an expensive undertaking. It is said that this church cost to build not a penny less than did the Stone Bridge itself.

When it was completed and the first sacred service held in it, the priests at the altar sang in the Slav language, and they read Holy Mass in the ancient ceremony from Slav books, for the first time for centuries in a Czech church.

Then there was joy in the heart of the pious Czech king who had brought these Slavonic monks here from Dalmatia, and all the people rejoiced with him.

And they gave to both monastery and church the name of Na Slovanech, the place of the Slavs, and so they are called to this day.

Before they had been working three full years on the building of the Slav church, Charles the Fourth had already laid the foundation of a new church, on the highest site in the New Town, opposite Vyšehrad. A certain young Prague

architect had submitted the plans for this building. The emperor, seeing the scheme he had drawn out, marvelled to see a conception so beautiful and at the same time so audacious.

He marvelled, and the knowledgeable people marvelled with him, the experienced and proved builders; and they said that their young fellow would not fulfil his plan for the church, that he would be unable to erect that enormous vault he had designed. But the king believed in the work of the young artist, and he, eager to erect a building such as Prague had never seen at that time, set to work with enthusiasm and ardour.

He built and built, and the church on its eight-sided foundation visibly grew. The walls were rising, the two-lancet and three-lancet windows with their beautiful arched ribs already stood in them, and the portal displayed its rich courses of masonry, ornamented with luxurious leaves, figures and knots of flowers. Already they had begun, in accordance with the plan of the young master, to arch over the interior of the church with the bold, hitherto unheard-of starry vault in the form of a dome.

All the vault was still covered with scaffolding, and could not be seen for a forest of beams and joists and a great number of planks, and already the experts were marvelling at it. But all the more positively did every one of them assert that the young architect would not finish his work, that the vault could not hold, for it was impossible, no such thing had ever been known. When it came to the point, they said, all that bold dome would surely give way and burst, and fall to ruin.

These speeches had their effect. The faith of the young master was shaken to its foundations. He began to be afraid, and doubt and distrust began to torment him. He no longer hastened to the site with such confidence and joy as formerly. And at home, in solitude, he had no rest or peace. He reckoned and estimated and drew, trying to determine whether the vault would hold. He meditated and considered day and night.

Anxiety and unease drove sleep away from him. Far into the night he sat in his tracing-house, and when he lay down in his bed he was still calculating, or recalling the speeches of his fellow-architects, old and young, their criticisms, their fears, their confident assertions that it was impossible to complete such a vault. Their mockery, too, came back into his mind, and when he considered what would happen if he should not complete his design, or if the vault should collapse, how he would be overwhelmed with laughter and shame instead of praise and honour, he clutched at his burning head, or walked his room heaving desperate sighs. Once in such a night he ran out of the house and hurried uphill to the New Town.

There in the dim light his work towered darkly, the uncompleted church still in its shell of scaffolding. There was no ring of hammers now, the building was silent and deserted. Only its creator paced round it, pondering on it, lifting his gaze on high, where the vault began to soar. Then he crept within, into what would some day be the nave of the church, where the holy hymns and prayers would some day be uplifted.

Through the still unglazed windows the starry sky looked in upon him, and the moonlight streamed in. By its gleam the oppressed and agitated artist looked round his work, but immediately lifted his eyes to the vault, dim and dark among its framework of beams.

But the builder saw it at that moment in its completed perfection, his bold conception, with its ribs forming a great, eight-rayed star, and in it two smaller ones. He saw the vault decorated with colour and with gold, he saw the church already flooded with sunlight, glittering with ornaments. And the king entered with his court, and the people after them, and every man looked up at the ceiling, to that magnificent vault, marvelling and amazed.

When he wrenched himself out of his dream to the realisation that he might be cheated of all this, that it would never happen, that the vault would fall, defiance flared up in his spirit.

As he left he told himself that he would complete his building, in spite of all. He would finish the vault, he must; and if he could not do it alone, then with the help of the devil himself! And so it happened. He invoked the devil, and when he had signed away his soul to him, the devil promised him that the church of Karlov would stand. So he completed the work. What his fellow-architects day by day expected, that the vault would collapse, did not happen. The keystone was set in place, and all the gigantic, unprecedented arch stood firm. All that remained was to remove the scaffolding that underpropped it, so that the glorious work should be exposed to view.

But not one of the masons or their workmen was willing to take down the scaffolding. Every one of them was afraid that the vault would fall as soon as the framework was removed. In vain the young architect ordered his men, in vain he promised them rewards. Then he wished to do the work himself, but the elders and his companions would not let him, and prevented him from touching the scaffolding.

'Then I'll burn it down!' he resolved, the devil himself prompting him.

Great crowds of people stood about the new building, anxiously awaiting what would happen, and agreeing that the vault would surely fall when the young master burned the framework from under it. They saw him come out from the church in great agitation, and hardly had he left it when there was a great sound

like thunder; a gigantic rumbling as though the church were falling to pieces shook the air. The watchers shrieked in terror, and turned in confusion to flee, crying out that the vault had fallen.

At that moment no-one thought of the builder, who stood, stunned by the deafening din, pale and demented, staring in despair at the church, through the windows of which billowed whirls of dust.

'The devil has deceived me!' he thought. 'This is the punishment of God!' And he waited no longer, for he did not wish to see his ruined work. He took to his heels and rushed away like a hunted creature.

The coils of dust dispersed, and when after a time the people ventured back to the church, and even into it, they cried aloud again, but with wonder and amazement. Boards and beams lay in confused wreckage on the ground, but above them, above the whole interior of the church stretched the marvellous vault, such a vault as they had never seen before. They saw it in the flooding sunlight of the afternoon in all its unveiled perfection, the masterly assembly of its ribs; and they were filled with wonder and joy.

Then they remembered the young architect. They called him, they searched for him, they sought him until they found him at last in his own dwelling, dead. In his despair he had taken his own life.

What he had dreamed of and seen in the spirit, on that night when he had rushed out to the church, was fulfilled. The church was completed and beautified with many ornaments, and every man who entered it for the first time, king or courtier or commoner, turned his gaze first to the mighty vault, so audaciously poised over the holy place, and every man remembered the uhappy young architect who had paid for his work with his life.

At Hradčany, at the castle of the Czech kings, they were raising at this same period the magnificent building commissioned by Charles, the new church of Saint Vitus, while across the river on its wide eminence the New Town appeared in vigorous growth. And between these two glorious monuments of his piety, and his love for art and for his best-loved city, Charles began to build a third great work, the Stone Bridge.

This bridge has survived the centuries; the triumphs and humiliations of our nation have passed over it. Many things in Bohemia have changed and are still changing since its foundation, quarrels and disputes have torn apart people of one blood and one tongue. Only the bridge has remained dear to all through all ages. It has endured firm and strong through all storms and all times of subjugation and weakness, a reminder of better times, and of the glory from which it arose, and which has been always the comfort and stay of the feeble. They say that Charles Bridge is of all bridges the strongest, because at its building the mortar was mixed with eggs. And they were needed in incalculable quantities for its sixteen mighty arches, and its numerous pillars and gigantic walls.

They could not amass so many eggs in Prague, even the surrounding districts had not the full total that was needed. So Charles the Fourth sent out an edict to all the towns in the kingdom of Bohemia, desiring each one to send a certain number of score of eggs for the building of Prague bridge. And they sent them; wagon after wagon came, and from each the eggs were unloaded and beaten into the mortar.

From Velvary also they sent a whole wagon-load, willingly and gladly, priding themselves on their contribution. When the masons broke the first egg from Velvary, and then the second and the third, they could not believe their eyes. But when the fourth and fifth, and the whole of the first three score were broken, they burst into hearty laughter. The masons laughed, the architect laughed, everyone about the site laughed, and soon the whole of Prague was laughing, and everywhere they recounted with delight the story of how the good people of Velvary had sent to the building a whole wagon-load of hard-boiled eggs.

When the Stone Bridge was built it had no statues. Only a wooden cross was erected on the ascent, where now stands one of metal and gilt. Near this spot, they say, in ancient times executions took place, and the condemned man made his last prayers at this cross.

On the wall which connects the Bridge Tower with the monastery of the Crusaders, on the side turned towards the river, a relief of a bearded head can be seen. This is the Bearded Man. They say it is a portrait of the first architect, who had his stone likeness carved into the bridge pillar as a perpetual remembrance of him.

As you pass over the Stone Bridge towards the castle of our kings you will see to the left on Petřín a long, battlemented wall. It shows white among the rich green of the trees on the crest of the hill, and descends its steep slope to the former Újezd gate. This wall is the work of the 'family' of Charles the Fourth.

A time of great scarcity had set in; the poor people were dying of hunger, for there was no work for them, and therefore no wages. At one period in these lean times there were gathered together in Prague some two thousand poor people, and when King Charles was coming out of church they came flocking before him, and begged him with tears to provide them with means to live, saying they would be glad to work without wages, if need be, only for food, and that they could live on very little, just enough to keep them from dying of hunger. Moved by their misery, the king commanded them to meet at the same spot the next day; and when they did so, he told his agents to conduct them to the summit of Petřín, and himself appearing among them on horseback, set some to breaking stones, some to digging foundations, others to begin the building of the masonry of a wall from the Vltava over Petřín to the monastery of Strahov.

The workmen did not receive money in payment, but bread and other eatables as much as they desired, and also shoes and clothes. And when others who were also hungry heard about it, they ran in great numbers to the site, and worked with a will. King Charles often rode out to see them on Petřín, and often distributed their rewards to them with his own hands, saying that these working people were his family. Thousands of people blessed him, and prayed for him daily when they rose, and nightly as they went to their rest.

Out of this stone which they carried and cut and built into the wall, bread grew for them. Therefore they called this wall 'the Bread Wall', and also 'the Hunger Wall', because it had driven away hunger and misery. And it is battlemented with great teeth, because King Charles the Fourth had it built in order that the teeth of the hungry people might have something to bite.

At that time there lived in Prague a rich citizen named John Rotlev. He had bought a deserted mine in Jílový, being convinced that there was still plenty of gold in it, and that he would surely find it. He hired a great number of miners and dug and mined untiringly, endlessly, shrinking from no expense. And he had need of much money to pay his costs. But he could not hit on the gold.

The mine led only through gravel and barren stone; not a single gleam of gold anywhere. Hundreds and hundreds of good coins Rotlev had already poured into this undertaking. His money had run out, and he was already beginning to incur debts, so that the work should not stop. His friends and acquaintances warned and exhorted him to give up his efforts, saying that he would not find gold, and that instead he would surely bury here all that he now had left to him. But Rotlev was convinced that he would certainly find gold; and so strong was this conviction, that he would take no warnings and no advice, but began to sell his property piece by piece in order to have money for his mine in Jílový. So he lost all, and had nothing left with which to pay his miners. He was downcast and in despair, not because he had buried all his possessions, but because he could not go on with his digging. He insisted again and again that very soon now he would find gold, if only he could go on for a short time longer.

They all mocked him, and no-one believed him. Only his wife never doubted what he said, and she was sorry for her husband, but she had no way of helping him. All that she had, her jewels and trinkets, she had given to him long since.

A precious veil woven of gold thread was all she had kept of all her wealth, in memory of the years of her youth. This veil was particularly dear to her because her husband had given it to her when she became his bride. But she gave up even her veil. Rotlev took it and hastened to a merchant with it; and in still greater haste he hurried to Jílový with the money he got for it, to set the work going again.

And they had no more than turned their hands to the work on the very first day when they struck a rich vein of pure gold. There was so much gold that in a very short time he had recovered all that he had put into the mine, and from that time on he continued to mine it until he had amassed an enormous wealth of gold.

The mine which had brought him fortune he called, in gratitude, the Veil. And in Prague, in the Old Town opposite Saint Gallus, he built for himself a magnificent house, one of the largest and most beautiful in the whole of Prague. Three gates led into its courtyard. It had an arcade on the ground floor level, and turrets and a beautifully carved oriel above. Rotlev lived here in richly furnished halls and chambers, until later he handed over all of them, including the spacious hall, to the university founded by King Charles. This splendid house, which had emerged from a gold-mine, became itself a mine from which many generations of the Czech race and of foreigners have drawn up the gold of learning and culture.

In the autumn of the year 1378 it was quiet and sad at the celebrated castle of Karlštejn. The drawbridges were not lowered. The king and his court did not ride in, as was their custom at this time of year, for gay hunting parties. The royal rooms remained closed, and in the early twilights the windows of the palace showed no blaze of light. Silence hung upon the castle, and only the cold autumnal wind broke it, bearing into the distance the voices of the watchful guards from the four turrets round the great tower, from the fifth in front of the castle well, and the sixth beneath the royal palace.

'Stand off, stand off from the castle!' rang out from them every hour of the night, echoing plaintively and sadly through the chill and unfriendly night. And when dawn came, and the red and gold leaves glowed in the forests around as the sunlight touched them, it was not more cheerful.

No note of the huntman's horn resounded in the silence, no coupled hounds bayed and no hunters hallooed through the valleys and over the brightly coloured hillsides. The old oak-tree in the forest, on the way from Karlštejn to Saint John under the Rock, stood forsaken; for good King Charles did not come, as he used to do every year, to rest beneath its broad crown in the nest of projecting mossy roots as in a carved chair.

The country people going by looked round sadly at the oak-tree, the 'king's bench', where they had often seen him taking his repose. It was vacant now, and the 'king's spring', close by, at which Charles always used to stop and drink, was choked with the yellow and red leaves of the maples, beeches and hornbeams.

The king was ill; he lay in Prague castle sick with fever, and already people were saying that he would never rise again. He himself knew it, and lay awaiting death. Beside his bed waited the archbishop, the king's sons, all his family. The king bade his successor Wenceslas rule wisely and justly, and blessed him with a feeble hand.

At that moment the bell in the tower of Saint Vitus pealed, once, twice, thrice, and immediately after these great strokes the death-bell began to toll with a solemn and mournful sound.

All those about the bed stood aghast, only the king's face lit up with the radiance of holy peace, and in a soft, calm voice he said: 'Listen! The Lord is

calling me. God be with you eternally!' At that very moment the bellringer of Saint Vitus was rushing to the tower in consternation. It was locked, and he had the key, and yet the death-bell was ringing. Hastily he opened the door and ran up the staircase. There he stopped and stood gazing, frozen to the spot.

The death-bell was ringing by itself, and at that instant all the others, the great bells, burst into a peal. They swung by themselves, pouring forth a great torrent of sound, in all the other towers. The tolling of bells drowned all the sorrowful city of Prague, and in their splendid, solemn lament the soul of the good and glorious king, the father of his nation, soared into eternal glory, where 'the courts of heaven are heavenly fair'.

II

Žito the Magician

During the first years of the reign of Charles the Fourth's son the whole
kingdom was at peace, and for ages there was a saying that in the days of King
Wenceslas every man could walk through the land with gold on his head, or
ride out at what hour of the day or night he pleased, and no-one would meddle
with him.

The king cared greatly for justice, and wished to ensure that the poor received
it from the rich, and to this end he took personal measures. More than once he
disguised himself as a workman, a peasant or a student, and went among the
bakeries to buy bread. If it was good bread and of a fair weight he paid for it and

departed. But if he saw that it was poor and underweight he revealed himself, and confiscating all the bread in the shop, ordered that it should be given to the poor, or distributed to the schools for the needy scholars. Then he punished the baker by levying a fine on his property, or had him ducked in a basket in the Vltava.

He did the same with the butchers and the other tradesmen. And once he went, dressed as a labourer, to dig in a vineyard, so that he could see for himself how the people fared even there. He dug among the vines all day long, and when he realised what hard and laborious work it was, he ordered that the labourers should have a longer rest in the middle of the day, and be allowed to go home from work earlier at night.

He loved to wander about Prague at night, too, in disguise, and visit the inns to see whether they were giving fair measure. And this he did also in order to hear what was going on, how people were talking and thinking and feeling. His favourite haunt was the Blue Pike in the Old Town, and there and elsewhere he indulged in many a frolic with his boon companions.

He also loved jugglery and conjury and all kinds of magic feats. These were staged for him usually by his magician Žito, a skilful and accomplished fellow and a notable wizard, who could freeze whomsoever he pleased, and was especially expert at changing his appearance, often even his face. He might come before the king in a cloth gown, old and badly worn, and narrow hose with feet; but when he stood before him he was suddenly seen to be wearing a silken tunic and parti-coloured hose, and the brazen toes of his shoes shone like those of any dandified young blood. So he stood before the king; but when he went away he would change before the eyes of the whole court without putting off his clothes, and drape round him the voluminous folds of a pilgrim's cloak.

And at the king's table what pranks he sometimes performed! And worst of all at the expense of the king's jester. Once at dinner this poor fool reached for the fish served in sauce; but as soon as he took a portion of fish it fell from his hand again.

The jester cried out in alarm, staring at his hand, which suddenly began to stiffen and stiffen, changing from flesh into horn, until it had grown into a hoof, a horse's hoof! And its fellow followed suit.

The terrified clown grimaced helplessly, examining his hooves with such despair that the king and his nobles burst into loud laughter, and laughed until the tears ran down their cheeks.

When at last the king gave orders that the jester should be relieved of these hooves, Žito made various passes in the form of circles and crosses over them, and murmured strange words. The hooves vanished, but—imagine!—they became the feet of an ox instead, and these did not disappear until Žito, touched by the poor fool's tears and laments, charmed them away.

Once King Wenceslas wished to drive out from the castle. In the courtyard his painted and cushioned carriage, under a canopy raised on four columns, was already waiting, four beautiful white horses in glittering harness already yoked to it. The king's retinue in full panoply stood waiting around, already mounted, and the royal jester on a pied mare. Only Žito was missing, although he had received his orders to take part in the procession. The king himself arrived, and no sign of Žito. As the king was getting into his carriage he asked after him, and when he heard that he had not put in an appearance he was gravely displeased.

At that moment there arose from the next courtyard a furious crowing of cocks, a terrible din, as though a great number of cocks were crowing in competition. And through the passage from this courtyard hurtled a carriage, a little carriage, a tiny two-wheeled chaise with a team of three pairs of black cocks harnessed to it. The first pair were smallest, the next bigger, and the third pair the largest. Their black plumage shone with a green lustre, their rosy combs burned. Every cock had in his beak a slender rein, and all the reins came together in Žito's hand. The wizard stood in the tiny chaise and drove this extraordinary equipage.

The king laughed, and said that as Žito had more in his team than he, he should drive immediately behind him. Off went the king with his white horses, Žito after him with his black cocks, and wherever this extraordinary carriage and team appeared, everywhere people flocked to see. After this he drove out in similar fashion on other occasions, and every time people came running when they heard that Žito was coming, or else they were already waiting for him in front of the castle. This continued until he performed some new freak, and word of it ran through the whole of Prague and the surrounding regions.

Žito made for himself thirty wisps of straw, and by his arts turned them into thirty little pigs, plump, as though they had been very well fed. This herd he drove out to pasture in person beside the river, where the pigs of a certain wealthy but miserly baker named Michael were feeding. Michael eyed Žito's stock with appreciation, and when he heard that they were for sale cheap he struck a bargain with the magician, bought the pigs and paid in ready money on the spot. When they reached agreement Žito warned him: 'Let me tell you this, though, they're good little pigs, and well fed, as you can see for yourself, but they can't abide water. You remember that!'

But the baker did not remember; he drove the pigs he had purchased down to the ford, not realising what he was doing. As they trotted into the river they sank at once, and in their place thirty wisps of straw floated to the surface. The

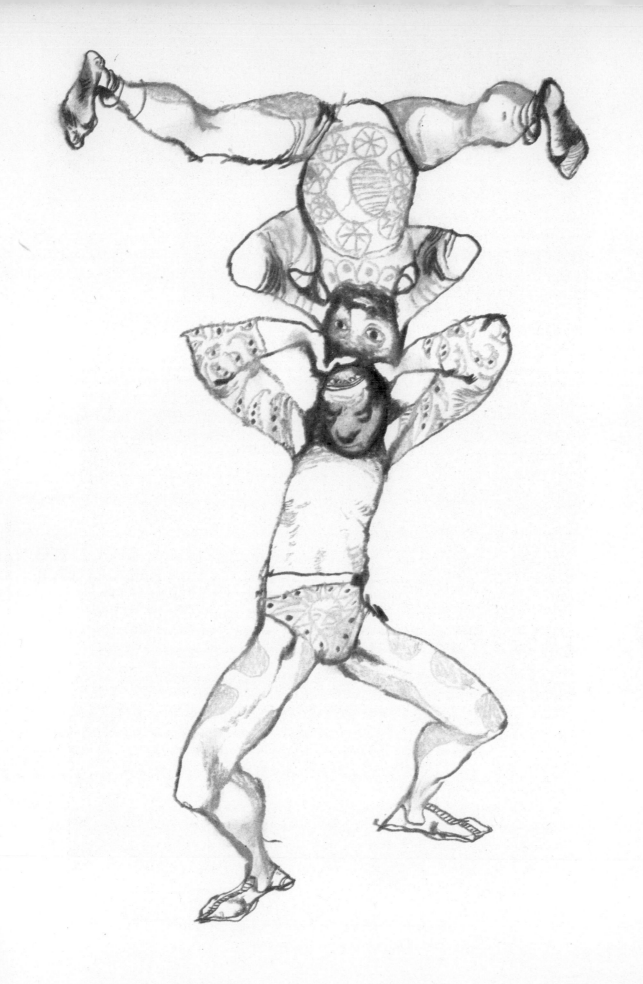

baker waited for his pigs to reappear; but they never rose, and the wisps of worthless straw were floating farther and farther downstream. The miserly baker ran along the shore, shouting and complaining, now calling on his pigs, now pointing at the wisps of straw and yelling that they were floating away, that someone should catch them, that they were floating out of reach. And so they did. The baker, enraged at having lost so much money and so many pigs, ran to look for Žito, but he could not find him in the king's court. He hunted for him, he asked after him, until he found him at last in an inn. There sat the king's magician in a vaulted room, in a recess in the thick wall beside the window; his legs were stretched out before him, and his back leaned against the panelling. An emptied tankard stood before him, and he was asleep.

The baker grew green with rage as he beheld him. In the very doorway he began to abuse him, and flew at him in a flurry of curses. But Žito slept on placidly, as though he heard not a sound, or at the most only a fly buzzing. The frenzied baker seized him by the leg and shook him, and when he did not open his eyes even then, gave a great jerk at his leg. And at that he grew pale as the wall.

The leg fell away in his hand, pulled off at the joint, and Žito leaped howling out of his sleep as though he had been bitten, and seized the baker by the throat. The man was half-dead with fright and shock. Žito would take him to a court of justice. What was there to be said? The injury was plain to be seen, the innkeeper and his guests bore witness that it was the baker who had done it. There was nothing he could do but beg humbly for forgiveness, and pay a large sum in compensation into the bargain.

On this Žito consented, and gathered up the money into his purse. Then he touched his severed leg and healed it in an instant, so that without any crutches, with a firm and springy step, he strode jauntily and victoriously out of the court of justice. The miserly baker had to put up with a great deal of teasing into the bargain. Everywhere they were telling the story against him in high glee, until it started a saying: 'You'll make as big a profit as Michael did on his pigs.'

Not long after this Žito had a spell of being out of spirits and out of temper. The Duke of Bavaria had come to pay a visit to King Wenceslas, and with him came several conjurors from Germany, in carts full of strange implements and machines. The duke himself had provided them to while away the time for the king.

These conjurors were clever fellows, men of the world and well-known for their arts. The king admired them, but gave credit to his own Žito, too. Žito had to show the duke what he could do; but whatever he did the Germans did after

186

him. There was nothing they could not achieve, and he was unable to outdo them. This upset Žito, and so he played a trick on them with which they really did not know how to deal.

It was during dinner, after which the Schwabians were to give a public performance of their most accomplished feats on a stage in the castle courtyard, before the king and his guest, the court and the people of Prague. At this dinner the king was seated apart with the duke and the foremost of his lords at a raised table, and below them at a special table the jesters, Žito and two of the duke's wizards. Suddenly a cry rang out from beneath the windows, and a voice called out in German; and the two Germans, who were seated by the window, stood up and leaned out to see what was going on below.

And they were in the trap.

There was nothing below. The Germans wished to take their seats again, but they could not. They could not withdraw their heads into the hall again. The windows were not big enough for them, and for good reason, for in the moment when they leaned out they had grown antlers, great, many-branched antlers. They turned and twisted, they jerked their heads, they twisted themselves into weird shapes, and the antlers clattered and clashed against each other.

Behind them there was laughter, tremendous laughter. King Wenceslas was particularly delighted. He laughed at the conjurors, and was glad that his Žito had had such a success.

But later in the afternoon these Schwabians, relieved of their antlers at the king's order, performed wonders in public in the castle courtyard before the king and thousands of people. Everyone marvelled at the miraculous and devilish arts they had mastered. And Žito was nowhere to be seen. He did not even show himself. So they were remarking to one another in the crowds, while others again were saying that he had been present, but had left in anger, because he was ashamed and annoyed, knowing that he could not do such things. He had fled the scene and hidden himself in order not to hear the thunder of applause all around, or perhaps for fear the king should urge him into a contest with these Germans.

But suddenly Žito did make an appearance. Just as the crowds had grown quiet for a moment, his voice was heard from the gate. They recognised it, and at once there was a stir of curiosity among the people. Everywhere they drew back and gave passage to the sunburned, brownhaired figure of Žito in his red gown, until he came to the stage of these Bavarian performers, two servants at his heels. As he stood in the middle of the platform he rolled up his sleeves, and then began to stretch his mouth, and stretched and widened it until it was enormous. The Bavarian conjurors suspected what was coming. They began to shrink away and draw back from him.

But Žito's two servants seized the most distinguished of them all, and offered him to their lord. Before anyone knew what was happening, Žito took the German, who was slightly built and not very tall, adjusted him to his liking with hands pressed against his sides, and twisting and rolling him to a convenient size, opened his gigantic mouth like an oven and began to stuff and cram the German into it, paying no attention to the feeble kicking of his dangling legs, until he had gobbled up everything but his boots. These Žito spat out.

There was such an uproar of applause and cheering and laughing all round that it was a wonder the windows of the castle were not shaken from their frames. Then his servants brought Žito a vat of water, which the Bavarian wizards had on the stage. Žito, as though exhausted by his heavy meal, leaned over the vat and spat out the Schwabian, who had evidently been too much for his stomach.

The Bavarian fell into the water until it splashed high, grovelled in it a moment, and then clawed his way out of the tub like a drowned rat.

The onlookers shouted, clapped and exulted, all laughing and chuckling until they bent double and held their sides. Crimson with laughter and running with tears of mirth they pointed at the Bavarian, from whom streams of water were trickling, as at length he crept under a canvas and hid himself.

The Bavarians performed no more marvels.

No-one was paying any attention to them. Everyone looked only at Žito. He had to go before the king, who praised him before everyone. And when thereafter the great magician descended from the stage, the crowds greeted him with such a thunder of applause that the echoes rang throughout the royal castle.

This was Žito's most celebrated feat.

But from then onwards to the end of his life he knew only decline and loss.

III

Concerning King Wenceslas The Fourth

After years of peaceful government, law and order in Bohemia began to suffer greatly when King Wenceslas the Fourth was in disagreement with the lords of his land. He paid little attention to them and ignored their advice, placing more confidence in his favourites from the ranks of the landed squires and the citizens.

When therefore they failed to get their way, they conspired against him with the king of Hungary, his brother; and after a long period of calm and prosperous rule the storms of warfare gathered and burst upon the land. Things went so far that the nobles fell upon their king as he was riding from the castle of Žebrák to Prague, and carried him off a prisoner to the Old Town Hall. There they kept him captive in the prison which was known as the Dirt Pit.

In this prison he was held for more than fifteen weeks, and he grew deeply depressed.

In the sultry heat of the summer, about the season of Saint Bartholomew, he sent his warder to the citizens of Prague, begging that they would allow him to pay a visit to the baths which lay nearest to the Town Hall. The gentlemen of the council debated for a long time, but at last they consented to let the king go. And so King Wenceslas was freed once again from his cell, but only for a short while, and not as a king but as a citizen of Prague. He was allowed to go out only in the clothes worn by any ordinary citizen, and also he was guarded by four servants.

He went out to the nearest bath, which was close beside the Stone Bridge. So that he might not escape anywhere else, one of the servants stood in the hall, close beside the door of the house, the second kept guard on the king's clothes, while two went into the bath with the king and bathed with him. After a while, when the king came out of the bath, he asked his guards to allow him to go out into the fresh air for a while, where it was cool, for it was stiflingly hot and close indoors.

This they allowed, for he had no clothes, and could not run away. So the king went out, draped in a sheet, from the apartments of the bath on to the balcony of the house, close beside the river. The water glistened and murmured, and beyond it the green banks rose in thickets of trees and bushes to the slope of Petřín, beyond which at the summit gleamed the gilded roofs of the towers of the king's castle. Free and pleasant lay these smiling slopes under the clear sky, beautiful in the flood of God's sunlight.

The king longed for freedom here even more intensely than in his prison. Not far away on the bank of the river a boat lay, quiet and motionless, an oar lying across it. And just at that moment a woman came out upon the balcony, a girl attendant who served in the baths. As soon as the king caught sight of her he beckoned to her, and softly and swiftly he asked her if she could row. She said that she could.

'Ferry me over to the other side,' then said the king, 'and I'll reward you well, you shall never repent it. But quickly, before those inside come out of the bath.'

He ran down the staircase from the balcony, and the bath attendant after him. Into the boat jumped the king, and she after him still, and quickly casting loose the boat, she pushed off from the shore and rowed towards the opposite bank. She rowed rapidly and skilfully, with all her strength; before the guards emerged from the chambers of the baths the boat had touched ground in the deep shadows of the close-growing trees on the further shore. They leaped out on the bank, and fled into the shade of these thickets, and so travelled always upstream against the flow of the river under cover of the trees, until they drew near to the village of Chuchle.

Here they found an empty boat standing by the shore, and at once they climbed into it, and Susanna, as the bath attendant was called, again rowed across to the opposite bank. They reached it happily, and the king was saved. They took to the forests, and the forest and the twilight sheltered them; nor did they go astray, although night was coming on, for King Wenceslas knew all these regions very well, since he had often hunted here. Before two hours had passed they stood by the brook at the edge of the forest of Kunratice, beneath the hill on which towered the king's seat of New Castle. The castle was lighted up; the gleam of its windows pierced the darkness. In this castle the king had a garrison faithfully devoted to him. The burgrave could not even believe what he heard when the watchman announced that his Grace, the king himself, stood at the gate. When the burgrave had seen for himself that it was true he welcomed his lord with all honour, had kingly garments brought to him at once, and prepared a memorable supper. King Wenceslas invited to this supper Susanna the bath attendant, and when they had eaten he had a purse of a hundred gold ducats brought to him, and gave it to her before the burgrave, saying:

'Here is what I promised you for your services as ferry-woman. And for all the other help you have given me I shall yet repay you.'

Then the burgrave and all his men rejoiced that their king was again free.

King Wenceslas did not forget Susanna afterwards. When he was again on the throne and came to an agreement with his lords he had the old bath by the bridge demolished, and a new, large and luxurious one built in its place. As soon as the house was finished and furnished as a bath-house, the king sent for Susanna and gave her the new bath, together with a pension of twenty silver pieces annually, saying that all this he gave to her for her proved loyalty to him, in delivering him out of captivity.

And further he gave to all bath-keepers and their craft a very gracious charter, for by its terms he made them equal with all the other crafts. The charter allowed them to use as their sign a blue cloth girdle tied in a knot, on a gold field, and in the middle a kingfisher.

From that time forth until today this bath beside the Stone Bridge is called the King's Bath. And the gallant Susanna is kept in remembrance by a picture on the vault of the Old Town bridge-tower, showing a girl bath attendant in a white petticoat, holding in her left hand a pail, and in her right a bunch of green twigs.

The mind of King Wenceslas, formerly so clear and gay, grew more and more morose. He had experienced many disappointments and great ingratitude; he no longer trusted his people, especially from the time when his opponents tried to poison him. He actually swallowed the poison, not realising what he did, but he was able to take an antidote in time.

His life was saved, but after this poisoning he was left with a terrible burning in his stomach. In his efforts to rid himself of this distress, he deadened it by drinking; and when he had drunk deeply, and his wine-heated blood mounted to his head, he blazed into wild, blind anger, and indulged even in cruelty.

Gloom fell upon his spirit. Sorrowfully, with anxiety and dread, he considered the future, and ever more bitterly he feared it. He feared his lords, he feared the King of Hungary, his brother, and the lords who were his allies, he feared the fierce disputes about the faith, and dreaded to think how all this would end, and what must be the fate of his government and of himself.

One night, unable to sleep for his burden of care, worn out by his anxieties, he sent for his astronomer, a learned and scholarly master. The sad king sat at the window in his bedroom, from which he could see in the open courtyard of the royal castle the uncompleted church of Saint Vitus in its wilderness of scaffolding.

The learned court astronomer in his dark gown approached the window as the king beckoned to him.

'If you can see into the future,' he said gloomily, 'tell me what is waiting for me.'

The old man was silent for a moment, then he stretched out his right hand and pointed out of the window, where above the unfinished church the great tower soared blackly towards the night sky.

'My lord, beware of that tower. Let your Grace guard yourself from it.'

'Why?' cried the king in amazement.

'It is written in the stars and decreed by the eternal will that you will die before that tower of Saint Vitus.'

'And how am I to die? Will it fall on me, or will a stone drop from it and kill me? Speak!'

But the astronomer did not know. This was something he had not read in the stars. The irritable king, incensed by this, flew into a rage and cried:

'And what if I have that tower demolished, what then?'

'There is nothing written about that, my gracious lord.'

'Watch and see, then, learned master,' said the king with a burst of violent laughter. 'If I have that tower demolished it will be gone, vanished, and I shall not die before it.'

And on the instant he sent for the master of the work, and paying no heed to his amazement and grief and entreaties, he ordered him to tear down the tower of Saint Vitus immediately, to set to work on it as soon as morning came. And the king himself had a horse saddled as soon as day dawned, and rode out with several of his courtiers from Hradčany to New Castle by Kunratice.

The masons set to work on the task laid upon them; reluctantly, miserably they began the demolition of the beautiful tower. The work was slow under their hands, yet it did decrease, and with it the tower.

Meantime King Wenceslas lingered at the castle of Kunratice. Day after day passed mournfully; not even hunting could give him any pleasure now. And grave news came into his solitude, of great upheavals throughout the kingdom, of assemblies in the mountains, of general agitation in Prague, all portents threatening a great storm.

Then it broke. On Sunday, late in the afternoon, a mounted courier came galloping from Prague to New Castle and informed the king that, during the morning, there had been a great procession of all those who held by the new religious teaching. At the head of the procession the priest John Želivský had borne the Host, and when they had come from the church of Saint Stephen, which they had occupied by force, to the New Town Hall, they had demanded that all those who had been imprisoned there in recent times for religious disorders should be set free. The councillors had refused their request, and shut themselves in the Town Hall, but the people had stormed the place and thrown the councillors down from the high windows, down into the crowd, where others had caught the falling bodies on pikes, lances and swords, and killed all the councillors on the spot.

King Wenceslas grew pale, and his eyes burned. Rage convulsed him, his whole body shook. He could not speak, his voice stuck in his throat; but suddenly there burst from his lips a bellow like a lion's roaring, and instantly he fell in a stroke. And very shortly afterwards he died.

He died, as the old astronomer had prophesied, before the tower of Saint Vitus, that is, before its destruction was completed. He went on his last journey before the tower, and therefore died before it; and by his death the tower was saved. The masons stopped their demolition work at once. But a part of the tower had been pulled down, and only later was a new upper stage built, as can be seen from its appearance.

King Wenceslas had no peace even after his death. Some years were to pass before he could rest quietly in the church of Saint Vitus, near to his more fortunate father. There was silence in the royal tomb, and silence above it, in the church and round about it. No rapping and clanging of hammers now, no sound of the carpenters' axes on the scaffolding, the masons' lodges were empty, no creak of wagons bringing stone and sand, no voices of workmen calling, below or above. The building of the magnificent church which Charles had begun, and his son Wenceslas had continued, had come to a final stop.

The splendid work of Matthew of Arras, Peter Parler and his son John, the church of Saint Vitus, stood unfinished, and so it remained for centuries.

Nevertheless the people believed that it would not always be so, that it would be completed in all the splendour and beauty King Charles the Fourth himself had envisaged for it, and that the man who completed the work would be a mighty and renowned lord. When the church of Saint Vitus was perfected, he would drive the Turks out of Europe for ever, take Constantinople, and once again renew the divine services of the Christian religion in the church of Saint Sophia.

Leopold the First, Roman emperor and king of Bohemia, heard of this old prophecy, and since it was his longing and ambition to drive the Turks out of Europe, he wanted to complete the church of Saint Vitus, so that events might run in accordance with the prophesy. He had already laid the foundations for the completion of Charles's work and made many and various preparations for the building, when the Turks burst into Hungary, and the emperor, in order to halt their dangerous advance, had to divert the money he had amassed for the expenses of Saint Vitus to supply the needs of the army. And so the church of Saint Vitus still remained unfinished, and the Turks still remained in Europe.

IV

The Old-Town Clock

T here was no council of land-owners or
towns in session at the Old Town Hall, no important public meeting called there, no notable court
sitting, and yet the people came flocking in great
crowds to the Town Hall, and not for a brief
while, either, but from earliest dawn all through
the day. And all those who came were reluctant
to go away again; they stood there and waited
for a long while, an hour or more, and not in
conditions of ease and comfort but in jostling
multitudes.

They all craned forward towards the tower of the Town Hall, where was that wonder of wonders, the new clock, of which they had heard such marvellous stories. All round the district of Prague people were talking about it, in the king's court, in the houses of the nobles and the tenements of the citizens, in the inns and in the streets; and everywhere it was said that this new clock on the Old Town Hall was like no other, but so unusual and wonderful that it surely outdid all the clocks of the world.

Burghers, craftsmen, cloaked students, women old and young, all stood on tiptoe before the tower of the Town Hall, stretching their necks and straining their eyes at the great clock-face with its four-and-twenty hours, ringed with circles and strokes of gold, numbers and strange signs, at the round tablet beneath it, with its paintings of the twelve heavenly symbols, at the statues to right and left in their carved foliage, and most of all at the skeleton and the strange Turk, and the miser with his purse full of money. Voices murmured and roared round the Town Hall, constant and unwearying as a rushing torrent.

Then suddenly there was a great hush, as from above, from the new clock, rang out the chime of a bell. Only here and there a cry of wonder was raised, here and there hands were lifted to point at the skeleton Death as he reached for the bell and rang the alarm. Then, to the amazement of all, two windows opened above the clock, and the Apostles appeared in them. One after another they passed, all twelve of them, from west to east, each one turning towards the people as he passed, and at the end came Christ Himself, blessing the crowd. Many took off their caps, many crossed themselves, others pointed at Death, crying how his jaw gaped, or at Judas or the miser, how they quaked, and how that old man beside the skeleton shook his head, as though he didn't want to go yet, and wished Death would not ring the bell. But as a cock crowed higher up, above the windows, a new wave of excitement and merriment swept through the crowd. They laughed and shouted, and again there was the babel of voices murmuring and roaring, constant and unwearying as a rushing torrent. Everywhere in the throng they were talking of the master of this clock, and saying that he must be blessed with a special gift of God and with wit and skill above all others. Everyone talked of Master Hanuš, who had created this time-piece so skilfully and wonderfully made.

The scholars and doctors in their dark cloaks and tabards, who stood close to the tower examining the clock, also praised its maker. They stood gravely, fat scholars and lean scholars, speaking in Latin and Czech, and the invariable subject of their talk was the circles and signs of the clock. The cock, the figures, the skeleton, the old men and the rest of the toys they laughed at, and one of them said disdainfully in front of the graduates and students, when Death rang the alarm and the cock crew, that these buffooneries and mechanisms were meant only for show and to amuse the common people.

And he went on to state that this clock, for all educated people and especially for astronomers, was a wonderful and notable work without these toys, for it showed the progression of the sun in its course from west to east through the zodiac, at what degree it stood every day from year to year, at what hour it arose at any given date, at what hour it stood at the zenith, where it set, how high it climbed from the east above the horizon, how near to the zenith and how low to the west, also where it was after sunset beneath the horizon, that is, in the night when it was under the earth; and moreover, it showed the course of the sun's withdrawal from us in the dwindling days of the winter, and again in the waxing days of summer how it approaches us.

The learned man suddenly fell silent, as from the ornamental portal of the Town Hall emerged the councillors and officials of the Old Town, in their gowns and birettas and caps. They turned in the direction of the clock. Everyone drew back to clear their path, commoners and masters, graduates and students fixed their eyes upon them, but most eagerly of all on an elderly man in the dark gown of a master. He walked side by side with the mayor; his face was grave and pale, his hair dark.

A buzz of excitement followed him through the crowd, and everyone pressed eagerly forward, craning his neck to get a glimpse of this man. The word flew from lip to lip that this was Master Hanuš, maker of the new clock.

Everyone greeted him respectfully, even the masters from the college; and he thanked them modestly, and as soon as the mayor and councillors stood before the clock he began, at their request, to explain to them all the symbols and circles.

He spoke of the stars and the sun, and then of the moon, and all that the clock had to show them concerning that heavenly body; when it was new, when it reached its first quarter, when it was at the full, and when it declined to its last quarter, all the course of its waxing and waning. Then he explained the twelve symbols, and at what times six of them were above the earth and six below the earth.

And Master Hanuš further demonstrated that the clock also showed the holy days throughout the whole year, and in its signs was written the entire public calendar, with the twelve ordinary months and the golden number.

Everyone round him listened attentively, even the people in the crowd were silent; the masters and doctors looked on wisely and nodded their heads gravely.

When Master Hanuš finished his explanation, a loud chorus of praise broke out all round him. But he, as though this acclamation had not been for him, invited the elders to go with him into the tower and look at the machinery, the weights and the wheels, for the clock would shortly be striking the hour, and then they could see how the mechanism, and especially the wheels, faithfully fulfilled the task appointed.

They went, and in the tower they gazed at all the intricate instruments, the big and little wheels, the levers and weights, and were filled with wonder to think how the human mind could conceive all this, and how he could keep all the complex workings clear in his head, to every wheel and every cog of every wheel its appointed work.

Their astonishment grew as Master Hanuš showed and explained the four sides or parts of the clock, of which every one had its own balance, its own special mechanism and wheels, by means of which it fulfilled its duty. And everyone admired particularly the fourth side, the most complex and skilful of all, and its main wheel, the wheel of the calendar, which had in its rim three hundred and sixty-five notches or teeth, and which, as the master told them, turned once a year, every day by one notch or tooth.

All this intricate machine ran steadily and accurately, as though it had reason and soul. The wit of its master was in it and directed all, and only Master Hanuš, understood the whole machine, no other. One of the town officials, John, who was a clock-maker, said frankly before them all, without concealment, that he did not understand all this, that it sprang without doubt from a special inspiration of God. He was an old and experienced master of his art, he said, but he would not willingly take on him the repair and running of this clock, nor even its maintenance, for it would drive him out of his wits.

Then one of the masters from Charles's college added that he had been in Italy and in France, and had seen there great and famous clocks, but such a one as this he had never seen anywhere.

'I don't know,' he said, 'that there can possibly be any more masterly and wonderful clock than this to be found in any country of the world. I hardly believe there can be. Unless Master Hanuš here should make another elsewhere.'

The mayor started and stared involuntarily at his colleagues, and they at him, all in the same instant. They were stricken with the sudden dread that such a thing really could happen, and they turned in consternation upon Master Hanuš. But he, smiling, merely said that he was glad that he had been able to complete this complex task, and that he thanked God for it.

The mayor did not leave the clock in such high content as he had come to it. The anxious misgiving remained in his mind, and several of the town elders shared it: that Master Hanuš would some day make another similar clock elsewhere, that other cities would also be able to possess and boast of such a work, worthy of universal admiration.

The legend of the Prague clock spread through all the territories of the Czech crown, and beyond the frontiers into foreign lands. Everyone who came to Prague made haste to look at the clock, and everyone then carried its praise abroad with him into his own country.

Soon messengers were coming to Master Hanuš from various cities, both Czech and foreign, begging him to make similar clocks for them. This frightened the mayor and the councillors of the Old Town. They did not wish any other town to be able to boast of such a possession; Prague alone was to have this renowned work, and its clock was to remain the only one of its kind in the world.

They gathered together at a secret meeting and took counsel, speculating this way and that, until they all admitted that Master Hanuš must surely be easily tempted by foreigners who were making him such promises and offering him so much gold. He might already be working on a new clock, perhaps an even better and more remarkable one, for he was always in his workshop, and he was certainly experimenting with some new creation there. In order to make absolutely certain, they resolved upon a horrible deed.

Master Hanuš was sitting in his workshop at a great table, drawing out upon a large parchment some complicated instrument. Two candles burned on the table; the shutters were closed, and a fire blazed in the hearth. It was night, and the streets were dark and deserted. In the house it was still and silent, nothing moved.

The master was so absorbed in his work and so deep in thought that he did not hear the sudden soft sound of footfalls on the stairs as someone mounted them. He did not look round until the door of his room was suddenly burst open, and in upon him rushed three men in cloaks, with the hoods drawn low on their foreheads and cheeks. The master started up to ask what they wanted, but two of them sprang upon him while the third put out the candles, and muffling his mouth they dragged him to the blazing hearth.

All the inhabitants of the house were asleep; no-one heard the rapid footsteps overhead in Master Hanuš's room; not a soul in the dwelling knew that these three hooded men had opened the door into the court with a picklock and crept into the house, and thence after a long time had stolen out again. They slipped away like shadows and vanished, lost in the night's darkness.

Only in the morning did the dwellers in the house discover their tracks and their dreadful work. They found Master Hanuš on his bed, almost out of his senses. He was shaking with fever, and his eyes were bandaged. With horror his neighbours heard what had happened to him in the night, how the hooded men had fallen upon him and blinded him. It was they themselves who had bound up his eyes. But this he did not even know, for he had fainted as they did their ghastly work.

The news of this crime inflamed the whole of Prague. The people talked excitedly about the criminals, but they searched and hunted for them in vain. It was as if the earth had opened and swallowed them. And already there were strange rumours being passed round in whispers of what Master Hanuš had said when he came to himself a little, that they need not look for the criminals, for they would not find them, although they were so near.

He had said no more. They suspected that he could have said more, but he did not; silently, sadly, like a blind bird in the corner of its cage he sat in the corner of his room, the room where he had done so much and such wonderful work. His instruments stood silent, his handsaws and files and other tools hung motionless, and dust gathered on his books and on the scrolls of paper and parchment on which were inscribed his drawings and plans. For him everything had sunk into a black darkness. His quenched eyes saw nothing of all this, not even a faint gleam of light; now he could never again touch any part of his work. He pined and grieved, sickening and longing after his craft, which had been his life; without it he was failing and wasting away.

And their ingratitude tortured him, their horrible ingratitude for his great masterpiece. He never ceased to hear in the spirit the words one of the hooded men had called out to him on that terrible night: 'Now you'll never make a second clock!'

That was his reward, that was what he got for all his pains. He tormented himself, his body wasting away even more and more. Already he felt that he had reached the end of everything. He summoned his last strength, and went to the Old Town Hall, led by one of his former pupils.

Before the Town Hall tower stood a crowd of people waiting for the clock to strike. The renowned master passed by, and they did not recognise him, he was so sunken and changed. He had grown very thin, his cheeks were fallen and sallow, and his hair had turned grey with suffering. Close to the Town Hall he met several of the councillors, but they made haste to avoid him. None of the elders welcomed him now, and they were not pleased to hear that he had come to look at the clock, that an idea had occurred to him for an improvement which would enable the weights to move more freely.

He asked to be led to the fourth, the most intricate part. It was all a mere complex darkness to him now, this assembly of wheels and levers and springs. But he heard their movement and knew how regularly and accurately they moved.

Blind and sick he stood, the broken master, grey before his time, beside his great work; he listened to its steady sound and thought of the council and the officials, how they had repaid him with blindness so that they could preen themselves before the world, how they had paid as little heed to his torment and pain as now they paid to his very existence.

At that moment the bell chimed. Outside at the clock-face the skeleton had reached for the chain and rung the alarm, announcing that the hour was dying, dying at this very moment. Death called. The machinery began to operate, already the Apostles were in motion.

Master Hanuš trembled from head to foot. He stretched out his right hand, suspended it for a moment above the mechanism, then reached into it as though he could see clearly, and his bony fingers worked there for an instant. And as he withdrew his hand the wheels grated, and it seemed the entire machine went mad; in frenzy it rattled and vibrated and shrieked, wheels and springs flew, everything groaned, clashed, hissed, screamed, and Death went on ringing. Then abruptly everything was silent. The bell stopped ringing, wheels, levers and springs grew still, everything halted, the Apostles no longer pursued their journey, all the figures stood rigid, the cock crowed no more.

The frightened crowd outside shouted and cried out in consternation. From the Town Hall they ran to the machine. It stood motionless, and on the ground lay its maker, pallid and senseless. They had barely carried him home when he died.

And the clock stood mute and still, and there was no-one left, no-one who could mend that marvellous masterpiece.

Dalibor of Kozojedy

For long years the castle of Saint Wenceslas lay silent and sad. Its surrounding buildings had been laid waste during the great storms of the Hussite wars, the church of Saint Vitus was damaged, and the royal apartments, splendidly furnished by Charles the Fourth, were left to moulder. Only occasionally, and then only for brief interludes, did they revive, when the king came there from his court below in the Old Town.

He came, and remained for a while, but he never stayed long. Even the young Ladislav the Posthumous, and his glorious successor King George of blessed memory, reigned for the most part from the royal seat down in the city. And so, after George, did Vladislav the Second of Jagellon during the early years of his reign. But after that came a great change.

After twelve years of sovereignty he changed his seat. It occurred to him suddenly that he was not sufficiently secure in his court in the Old Town, at which he had had built at great expense a very fine and beautifully ornamented tower. So he returned to the old seat of the Czech kings on Hradčany, and had all the buildings that had lain damaged and deserted restored and renewed. Beneš of Louny built for him a vast and wonderful hall, and at the same period he also made the king's oratory in the church of Saint Vitus, to the right of the high altar, decorated with remarkable stone carvings.

The king also had the bare walls of the church draped with brocaded hangings, notably in the chapel of Saint Wenceslas, and through his care and at his expense the chambers of the royal castle were again bright with splendid tapestries and pictures. In one of the rooms hung nothing but pictures of the Czech princes and kings.

But the king's interest was not totally taken up with ornamenting and beautifying his seat, he also took pains to see that the castle was more strongly fortified. The walls were reinforced at his order, the ditches were made deeper and the ramparts higher where there was need, and he built a very lofty roof to the Mihulka tower and covered it with glazed tiles, above which on the topmost pinnacle shone a silver-gilt lion.

Not long afterwards King Vladislav had a new round tower built, behind the house of the burgrave, near to the rear gate. It was built out over the Stag's Ditch for the defence of the rampart, but also to serve as a dwelling, a sorrowful dwelling. Within it they made three prisons, one above another. The lowest one was beneath the earth, without door or window or light. The prisoner who was to occupy it had to be let down by a rope through a hole or 'bung' in the paving of the middle prison.

The tower was finished, but they had no prisoner to put in it, not even in the highest and mildest of the three cells, let alone the ones below. And therefore the tower remained for the time being without a name, for it was to be named after the first prisoner to cross its threshold. But it did not remain nameless for long.

At that time a great many flagrant injustices were being inflicted upon the country people. Their lords and rulers oppressed them with new and unauthorised forms of forced labour. In certain regions they could no longer bear these impositions; they forsook everything they had, and fled from their homes into the forest, to other districts, and became bandits and robbers. But others rose in rebellion against their lords.

Among these rebels were the peasants who rose against Adam Ploskovský of Drahonice, in the district of Litoměřice, for he had used them cruelly, and inflicted on them unlawful feudal labours and many and great injustices. They attacked his stronghold, stormed its ramparts, and although their cruel master defended himself stoutly, they wounded and captured him. To save his neck he fell in with their wishes, and on his honour and faith and with his own signature and seal he released them from his power, and further promised that he would lodge no complaint against them.

On the estate bordering Ploskovský's there was at that time a fortified manor belonging to the young squire Dalibor of Kozojedy, a man of ancient family, whose ancestor had fought with King John of Bohemia at Creçy, and there died with his king. The liberated farmers of Adam Ploskovský hurried to this Dalibor and joyfully told him that they held the stronghold of Ploskovský in their power; and they begged Dalibor to accept it, saying they wished to place themselves under his lordship, as they already acknowledged him as their lord. This they would do of their own free will, and gladly, they said, for they knew that Dalibor would be a good and gracious lord to them.

They were well aware from their own experience that Dalibor of Kozojedy was always generous and kind to his serfs, indeed they knew he had taken in more than one poor wretch in flight from other lordships, and helped him by his intercessions and in many other ways.

Dalibor did not refuse them; he accepted what they offered as soon as he heard that they had the signature and consent of their former lord to all that they wished. But Ploskovský, as soon as he had escaped and recovered his health, claimed back his property. He called forcibly for help from the government, and the headmen and officers of the region, reckoning Dalibor's act as a territorial offence and that of the farmers as rebellion, summoned the armed might of the province of Litoměřice, gathering to the muster all the men-at-arms of all the lords of those parts, together with the citizen force of Litoměřice.

This great army descended upon the embattled farmers; many were killed in the fight, many taken prisoner and cruelly punished, and Dalibor, their ally, was also made captive. So the young champion of the oppressed peasants came himself into fetters. In chains they dragged him to Prague and cast him into the central prison in the new round tower behind the burgrave's house, overlooking the Stag's Ditch.

Dalibor was the first to cross its threshold as a prisoner, and so it is called after him the Daliborka. In the castle and throughout the whole of Prague there was much talk about the young squire for the very reason that he was the first captive in this new tower, as well as by reason of the events which had brought him there. The haughty lords were glad of his downfall, holding that he had his just deserts, but the people pitied him.

It was gloomy and sad for him there in his tower. This vaulted cell with its thick walls and small windows was now his domain. At home he could look out from his stronghold into the beautiful, open countryside; here he could scarcely see a narrow band of sky, and beneath the tower the deep, overgrown ditch. Down there the leaves were already changing colour into gold and red, for the mournful autumn days were coming.

Silence in the tower and silence round about it. The birds were hushed, only the wind whistled and tossed in the bushes and trees. The leaves fell, mist lay in the deep ditch, veiling it in the morning and in the early twilight, and in between the rain rustled and pattered in the naked bushes and the tops of the bare trees. The short day was all too long in the prison, and the long night was endless. The interminable hours and his own yearning tortured the young squire.

He ordered for himself a violin, out of the modest supply of money they had left to him, and from which he had to pay for his food. As soon as the gaoler brought him the violin he began to practise on it. He had never before held a bow in his hand; now he seldom laid it down. He taught himself, he played and played, the long hours were whiled away, time went more quickly, and the more he practised the better he played, the more sensitively and beautifully.

Soon the gaoler and the warders began to stand at his door and listen. Soon more than one of the lords attendant and the officials of the castle came to hear

how the squire of Kozojedy had learned to play the violin in his prison. Already they were talking of it in the city, and people began to come up to the castle to hear themselves; first the curious, then the doubting Thomases. Every day there were more of them, until at last it was a regular thing to find a great crowd standing waiting at the rear gate of the castle, on both the roads between which the vineyard of Saint Wenceslas extended down the slope.

This was already in the spring, when the soft south wind was blowing, and the crowns and branches of the trees were budding and flowering, when Petřín and all the heights around grew delicately green, and new leafage filled the Stag's Ditch, now tremulous with sweet sounds. But more beautiful far than the songs of the birds was the delightful voice of the violin, stealing forth from the round tower.

Everyone marvelled and stood charmed into stillness at the first whisper of those soft, sweet and sorrowful strains from the barren and gloomy prison.

The desolation from which they came made them all the more moving. Grief and longing filled them; and then again they changed, stealing into the well-known melodies of sacred hymns. Humility, hope and the prayers of a sad heart breathed in their notes. And at other times they sang the delights of the world, of love songs and the valiant panoply of war.

More than once Dalibor played the old lamenting balled of King John of Bohemia, and of young Klimberk, of Plichta of Žerotín and Bavor of Strakonice, and all those Czech lords and squires who died with their king at Creçy, like the ancestors of the imprisoned musician.

With deep emotion the Praguers listened at the tower. And one day, looking up, they saw a crude linen bag let down on a cord from the window of the prison, and gladly and eagerly every one of them gave whatever he had on him, large coins or small. Everyone had thought that the squire was living on his own money. Now they saw that things were very ill with him, and he had been brought down to poverty. A man of noble birth, he had not been willing to be led in chains to beg for his needs in the town, and he had received no gifts in his cell. Now he had nothing left but his violin.

But after that day, as often as he played and let down the linen bag from his prison, the people listening below filled it for him, sending him money and gifts so that he might not languish in hunger and misery. More than one kind-hearted city wife, more than one good neighbour helped to better his lot; they sent him a pillow for his head, bed-linen and food, and more than one tankard of wine to drink. In return he played to the crowds whenever they gathered at the tower at noon or in the evening. They listened with held breath, and when they dispersed they were all of one opinion: that there was no-one in the whole of Prague who could play like this young squire. Misery had taught Dalibor to play the violin. By day he played for other people, and often in the night he played for himself.

When the royal castle was silent and dark, towering against the night sky like a wonderful blue-grey shadow, when the thickets and trees of the Stag's Ditch lay hushed in the pale light of the moon, still the entrancing sounds of Dalibor's violin distilled out of the darkness of the round tower. And there were tears in the sound, yearning for freedom, and outcries of anger. They gave him consolation, but not liberty. God was very high, the king very far away, and the lords had no sympathy.

For a long time they left the squire of Kozojed in his prison, until at last they brought his case into open court, and issued their decree concerning him to this effect: that Dalibor had taken to himself an estate acquired by unlawful means, and had been taken in possession of the said estate; that this was in itself unlawful, and he had acted dishonourably and in contravention of law and order, for which rank offence he was to lose his life.

So they decreed, paying no heed to his argument that they should take into consideration who had first begun the offence, who had committed flagrant breaches of justice and so inflamed the people into revolt. He, Dalibor, had done no more than stand up for the people. But indeed this was in their eyes a crime and a sin; and so they adhered to their verdict, but the day and the hour of his execution they kept secret. On the evening before it the voice of Dalibor's violin rang out for the last time. From the depths of the gloomy prison it quivered and cried into the hushed night, a last consolation, a last light in the darkness of his grief, and faded above the Stag's Ditch in the radiance of the moon. When the people of Prague again came to the new tower on the morrow, they saw no linen bag let down from the grating of Dalibor's cell, and the tower was mute and still. When they asked if Dalibor was ill, or what was the matter with him, the gaoler replied that on the contrary all was well with him now, for that morning he had been executed in the court of the castle.

'But before he left his prison,' said his guard, 'he took down his violin from the wall and looked long at it, and took his leave of it. Then he walked unfalteringly to the place of execution, and there he kneeled and bowed his curly head on the block. He died gallantly, believe me, like a true Christian.'

Many eyes were full of tears as the gaoler spoke; and sadly the people of Prague returned to the town, looking back at the silent Daliborka.

And the tower behind the burgrave's house at the rear gate of the castle is called by the same name to this day, to keep in constant remembrance the unhappy squire and the glorious musician.

VI

Stories from the Jewish Town

I

The Jewish Town was once part of the Old Town. It lay alongside it and yet it was set apart. Six gates divided it from the Old Town, and these gates had to be kept closed day and night during Passion week. Within the gates everything was different; different buildings, poorer and shabbier, and in ancient days built more of wood than of stone, with strange annexes, balconies and porches, and faded black doors; and the streets were different, narrow and short but very crooked, and dirty and unpaved. And no-one but Jews to be seen, people of other manners and customs, living a different kind of family life. Even their dress was different. The most noticeable feature was the yellow horn in which the Jewish hat terminated, and the yellow or red cloth circle they had to wear on their cloaks.

They lived humbly and only in their Jewish Town. But this they believed, and the belief was passed on from generation to generation, that it was older than proud Prague itself, for their fathers, they said, had had a settlement here before Libuše founded Prague castle. They also said with pride that their Old-New Synagogue, on the doorstep of which they took the oath on the holy book of the law in any law-suits against Christians, was of older origin than the church of Saint Vitus or any other of the churches of Prague.

Every Jew looked with reverence at the old, gloomy building with its narrow windows, high gables, and tiled roofs already worn to a faded brown by the ages. It stood solitary, like a giant towering above the maze of narrow streets, a sad memorial of old times and of great storms.

The Jews believed that, apart from the house of prayer in Worms, it was the oldest of all synagogues, and that in its foundations was embedded a stone from the ruined church of Jerusalem. The angels themselves had brought it long ages ago from the promised land and set it down in this place. At that same time angels had appeared to the elders of the Prague ghetto, and ordered that the synagogue should always remain just as they had brought it, and nothing in it should ever be changed.

When in the course of the ages they did attempt to change anything or move anything in it, they never finished the undertaking, and they never escaped punishment. Either they fell lame at their work, or died suddenly.

But they had also another version of its origin and foundation. At first, they said, they had only a wooden synagogue. When this became inadequate, the elders resolved to build a new and bigger one of stone, on the spot where at that time a low hillock rose. When they had dug this away and removed it they came suddenly upon courses of masonry, on whole walls of mighty stones. And the more earth they dug away, the more clearly did they realise that these walls belonged to some very ancient synagogue; until at last they found a roll or parchment inscribed in Hebrew writing, and their last remaining doubts were removed.

At that time there were two Jews from Jerusalem staying in Prague, and they advised their co-believers to build their synagogue according to the pattern of the one at Jerusalem. The windows should be made wider on the outside, narrowing within through the great thickness of the wall, and the holy place itself should be so deep that they must descend into it by a staircase, for it is written: 'Out of the depths I call unto Thee, O Lord!' And all this they did. The synagogue was built on the recommended plan, by the architect Lirenský, so it is said, and stood and still stands unchanged. Generation after generation have passed through it with their prayers and their psalms.

Even the unbelievers entered it at last, but by force, and without reverence for the place so holy to the Jews. Twice the eternal light was extinguished, and the tabernacle of the Lord, *Árón hakodesh*, veiled with the precious embroidered curtain *poroches* destroyed by the enraged Christians.

The first time was in the reign of King John, who sent his agents to dig in the synagogue for the buried treasure of the Jews, and for whom his men unearthed here more than two thousand talents of gold and silver. In the same reign blood was shed here, and again in the reign of his grandson, King Wenceslas the Fourth. It happened at Easter on this second occasion; all the space beneath the vault, borne up on two eight-sided pillars, shook with the grievous and despairing cries and wails of murdered Jews. Their blood splashed on the walls of the old synagogue, and spattered the ancient and holy Hebrew sayings inscribed there.

In the Jewish Town they remembered that terrible Eastertide for a long time and with horror, and thereafter every year on the Day of Atonement a *selich* was intoned in the synagogue, a lament for the horror of those days. It was composed by Rabbi Abigdor Karo, who was himself a survivor of that persecution.

The old synagogue itself retained a souvenir of those days. After that time its walls were never cleaned. No-one washed or painted them, and so they darkened ever more until they were quite black. The rabbi would not allow anyone to touch them, for the dried blood of the believers clung to them. Jews for all time held it in reverence as the blood of martyrs.

The old building lived through many later storms and dangers. Four hundred years ago, when a huge fire engulfed the Jewish Town and everything there was ablaze, the old synagogue stood untouched above a living sea of fire. The flames destroyed and consumed everything around it, on every side rolled billowing clouds of black, choking smoke. Only the synagogue escaped even a flying spark, and not so much as a tile fell from its roof.

On the dark gable sat two white doves, and there they remained, and not even the fierce blaze or the suffocating smoke could drive them away. They stayed there until all danger was past. Then suddenly they soared on white wings and vanished in the clouds.

2

A long time ago, more than four hundred years, the mayor of the Jewish Town, Rabbi Jizchak, was returning to Prague one autumn night. He was on his way home from some country town, where he had been on official business, and for some way he had to drive through the forest. As he did not know the vicinity, and neither did his coachman, they went astray at a crossroads, took the wrong road and got lost. They soon realised that they were astray, but they could not hit on the right road.

It was already dusk and, in the solitary forest, darkness came very rapidly, and all paths and tracks were lost to sight. Just then they saw flickering before them a gleam of blue light, far off among the trees. As soon as they sighted it they stopped, for the horses halted of themselves. They were very uneasy, they pricked their ears and snorted, and then began to rear in terror as the light before them burned into a fiery red glow.

The coachman also was frightened, only the mayor kept his head. He ordered the coachman to cover the horses' eyes and wait for him there, while he went ahead to see what this could be. And he walked forward between the trees, straight towards the blaze, until he stood in a small clearing, and beheld before him an astonishing sight: a vast, an enormous, pile of gold and silver coins. Two dwarfs, both grey-bearded, were taking coins from this heap of gold and silver, and filling purses with them.

They were both so absorbed in their work that they did not even notice the mayor. He watched them for a while, then he asked for whom they were filling these bags of money. He had hardly got out the words when one of the manikins glowered at him and said crossly:

'Not for you!'

And on the instant he vanished. And suddenly the gold was gone, too, and the silver, all that shining heap, and all the bags which had already been filled. Only a few scattered gold coins lay on the ground. But the second dwarf remained, and the curious Jew again asked him for whom they had been filling all those purses.

'Not for you!'

'For whom, then?'

'One of your people,' replied the dwarf, and added. 'But you shouldn't have asked. You've interrupted our work, and it's a bad thing you've done to him.'

'Who is this fortunate man? Won't you please tell me?'

'I must not.'

'If you can't tell me his name, at least tell me what he looks like, give me some sign—'

'I must tell you nothing.'

'Only this one small thing, then, when is he to receive this treasure?'

'When your daughter gets married.'

The mayor started in astonishment, but again he pressed the manikin:

'My daughter? What has my daughter to do with it?'

'You'd never guess.'

'Such a treasure! *Sbadaj!* And nothing for me! At least allow me to pick up these few gold pieces from the ground.'

'I mustn't give you anything,' the dwarf rebuffed him sternly. 'But if you wish, you can exchange gold coins for them—'

And so it happened. The mayor laid down three ducats, and kneeling on the ground, gathered up three gold pieces of the dwarfs' hoard that lay here and there. When he rose from the ground there was nothing to be seen. The red glow had faded, the dwarf had vanished, there was nothing round him but the darkness of the lonely forest, through which howled the cold night wind. Rabbi Jizchak turned and hurried away. He did not tell the coachman what he had seen, but made him some likely explanation and bade him drive on. The horses were now quite calm, and strange to relate, they went forward confidently, and very soon it grew lighter about them. They had emerged from the dark forest and were on the right road. The rest of their journey was in open country, and they travelled the whole night, and in the first light of dawn they drove in at the gate of the Jewish Town.

Rabbi Jizchak brought back with him from this journey a load of care. Who was this most fortunate of men who was to inherit such immeasurable wealth, and what had the dwarf meant by what he had said about the mayor's daughter? He pondered, he examined the three ducats from the forest, he made enquiries, but all in vain. Burning curiosity never stopped tormenting him. At last it occurred to him that perhaps by some revelation, some sign, he could arrive at certainty. He wrapped the three gold pieces in paper, each one separately, and threw one of them out of the window into the street.

He himself lurked on the watch, to see who would pick up the coin. Plenty of people were walking along the street past the mayor's house, up and down, but not one of them so much as looked round at the little paper packet. The day was already drawing to a close and the mayor was about to send out for the money, when up ran a little boy, tattered and dirty, who looked round placidly for a moment, and then pounced straight upon the ducat and ran off with it.

The mayor was displeased that such a puny ragamuffin should be the prospective inheritor of such a treasure; but he consoled himself with the thought that it was by no means certain. The next day he tossed out the second ducat, wrapped in paper, into the street, and again waited to see what would happen. Again the whole day passed, with people walking up and down past his door and taking no notice of the coin, and again at twilight the boy ran up, pounced on the money and trotted away with it. And so it happened the third day with the third ducat.

It was quite evident by this time that this was no accident. It was a certain sign. It did not please the mayor at all. The one thing he still needed to know was who this boy could be. So he ordered that it should be proclaimed throughout the Jewish Town that he, the mayor, had lost three ducats, and that he desired whoever found them to return them to him honestly. The crier had hardly made his round with the announcement when the poor boy ran to the mayor's house. He brought the ducats with him, but only two of them; and he asked pardon for not bringing the third one, but he had given it to his mother to go marketing, and his mother would bring back faithfully the whole of it as soon as she could earn something. He said he would have returned all three at once if he had known to whom to take them. And then, he had come by them so strangely, for three nights running he had had a vivid dream that he must go to the street before the mayor's house, and there he would find a ducat wrapped in paper.

Rabbi Jizchak listened in astonishment, and no longer doubted that this poor boy, Mordecai by name, the son of a poor Jew named Shalum Maizl, was the intended heir. He praised him for his honesty, gave him the two ducats he had returned, and invited him to remain at his house, saying he would clothe him and have him educated as his son. Young Mordecai was delighted, but he said at once, with polite thanks, that he could not, for his mother was all day long in the shop, and his father was blind.

'He's alone, and he has no-one to lead him to the synagogue. He goes there three times every day,' added the boy.

'I'll pay for a guide for him,' offered the mayor.

'A stranger would never serve him so well as his own son,' said the boy.

And young Mordecai would not stay. A few days later the mayor went to his parents, and asked them at least to send their son to him every day for several hours, and he would have him educated for business, so that he should have a better living than they had had.

'I like your boy,' he said, 'he's a good boy, and if he grows up as well as he promises I'll give him my daughter as his bride.'

Shalum and his wife, already delighted by the visit of the wealthy mayor, were overwhelmed by this, and in their joyful excitement could hardly believe their ears. Gratefully they accepted the mayor's offer, and promised faithfully that for the time being they would say no word to anyone of their arrangement, since that was what Jizchak wished.

So the fifteen-year-old Mordecai Maizl entered the mayor's household. But every day he led his father to the synagogue, and also helped his mother as well as he could. In learning and in business he made remarkable progress, and when he was twenty years old Rabbi Jizchak married him to his daughter, who had fallen sincerely in love with the young man.

Only seven days after the wedding the mayor had his horses yoked to his carriage and drove out of Prague, taking his young son-in-law with him. He led him to the forest where six years earlier he had had such a strange vision. But he did not tell the boy why he was going there, and he said no word of the purses of gold and silver. They watched in the forest all night long until dawn came, but they saw nothing, no red glow of treasure, and no dwarfs.

Rabbi Jizchak returned to Prague very discontented, but not without hope. He was confident that at a second attempt they would be more successful. But they were not. Nor yet the third time they visited the forest. After a time the mayor went there again with his son-in-law, to whom, however, he had still said nothing about the reason for these journeys. But even on this occasion they had no luck. Now the mayor was convinced that everything he had seen in the wood had been a deceitful trick, that the devil had fooled him thus and made him marry his daughter to a poor man. And this greatly angered him.

He could no longer conceal his ill humour. His son-in-law, whom he had formerly praised so highly, could do nothing to please him now, and the old Jew let his dislike be plainly seen. Daily he addressed him more coldly, and then more harshly. This was hard for young Maizl to bear; at last he resolved that he would leave the mayor's house, where he was plainly only a nuisance. His young wife put no obstacle in his way, and so they left Rabbi Jizchak's house.

Mordecai Maizl took over his mother's ironmongery business, and soon improved it so much that it became one of the finest in the Jewish Town, indeed in the whole of Prague. The young merchant did his best, and God gave His blessing. Mordecai Maizl soon became a wealthy man; but he did not grow proud, nor did his heart harden. He always remembered the poor, gave away generous alms and gifts, and took the part of all those who through no fault of their own were in poverty or debt, buying them out of prison. It happened once in the summer, before the harvest, that a farmer whom he had never seen before came into his shop. The farmer chose some brand new tools, scythes and sickles, but said at once that at this time, with the harvest still to come, he had not the money to pay, and asked if Maizl would be good enough to trust him for the price of the goods. And Maizl, to whom the farmer seemed to be a thoroughly honest man, let him have the things he had chosen on credit. At this the farmer was pleased, and said:

'Now you're indeed a good fellow, to trust me like this, when you don't know me. I tell you what, I've got an old iron chest at home, a very heavy one. I can't open it, though I've tried hard, and I don't need it. I'll bring you that and give it to you to pay my debt.' And the third day he came with the chest. It was indeed very heavy; it weighed so much that, with the price of its iron, the farmer was able not only to pay his debt, but to get some ready money back for himself.

Late in the evening Maizl wanted to open the chest. But no sooner had he set his chisel to it and lifted his hammer when the lid gave of itself, and sprang open. And under the lid! Maizl stared in amazement, dazzled and blinded by the hoard of gold and silver of which the iron chest was full to the brim. The young merchant was overjoyed, but he pulled himself together at once, shut down the lid, locked the chest, and said not a word to anyone, not even his wife. He waited a day, a week, a month, for the farmer to remember and come for his treasure. But months passed and no-one came or sent word. Maizl did not know the farmer, he did not even know where he came from; so when a year had passed thus, he began to use the treasure as his own.

The first thing he did was to go to the chief rabbi and give him a great part of the money to finance the building of a new synagogue. But he made a stipulation that no-one was to know it was he who had given the money for the building. But when the synagogue was completed and consecrated, the rabbi announced publicly before them all who had built the new house of prayer in which they stood, and pointed at Mordecai Maizl, who was standing modestly in a corner.

Everyone rushed to congratulate and thank him and wish him well, and the foremost of all was Rabbi Jizchak, his father-in-law. The rabbi now made his peace and was reconciled with him, and when his son-in-law confided to him the story of the farmer and the iron chest, the mayor at once told him with certainty:

'Don't wait for that farmer. He was surely one of those dwarfs.' And only now did he reveal to his son-in-law what had happened to him so many years ago in the forest, and why they had made all those journeys to the same spot after the wedding and later.

'Who would have thought that it would turn out like this,' cried Rabbi Jizchak. 'So strangely and wonderfully! But praised be the Lord to all ages!'

Mordecai Maizl remained a rich man to the day of his death, but he was no miser; he wished well to all his co-believers, and did many good things for them.

The synagogue which was built at his expense is called after him to this day. Besides this he built a town hall in the Jewish Town, a women's bath, a poor-house and an orphanage for Jewish children, and the paving of the crooked, dirty and muddy streets and lanes of the Jewish Town was his work. He also enlarged the cemetery, and at all times and in all places he remembered the poor. And so he did to the day of his death, which happened in the year 1601.

3

During the reign of Rudolf the Second there lived in the Jewish Town of Prague a certain Rabbi Jehuda Löw ben Bezalel, a profoundly learned and experienced man. He was of a tall and commanding figure, and therefore they called him 'the great rabbi'. He was deeply versed not only in the Talmud and the Kabal but also in mathematics and astronomy. More than one secret of nature, hidden from others, was plain to him, and he could do such wonders that people marvelled at his magical powers.

His fame spread far and wide, and penetrated even into the castle of Saint Wenceslas, to the court of King Rudolf. His astronomer Tycho de Brahe greatly esteemed the learned Rabbi Löw, and his sovereign lord himself met with the rabbi in a strange manner.

He was driving once in his coach from Hradčany to the Old Town in a procession of mounted courtiers. It was just at the time when he had given orders that all Jews should move out of Prague. Rabbi Löw had gone to court to plead for the Jews; but he was not able to do so, for they would not even let him in to the king. Now he waited for him in the very middle of the Stone Bridge, for he had reliable word that he would drive that way.

When the people saw the king's splendid coach with its four horses in beautiful harness gleaming with hammered metal ornaments, and the glittering mounted procession after it, they called out to the rabbi to stand out of the way. But Löw stood his ground as though he had not heard them, right in the path of the royal carriage.

Then the crowd began to shout angrily at the learned man. They hurled stones and mud at him, but flowers fell on him, on his head and the folds of his cloak, and on the ground at his feet.

At this moment the royal coach reached him, but the rabbi did not move a step out of the way. Nor did the horses run him down, for they halted before him of their own accord, though the coachman had not stopped them.

Only then did the rabbi move. He walked with uncovered head through the roses and other flowers to the carriage, and there, kneeling, he begged the king for mercy on the Jews. The king, astonished by his appearance and by what had happened, commanded him to come to the castle. This was a great honour and favour.

So at his second visit he was received into the king's palace, and prospered well with his request.

The Jews did not have to depart into exile, and their Rabbi Löw from that time forth was invited more than once to the castle to the king's presence, and

whiled away many an hour for him with his magical arts. Once the king asked Rabbi Löw to show him his forefathers: Abraham, Isaac, Jacob and the sons of Jacob. The rabbi pondered, but at length he promised that he would fulfil the king's wish; all he stipulated was that no-one must laugh when the sacred figures of the patriarchs appeared.

The king and his courtiers, gathered together in a spacious hall, promised, and gazed eagerly into the deep opening of the window, where stood the tall, grave figure of the rabbi. In a moment he vanished as though into mist, and out of the grey cloud towered the figure of an old man of more than human stature, in a voluminous robe, a solitary figure bathed in clear light. It appeared, growing in grandeur before their very eyes, paced across their vision, and then as suddenly vanished as though it had dissolved into the grey cloud. This was the likeness of Abraham. After him Isaac appeared, then Jacob and his sons, Judah, Reuben, Simeon, Issachar and the others. They manifested themselves one after another, and the king and the court gazed silently and solemnly at the forefathers of the Jewish nation. Then from the cloud emerged also Jacob's son Naphthali, a red-haired and freckled fellow who trotted quickly past as though he did not want to be late, but was hurrying to overtake the others. At that the king could not contain his amusement; but as soon as he burst into laughter the cloud vanished and all the vision with it, and suddenly all the great hall echoed with shrieks of dread and horror.

The courtiers leaped out of their chairs, and one and all were staring and pointing up at the painted ceiling.

The ceiling was moving; it was visibly descending, sinking steadily towards them. The lofty hall dwindled before their eyes. Pale as death the courtiers tried to rush to the doors, but they could not move from their places. They stood as though frozen to the spot. They all called hoarsely upon Bezalel, to stop the ceiling from falling.

The rabbi stepped out of the alcove, stretched out his right hand and said something; before the words were completed the vault ceased to move, and sank no lower. The king did not ask for any further revelations. He rushed out of the room, and all the court after him.

The ceiling never returned to its original height. At the point to which it had sunk, there it remained. The king never entered that room again. They locked its doors, and so they remained locked for ever.

But Rabbi Löw ben Bezalel did not fall into disfavour for this incident. It even came to pass that Rudolf visited him in his own house. The Jewish Town had never before received such an honour. And Rabbi Löw was also grateful for it, and in his gratitude he prepared a great surprise for his king and lord.

Löw's house was old and not at all imposing. But its surprises began as soon as the king and his courtiers had entered under the low lintel. For this was not the entrance hall of an ordinary house, but a fine vaulted room fit for a prince's palace, painted and ornamented with stucco. And the staircase leading to the main hall, which anywhere else would have been of wood, glistened with marble where it was not covered with rare carpets. Nor did it lead into a simple domestic reception room, but into a splendid hall decorated with pictures and expensive tapestries. Through the open side doors they could see into an array of rich apartments, and through one in particular into an open gallery of Italian design.

Rabbi Löw, respectfully conducting the king, led him with his courtiers into a large chamber where the table was laid for them, and begged him to partake of his hospitality. The king sat down to table, and the rabbi entertained him and all his retinue with such a feast that it equalled the royal table. The king, charmed by this magical art by means of which Löw had enlarged his modest house and ornamented it with such rich treasures, stayed for a long time, and went away very content. From this time forth he showed his grace and favour to the learned rabbi more than once. And he, to keep alive the memory of the visit paid to him by the King of Bohemia, had a lion carved on his house beside his own sign, a bunch of grapes.

But a marvel even greater than the visions of his forefathers which he raised at Hradčany was Jehuda Löw's servant, the Golem. The powerful rabbi fashioned him from clay with his own hands, and then brought him to life by placing a 'shem' (a tablet with a magic Hebrew inscription) in his mouth.

The Golem did the work of two men. He served, he carried water, he hewed wood, he swept the rooms, and in fact he did all the rough work. In addition to which he did not eat or drink, and he needed no rest or recreation. But every week when the Sabath began, on Friday evening, and all work had to stop, the rabbi took the 'shem' from his mouth; and at once the Golem became rigid and inanimate and stood like a doll in the corner, mere dead clay, which at once revived again after the Sabbath was over, when the rabbi replaced the magic 'shem' in his mouth.

But once Löw ben Bezalel, as he prepared to go to the Old-New Synagogue to celebrate the Sabbath, forgot about the Golem and neglected to take out the 'shem' from his lips. The rabbi had entered the synagogue and was just beginning the psalm, when people from his own house and the neighbouring houses came running in terror and alarm to look for him, all crying out in horrified chorus and wanting to know what had happened, for the Golem was running amok at home, and nobody dared go near him, for he would surely kill them.

The rabbi hesitated for a moment; the Sabbath was already beginning, for he had commenced the psalm. All work of every kind, even the least effort or exertion, from that moment became a sin. But the psalm by which the Sabbath is sanctified was not yet completed, therefore the true first hour of the holy day had not actually begun. He rose and hastened to his own house, and before he reached it he could hear a frightening uproar and the sound of crashing blows. When he entered, the rest of the people in their terror kept well behind him; he saw before him, smashed crockery, broken and overturned tables, chairs, chests and benches, torn-up books. All this work of destruction within the Golem had already accomplished, and at this moment he was 'at work' in the yard, where hens, chickens, cat and dog already lay slaughtered, and where the Golem was just tearing out of the earth a great lime-tree with a thick trunk. He was red in the face, and the black curls danced round his forehead and cheeks as he ripped out the tree as though it had been a mere stake from the fence.

The rabbi walked straight towards him; he gazed at him fixedly, his hands outstretched. The Golem shuddered and stared wide-eyed as the master touched him, gazing intently into his eyes as though transfixed by the power of his glance. And in that instant the rabbi reached between the Golem's teeth, and snatched the magical 'shem' from his mouth.

The Golem dropped as though he had been felled, crashing stiffly to the ground and lying senseless and motionless, nothing but a clay doll now, inanimate matter. All the Jews who had looked on, old and young, shouted for joy, and full of courage now, approached the fallen Golem and laughed and derided him. But the rabbi, heaving a deep sigh, turned without a word and paced back to the synagogue, where by the light of the lamps he again began to say the psalm and consecrate the Sabbath.

The sacred Saturday passed, but Rabbi Löw ben Bezalel never again laid the 'shem' in the Golem's mouth. So the Golem never arose again; he remained nothing but a clay image, and he was put away in the loft under the roof of the old synagogue, where he crumbled away and fell to pieces.

4

Centuries passed, and many things changed in the Jewish Town. The strict segregation ended, the gates vanished, the town itself was transformed, streets, houses and inhabitants.

Only the Old-New Synagogue remained just as it had always been, unchanged, and with it, among the houses of the new development, the quiet 'garden of the dead' lay hushed and changeless. Here reposed all the past generations of the

former ancient Jewish Town, from most remote days before Prague existed, as the Jews claim, to the time when the ghetto attained freedom with all its inhabitants, when the last funeral was celebrated here, and for the last time they said the mourning prayer over the open grave.

In the shadow of the elder-trees and bushes the crowded stone monuments bristled, simple and elaborate, the flat slabs reared on end or leaned one against another to resemble a roof. And on all some sign is graven: the grape, which invariably proclaims a Jewish origin; a hand-basin, signifying that here rests a branch of the tribe of Levi; hands, the sign of the family of Aaron. Here the image of a maiden, there of a lion, a wolf, a stag, and so on, according to the name of the dead.

And everywhere inscriptions in Hebrew script, some brief, some diffuse, announcing the name and the tribe, the year of death and some account of the dead. You may read here many and strange names: Hebrew, German, and from the more remote period of the sixteenth century, when Jews more frequently acknowledged themselves to be members of our nation, many Czech names.

In the ancient days, when they were still burying the dead here, the Jews used to lay on the monuments various coins, always secretly, as a gift of grace to the needy, who were ashamed to come and ask for support or alms. Now you will find pebbles and stones lying on many of the memorials, here a few only, there a great many, all put there in token of respect. Whenever a believer visits a grave here he lays a stone on it, and by the size of the piles you may know who is most remembered and for whom the blessing is still uttered: 'Secher Zaddik livrochi'— 'Blessed be the memory of the righteous!'

All the generations of the former Jewish Town sleep here, poor and rich together, those forgotten and those who were celebrated in their own time.

They rest in the shade of the scented branches, and nothing disturbs their sleep. But one lies here who has found no gentle rest even in the 'garden of the dead', and the pious 'Shalom alechem!' is whispered over his forsaken grave in vain.

In youth this Jew was estranged from his family. He took the Christian faith and even became a priest; he was chaplain at the church of Saint Vitus. But when his last hour was approaching he remembered his origin, and longed to rest in the 'garden of the dead' in the Jewish Town. Among those buried there was a young Jewish girl whom he had loved when he was young. He died as a Jew, and the Jews buried him, as he had wished, near to the grave of his beloved. But the peace of which he had surely enjoyed so little during his life was not to be found even in the grave. Every night he rose from his tomb and was forced to go down to the Vltava, where there awaited him a little boat, and a spectral oarsman in the form of a skeleton. Through darkness or moonlight, whatever manner of night it might be, they rowed across to the opposite bank. There the bygone priest disembarked, and his rower accompanied him up the hill to the castle, and the church of Saint Vitus. There the Jewish priest sat down at the organ and played, while the skeleton worked the bellows for him. Suppliant hymns, intercessions, penitent psalms stole through the dark and silent nave of the church; by these passionate and sorrowful sounds the priest offered his atonement and begged for the forgiveness of God. But the pleading laments went unheard. Before the last of the strokes of midnight pealed from the tower of Saint Vitus the organ ceased to play, and the organist returned disconsolate to the riverside.

The skeleton rowed him across the water again, and the priest went back to the cemetery of his fathers and his own unquiet grave, only to rise the next night and cross the river as before, to play at Saint Vitus his threnody of penitent psalms and hymns.

Sorrowful Places

In the night before the twenty-first of June, 1621, there was such fear and foreboding in Prague that every heart shrank with dread. Everywhere was dead silence, all the houses were fast closed, no-one ventured into the streets; only patrols of foreign soldiers marched through the city. Their footsteps echoed hollowly, and the clash of their arms rang like a threat.

In the Old Town Square wagons stood in the darkness of the night, and from them men were unloading boards and beams, and carrying them into the centre of the square, where the carpenters were working. The dull blows of their axes and the staccato of hammering echoed through the deathly quietness. In the obscurity of the night they raised by the light of pitch-flares a great stage, which grew higher and higher until at dawn it stood completed in the cold, pallid light, draped with a black cloth, and with a wooden cross erected at one side.

A scaffold! And as yet it stood empty. But as the sun rose the report of a cannon thundered from the castle, the signal for the executions to begin. In a few moments the square was encircled by the imperial army, both foot-soldiers and cavalry, and on the platform stood the dark, hooded figures of the grave-diggers and the executioner's assistants; and soon came the executioner himself, John Mydlář.

The emperor's officials took their seats, and called the name of the first of the condemned directors, who had spent their last night imprisoned in the Old Town Hall. The lord Šlik walked bravely to the place of execution.

In the ranks of the army the drums rolled; but in the city, in the houses, there was a terrible silence. The faithful Czechs trembled with grief, weeping and praying for the Czech lords and their comrades of the directorate, who were dying on that black-draped stage or on the gallows beside it. And there were twenty-seven of them!

In the place in the Old Town Square where this happened there used to be sixteen great stones set at intervals in the form of a square. The old Czechs, walking across this space, never walked over these stones, nor ever set foot on them. They always avoided them or stepped round them, out of reverence for the sorrowful place and the shed blood of the Czech lords. And they say that in this spot these executed noblemen and citizens appear once a year, during the night preceding the day on which they died on the scaffold. They assemble with the oldest of them all, the lord Kaplíř of Sulevice, who was nearly ninety years of age, at their head, after him Budovec of Budov with his long grey beard, old Konecchlumský, Kochan of Prachová, Kryštof Harant, Diviš Černín, the lord of Michalovice, Šlik, Otto of Los, the lord of Bílá, Hošťálek, Jesenský, Vodňanský, Vokáč, Jiří Řečický, Kobr, Jizbický and the rest, old men and younger men, down to the youngest of them, John Kutnaur, who was barely forty years old, and died like a hero, singing. They gather on the site of the scaffold, and then silently, without word or sound, they cross the square and enter the Týn church. There they kneel before the altar and reverently receive the Blessed Sacrament in both kinds. And then they vanish.

At that time there were houses standing even in the centre of the Cattle Market, and one of these houses, on the side nearest the New Town Hall, was called the Locksmith's House. About thirty paces from this building towards the Town Hall there stood in an open space a stone, one and a quarter yards high and a yard wide. On this stone was carved a cross, and beneath it a death's-head and the date 1627.

On this spot, beside this stone, they say executions used to take place during the night-time. And in this year 1627, so it is said, several priests died here under the executioner's sword; while in the year 1743 certain Czech lords were executed here for having joined the Elector of Bavaria, Charles Albert, when he captured Prague with the French, and had himself declared King of Bohemia and crowned in the church of Saint Vitus.

An underground passage led from the New Town Hall straight to this stone, which remained in its place until well into the nineteenth century, and from the stone it continued under the whole of the Cattle Market, up the slope to the House of Faust.

VIII

The House of Doctor Faust

This ancient house stood at Skalka, at the end of the Cattle Market, on the corner opposite the Slav monastery. For a long, long time no-one had lived in it, and for that reason its appearance was shabby and neglected. The once red roof had darkened, the walls were cracking, the windows filmed over with dust and rain were like blind eyes, full of cobwebs. The heavy oak door studded with enormous nails was never opened, nor even the smaller wicket door in it, and nobody stopped at the portal to reach for the graceful wrought-iron knocker.

Within the gate all was silent and deserted; no dog barked there, no cock crowed, and in front of the gate grass grew thick among the cobbles.

No less mournful was the garden behind the house and beside it, along the road directly opposite the Slav cloister. No-one took care of it now. It had no flowerbeds, no plots of herbs or vegetables. Even the paths in it had vanished, overgrown with grass. Nothing but grass everywhere, luxuriant, tall grass, smothering even the trunks of the old maples, limes and fruit trees, whose boles and boughs were muffled in lichens and mosses.

Only in spring, when the flowers came, when the thick grass was starred with dandelions like golden coins, and later grew white with goat's-lip and hemlock, did the garden look a little gayer. But in autumn, when the leaves fell and drowned the whole enclosure of the garden, when the sky loomed low and heavy with menace and the wind wailed through the bare branches, and after the early twilight the darkness closed in on the whole house, the place became more dismal than ever!

Melancholy exhaled from garden and house, and a strange dread fell on the people who passed by it. It was an accursed place; in the night the soul of Doctor Faust walked there, unable to find peace after death as he had failed to find it living. For long, long ago Doctor Faust had lived in this house. Here he had cast his magic spells and pored over his books of sorcery, here he called up the devil and signed away his soul to him. In return the devil served him, and performed everything the doctor desired of him. But in the end, when his time had run out, the devil said: 'Enough! Now, come!'

But Doctor Faust was not yet ready to go, and he resisted as well as he could. He fought with curses and exorcisms, but in vain. The devil pounced on him and gripped him in his talons, and though Faust still resisted him, he burst out of the house with him, straight through the ceiling. And so Faust received what he had bargained for; he had sold himself to the devil, and the devil took him.

And the hole they made as they shot through the ceiling remained. It is true they tried to build over it several times, but every time the masonry had fallen out by morning, and there was the great black hole, just as before. At last they gave up trying, for they were frightened, especially when the spirit of Faust began to walk the house. Every night he haunted it, and soon not even the boldest tenant would remain in it.

From that time on no-one moved in there, the ancient building stood empty. It decayed and mouldered steadily. No-one so much as entered it, everyone preferred to avoid it and walk round its grounds, especially in the evening or

232

night. But once in the autumn, when the day was already nearing twilight, a young student halted at the gate of Faust's house. That he was by no means well off was plain to be seen from his battered three-cornered hat, his worn-out coat and shiny knee-breeches, his darned stockings and down-at-heel shoes.

He was as poor as a stray greyhound. He had not even a roof over his head. He wandered through Prague, searching for lodgings, begging for a little time, but everywhere they refused him, and no-one would take him in. So he had walked the whole day long, until weary and exhausted he stood before the house of Faust. He did not know himself how he had got there.

It was growing dark, a drizzling rain was falling and the wind blew bitterly cold. The student's shabby coat, though buttoned up to the neck, could not keep out the chill, and his miserable shoes let in the wet. He was already trembling with cold. The rain grew heavier, the night closed in; here he was in the autumnal evening, and where was he to spend the night?

He had nowhere to lay his head. He looked round him, and then fixed his eyes on the old and gloomy house. 'They won't throw you out of here,' he thought, and bitterness filled his heart. He hesitated for a moment, then he seized the latch; the door gave to his push, and he stood in a vaulted passage. It was dry, and no wind blew here. And since he had ventured so far, he mustered his courage and went on.

By a staircase, above which on his right hand curious statues stood in niches, he reached a corridor. It was long, and its distant end was lost in darkness. All along this corridor he saw a row of dark doors leading to various rooms. It was silent and deserted here within, but from the courtyard and the forsaken garden he heard the howling of the wind.

The young man considered for a while, and then boldly reached for the latch of the nearest door and entered the room. Under its vaulted ceiling dusk was already gathering; the room seemed even more dim because the walls were covered to half their height with oak panelling, and all the furniture, the ancient table, cupboard and bench beside the wall, were of dark wood. Beside the table stood the dim shape of a high-backed armchair.

The student stood for a moment in the doorway, then he went in and sat down in the chair. He looked all round him, waiting and listening; but there was not a sound in the house, and no-one appeared. Only the wind outside wailed, and the rain slashed and battered at the windows. The student in the armchair waited and listened, until weariness overwhelmed him, and the voices of rain and wind lulled him to sleep. He fell asleep, and slept until eleven, on past midnight, an hour after midnight; he slept until daybreak, and nothing disturbed him. In the morning he awoke to wonder where he was, and when he remembered where he had passed the night, and how peacefully, he took heart. He did not take to his heels, but went curiously and even eagerly into the next room. It was furnished, and in addition there hung on the walls several faded and blackened pictures, in which he could distinguish little but the frowning faces of bearded men. But of the one-timer owner of the house, Doctor Faust, of whom he was now thinking constantly, there was no trace.

Until he came to the third room. There stood an old bed, under a canopy of faded material, worn pillows lay on the ground, together with two overturned stools and an old, tattered book in a yellowish binding which had once been white leather. And in the ceiling, a hole! It yawned blackly, as though torn out instantaneously and with great force.

The student halted at sight of it. He remembered what he had heard, and now he saw that everything in this room seemed to be just as it had been left when the devil carried off Doctor Faust. These stools he had overturned, that book he had probably thrown at the devil. The young man did not venture to touch it, nor did he linger long in the room. In the next room he saw nothing odd, except that a flight of wooden stairs hung from the ceiling. He stepped on to the lowest stair and began to climb them, until he stood under the vaulted ceiling, where there was an opening through which he might go farther. As he stepped on the last stair he heard a rattle behind him, and looked round in alarm and wonder. The steps by which he had ascended had rolled themselves up as though made of paper, and vanished in the ceiling, above which he now stood in a new room, larger than all those through which he had passed. In his astonishment and excitement over his new discovery he forgot the staircase and how he had come there.

The room was spacious, with a vaulted ceiling which bore pictures of the sun, stars and the heavenly bodies. Along the walls stood dark bookcases full of books in ancient bindings, small and large, and tables with various vessels of metal and glass, empty bottles and bottles full of tinctures coloured red, gold, blue and clear green. In the centre of this great room stood a long table on crossed legs, covered with a green cloth, and on it gleamed vessels of brass and copper, a variety of measuring instruments and gauges, and beside these a number of yellowed parchments and papers, some blank, some written on. There was also an open book beneath a pewter candlestick holding a wax candle, burned well down. Everything appeared as though someone had only recently left the room.

In this apartment the student lingered longest. When he returned to the opening by which he had entered it, and stepped upon the threshold, the wooden stairs unfolded and descended again of their own accord to the floor below, so that he was free to go down whenever he pleased. From the lower room he did not

enter Faust's bedroom again, but let himself out by another door into the entrance hall. There he saw a statue of a slender boy with a drum slung round him by a strap. As the young man approached him and touched the drum, the boy started as though he had been alive, and began to drum. The drumsticks fairly flashed, and the drum rolled until it was a wonder the window didn't rattle. The boy drummed and drummed, and the student in a fright ran out into the corridor.

Thence he hurried into the open passage, and so to the deserted courtyard, where on the edge of the garden there was a well. Yellow lichen and green moss had overgrown its sandstone ashlars, and the fallen leaves of maples and limes, gold and red, were strewn over the water and the chipped stone statue of a strange monster.

He explored the garden, too, but there he did not linger long.

Under the old trees, among the briars and undergrowth on a murky autumn day, it was not cheerful. He returned into the house. It was silent there now; the boy had stopped drumming. The young man did not go near him, but returned by the staircase into the great vaulted room and examined the parchments and papers scattered there. Beneath them he found a smooth, glistening dish of black marble, and in it a silver coin, bright and gleaming like new.

He was delighted but also frightened. For a while he stood over it considering what to do with it. He had not a farthing in his pockets, and he was beginning to be hungry. But what if Faust, or the devil himself—?

He hesitated, he dreaded, but in the end he took the coin and went off into the town. In the evening he returned, having eaten his fill, but with the haunting fear that some spirit might appear in the night. He sat down in the chair, as on the previous night, to sleep away the hours of darkness. He did not fall asleep so readily as before, and he awoke during the night. But neither the spirit of Faust nor the devil appeared to him.

When he again examined the library and the instruments on the table, once again there was a silver coin lying in the black marble dish. Yesterday there had been one also, just one, and he had taken it and changed it in the town; he had some small change from it still in his pockets. And now, in the same place from which he had taken it, there it was again, a coin gleaming white as milk against the black dish. This was surely meant for him. Doctor Faust or somebody had sent it to him. So the student reasoned, and he took the coin.

Before noon he left the house, and returned again in the evening, bringing the remains of the second coin in his pockets. And again he slept in the house, and as peacefully as before. The next morning on rising he went straight to the library and looked on the table. And there it was, a coin as pure as though fresh

236

from the mint, lying on the black dish. The young man no longer doubted that it was for him, and took it without hesitation.

And so every morning he found a coin there. He did not need so much for his daily expenses. He saved up the change until he had enough to buy new clothes, a cloak, a hat and new shoes. He was doing very well for himself. He did not bother about finding lodgings now; he was no longer afraid in the house of Faust, he had grown accustomed to his silent dwelling, where some spirit took care of his needs, and yet never showed himself. In winter he had plenty of wood there, both in the courtyard and the garden. He laid fires and lit them to warm his house, until the flames burned and crackled pleasantly downstairs in the stove, or up in the library in the hearth. He read and read in the books from Faust's library, and also in the book he had found on the large table, and the one below in the bedroom. It was a long time before he ventured to touch that one, but it was there in particular that he found what interested him, for it was full of strange signs and incantations. With dread he began to read, and sometimes his hair stood on end as he studied these sorceries.

Sometimes, too, his solitude oppressed him, but he did not want to move. He had peace here, and was comfortable enough, and moreover he had a coin a day without working for it! His companions at the college, where he put in an appearance less and less frequently, wondered what had happened to him and what was still happening to change him so, and make such a dandy of him. They froze in consternation when they heard where he was living, and were reluctant to visit him when he invited them. At last curiosity drew some of them to the house. He led them all through it, from the passage to the upper floor, through entrance hall, rooms, library; he showed them the bedroom, with the bed newly furnished, for now he himself slept in it. The hole in the ceiling was covered and blocked up with a carpet. He took them through the garden, and showed them everything that he himself had discovered during his stay in the old building.

They talked with amazement of the wonders of this secret dwelling, of the boy who drummed of his own accord, of strange statues that sang softly, of the metal maiden who poured water for them, of the miraculous latch on the door of one of the rooms, that shot out sparks and wounded whoever touched it, of the room into which a flight of steps let itself down from the ceiling, and again rolled itself up into the ceiling, of the strange instruments and magical books. He even told them about the iron door that led down into an underground chamber beneath the house, and thence to a long, dark passage.

The only thing about which the student did not boast to his friends was the black dish and its silver coins. But he laughed at his friends when they warned him not to stay in the house; all this was merely temporary, they said, suddenly something would happen to him, some evil spirit would ambush him.

They were not talking nousense. The charm of the black dish was a trap set for him.

He had a coin every day, there was no need for him to worry about anything or do anything. He grew accustomed to comfort and ease, and began to have more lavish fancies, to dress expensively and treat himself to luxuries; his expenses mounted, but the amount in the dish remained the same. A silver coin a day was no longer enough.

The student had got out of the habit of living modestly. He had forgotten what his state had been when he came here. And now he could not face the thought of working. He fell back upon his books, the one from the table in the great library, and the one he had picked up in the bedroom. In them he had read how to conjure, and how to call up spirits. They themselves had so far never revealed themselves to him, he had been at peace from them; and he himself, until this moment, had not summoned them. He was afraid, and still hesitated. But now the desire for gold urged and compelled him. Silver was no longer enough for him. Not even a dish full of silver coins would have sufficed; he wanted gold, and these books must help him to gain it.

One day he spent the entire day revelling in Prague, and frittered away borrowed money. During this revel he boastfully urged his boon companions and hangers-on to drink deeply and not spare the expense, for tomorrow he would have even more money. Gold, nothing but gold, and not borrowed, but his own; for he would force the spirit who had served him thus far to provide him with gold ducats instead of modest silver coins.

Late in the evening he left them to return to the house of Faust. Several of his drunken companions wished to go with him, but he would not allow them. Today he must be alone, he said, for tonight he would have important work. They gazed after him as he went in, and the wicket in the heavy gate closed after him. They never saw him again; neither they nor any other living soul. He never appeared again in the college, nor anywhere else.

When several of his friends who had already visited the house with him went to look for him there, they could not find him. Within the house it was hushed, silent, deserted, not a sign of the student anywhere. But in the bedroom they found the bed in disorder, the pillows on the floor, clothes scattered, a cloak torn to shreds, chairs overturned, and on the paving a battered old book of magic, an overturned candlestick and a burned-out candle.

Everything showed that someone had been involved in a struggle here. The carpet lay discarded on the ground, torn to pieces, and the black hole gaped wide.

Round its edges they saw on the ceiling stains, as though blood had spilled there. And not dark blood, but fresh, spilled not long ago.

All the students crossed themselves and fled in terror from the house of Faust. They were overwhelmed with horror at the terrible end that had overtaken their comrade. He had surely called up an evil spirit, summoned him proudly, and the evil spirit had settled accounts with him He had vanished with him through the hole in the ceiling, through which long ago he had flown with Doctor Faust.

The Story of John Žižka

I

Now down to the south of Bohemia.

Here in these southern regions is one quiet corner, the solitary farm of Trocnov, beside a low hill. All round it lie meadows, fields, an oak forest and dark coppices, beyond which in the distance to westward rear the blue ridges of the Krumlov mountains.

Stand and look at this country farmstead, its wooden walls and mossy roof dappled under the shade of the trees. Here were spent the early years of the greatest hero and general of our nation.

And there is his birthplace!

A little way from the farm, beyond the fish-pond, at the crest of a gentle slope where the fields border the darkness of the forest, a mighty oak-tree once grew, and under that oak he was born. In the summer it happened, at harvest time, when the farmer's wife of Trocnov had gone out to the fields to supervise the reapers. Here her son John first saw the light of day; and in all his life after he was as strong of will and spirit as that oak-tree.

He grew and flourished physically in the farmstead of Trocnov and its lonely surroundings. As a young boy he was sent to school, so they say, at Prachatice, which was even then a Czech town; to the same school attended by another John, a poor son of the village of Husinec. John Huss of Husinec walked to Prachatice daily beside the river Blanice, and often when he was tired he rested on its banks, on a rocky boulder which can be seen lying there to this day.

When John of Trocnov, who was known by the name of John Žižka, grew to man's estate, he inherited the farm from his father. But he did not live long in peace on his inheritance. He became involved in a dispute with Henry of Rožmberk, an extremely powerful baron and overlord in these southern regions of the country, who defied even the king himself in armed might. The lord of Rožmberk paid scanty attention to the rights of the small squires and yeomen who were his neighbours, and so it happened that the young lord of Trocnov, mindful of his honour and independence, took up arms and became a committed enemy of the lord of Krumlov and of the Germans of Budějovice, with whom he was also at odds.

The struggle was an unequal one. The young squire had not the wealth or the force to overcome a mighty baron and a rich royal city. But he took what revenge he could, and when they burned his farm and destroyed all his property in the quarrel he took to the forest and continued the unequal war from there, until friends rose to take his part, and interceded for him with the king.

And so through the grace of King Wenceslas the Fourth he came to the court of Prague in the year of our Lord 1409, and argued his case there. He became chamberlain to Queen Sophia. After some time he left court to go to Poland, to serve in the Polish army against the order of the German knights. On the fifteenth of July in the year of Our Lord 1410 he fought with many other Czechs and Moravians in the Polish ranks at Tannenberg, where the German knights suffered a crushing defeat.

In this battle of Tannenberg Žižka fought heroically, and it is said that it was here he lost an eye. When he had been for a considerable time in the Polish kingdom he returned to his own country, and came again to the royal court at Prague. As a servant of Queen Sophia he often accompanied her to the Bethlehem chapel to hear the sermons of the renowned preacher Master John of Husinec. The squire of Trocnov took a strong liking to this man and to his teaching. Being himself a man of grave and austere mind, he agreeds sincerely with the preacher of the Bethlehem chapel.

So great and deep sorrow possessed Žižka over the unhappy fate of the pious master when he was thrown into close imprisonment in Constance, fettered hand and foot, and then to the shame and disgrace of the whole nation was cast into the fire. It was not merely grief that burned in Žižka's spirit, but also anger and bitter indignation against all the opponents of Huss, both foreign and native Czechs; indeed, against these latter in particular. Žižka brooded ever more fixedly upon the tragic death of Master John and his friend Master Jerome of Prague. Many a time he walked alone in bitter recollection for long hours, in the courtyards of the royal castle at Vyšehrad.

Once King Wenceslas stopped him when he was like this, walking in solitude. Seeing him so deep in sorrowful thought he asked what was troubling him.

John of Trocnov replied:

'My gracious lord, it grieves me to the heart that our true Czech leaders should be thus pitilessly put to the fire, in disregard of the emperor's safe-conduct, and against all justice. Who can help but be sad here now?'

'My dear John!' said the king to this. 'Can we remedy it now? If you know any way to put it right, then put it right. We wish you well in the undertaking.'

And Žižka took the king at his word, saying that he would do so. And so he did.

I I

At that time almost all the citizens of Prague, as indeed the greater part of the nation, were ardent for the teaching of Master John Huss, and also for the right of communicants to receive the Holy Sacrament in both kinds. When the priests in the Prague churches refused to administer both bread and wine, the knight Nicholas of Hus approached King Wenceslas the Fourth at the head of a great throng of people in the street near the church of Saint Apollinaris, and begged that a greater number of churches should be devoted to the needs of those who believed in Communion in both kinds.

The king was much alarmed at this great assembly; he banished Nicholas of Hus from Prague, appointed new councillors to the New Town council, and

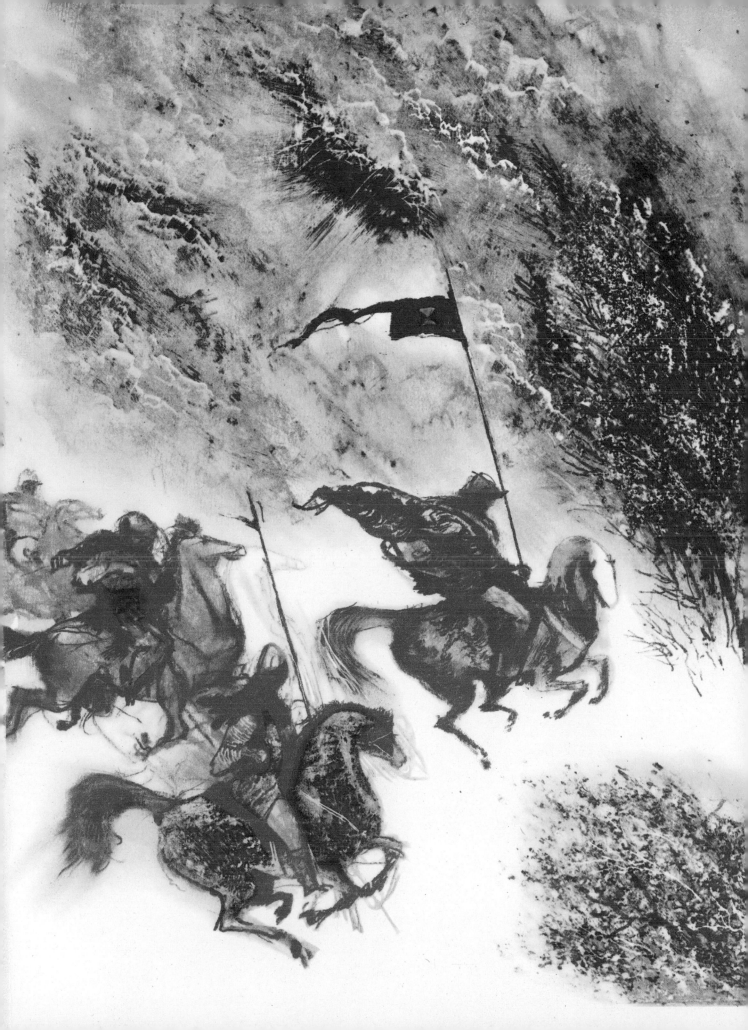

then ordered the Praguers to bring all their arms and armour, spears, lances, bows, plate-armour, helmets and shields, to Vyšehrad on Saint Martin's day, and there to lay them before the king.

The councillors were extremely frightened by this order. They were afraid that if they disobeyed the king would be dangerously enraged against them. But to give up their arms and thus leave themselves defenceless was something they were very reluctant to do. In this crisis John Žižka gave them good advice. He told the councillors to call a full public meeting, and to make it clear that this order came not from them but from the king, and at the same time to advise all citizens to arm themselves on the appointed day, and then march together in their full numbers to Vyšehrad. When the king saw them so, said Žižka, he would certainly not order them to take off their harness and surrender their arms. And it happened as he had said.

On Saint Martin's day all the citizens of Prague went in full panoply to Vyšehrad, and John Žižka, himself armed as a knight, led them as their general in the field. When they stood drawn up in the courtyard thus beneath their banner, in harness and bearing arms, the sunlight flashing from their serried ranks, the king looked out at them from a window alarmed and anxious. Then the councillors bade the knight of Trocnov:

'Brother, speak!'

And he, stepping forth from the ranks before the king, said: 'My gracious lord and king! Here we stand, your subjects, every man in arms and harness as you were pleased to command us to come before you. Here we are, at your service, your gracious Majesty, and now please tell us where you would have us go. Wherever you will send us, against whatever enemy, we'll go gladly, and protect your Grace and this kingdom gallantly to the last drop of our blood.'

The king, reassured by this, laughed and replied: 'Well said, brother! Turn your host, then, for I trust you. Let every man go as he came, back to his own home.'

And they all returned in good order and discipline to the New Town Hall, where they dispersed. They took home their arms and armour, and they had not angered the king. This they owed to the lord of Trocnov, who had solved their problem by his wise advice and witty speech. And thenceforward the citizens of Prague held Žižka in high respect.

But still more they relied on him after the death of King Wenceslas in the year 1419.

Those were evil and difficult times, for many and formidable enemies conspired together against the Czech nation, and the worst of all was Zikmund, king of Hungary, brother of the late King Wenceslas. This Zikmund had been heard

245

to say publicly that he would give his Hungarian kingdom to have the last Czech wiped out from Bohemia.

At this period, when our kingdom was threatened with utter ruin, and the Czech race with extinction, from the ranks of the country land-owners rose this renowned Czech, the bravest of leaders, one-eyed John Žižka of Trocnov, who now began to sign himself 'of the Chalice'.

By the grace of God he rose up and took the field against the enemies of his nation, against those who were of one mind with them as enemies of Master John Huss, and those who rejected the doctrine of Communion in both kinds. Everywhere he sounded the call to arms against them, summoning all who were not too old or too young for service, and bidding them be on the watch every hour. He called them to pluck up courage, urging that they should stand stoutly in the ranks, and never take into account that they were few against many, small against great, unarmed men against armed.

The foundation of his army was the farmers, and with them, in many a battle and skirmish, he defeated armoured knights and experienced soldiers. He never lost a battle. But he made use of more than his strength and passion to destroy his enemies, more than his genius as a military leader, for he was equally remarkable for his resource and cunning.

Thus in the year 1420 he was marching from Pilsen to his newly founded stronghold of Tábor with all his people, numbering at the most four hundred with the women of the brotherhood and the boy slingers. He had only twelve armoured wagons, and nine riding horses. And the lords of the confederacy of the Hungarian king's allies were hunting him from both sides. One force was hastening after him from Písek, and the lords of the region of Pilsen were advancing on him from Strakonice, led by the Grand Master of the Order of Saint John of Strakonice.

When Žižka had passed through Štěkeň and was marching towards Sudoměř through meadowlands among many fishponds, the army of the lords overtook him, so that he could not withdraw and evade their superior power. There were two thousand men at his heels, all cavalry and all heavily armed and armoured. These 'iron lords' inspired panic and horror; but Žižka did not lose heart. With his sparse following, armed for the most part only with flails, he withdrew beyond the large fish-pond which was called Škaredý—the Gloomy Mere—and which at that time was emptied of water, and there he drew up his ranks for battle, and marshalled his wagons on the tall dyke.

He also ordered the women of his array, so it is said, to scatter their veils and shawls and gowns in the grass and reeds on the soft bottom of the mere.

They had hardly completed this when the ranks of the 'iron lords' came into sight, and soon the fields and meadows round about and the bed of the broad mere were swarming with heavy horsemen, whose arms and harness glittered in the sun beneath the scintillating points of their many standards.

It was on the feast of the Annunciation of the Blessed Virgin Mary, late in the afternoon, when the iron lords erupted on all sides like a swarm of hornets and converged on the fish-pond, and the simple fortress of dyke and wagons. They charged upon it joyfully, with wild war-cries. They expected gleefully that without lifting a hand, without wielding sword or lance, by the very force of their impact they would trample this pathetic little force into the ground, and batter them to pieces under the hooves of their horses.

But they could not get all the way to the dyke on horseback; so they dismounted, and the greater part of their number advanced across the bed of the mere on foot. It was slow work for the iron lords in the soft soil. They slipped and slid, and then—close to the dyke itself—they began to fall. They had tangled themselves by their spurs in the veils and gowns and shawls, and the more violently they struggled to free themselves from these snares, the more helplessly their feet became entangled, the more frequently they fell and the more laboriously they rose again. From behind, their own rear ranks were over-running them; those behind pressed forward and those in front could not go on. The army stuck fast, fallen into disorder and confusion, and while like this, the brothers burst upon them, killing and lashing about them with their flails until plate-armour clanged and helmets rang.

There followed a terrible, confused struggle, and panic and horror among the iron men, especially when an unnatural wonder was added to their discomforts; for although it was still early, no more than late afternoon, the sun set before its time, suddenly and abruptly, as though it had dropped behind a mountain. At once it was dark, so dark that no-one knew with whom he was at grips. In this obscurity the iron lords were striking and thrusting at one another, until they began to retreat in disorder. They withdrew in various directions with great shame and heavy casualties.

Žižka remained that night on the battle-field, and at dawn he marched on to Tábor, which he reached without hindrance. And there they received him with joyful ceremony and great honour.

At Sudoměř Žižka used the veils and shawls of women to defeat greatly superior mounted forces of his enemies. On other occasions he employed for a similar purpose little three-pronged barbs with sharp points, which he had scattered on the ground. Then, when his enemies charged against his forces, the sharps points of the barbs lodged in their horses' feet. They fell lame suddenly, or in the shock of their sudden and cruel pain reared in terror, broke their ranks and caused others behind them to panic, so that the whole company was broken apart and fell into confusion and disorder.

Often, too, Žižka deceived his enemy by having the shoes of the horses ridden by his cavalry hammered on in reverse, so that the enemy, casting about for his tracks, might be led in the wrong direction. But he is most renowned for his most effective weapons, the wagons, of which he made such formidable use, in time of need, by turning them into a fortress for his army of peasants and foot-soldiers.

Žižka taught his people to handle and manoeuvre these wagons, which were both instruments of war and supply carts, to run them together and lodge them closely wheel to wheel in a powerful rampart, according to the need, which varied with the numbers and strength of the enemy and the site of the battlefield; he made them familiar, they say, with various forms of assembly, signifying which one was to be employed by means of signs well known to farmers, such as the hoe, the rake, the scythe, and others. If they were hard pressed, and had a position on a hill, he would have some of his forage wagons filled with stones, and place them among his cavalry in the front ranks, so covered that they should not be observed by the enemy. And when the enemy beneath his high position made ready to charge the hill, the cavalry would draw apart on Žižka's order, to give free way to the wagons which were stationed among them, and they thereupon launched these heavy wagons, full of large stones, down the hill upon the enemy. They gathered speed as they ran, the wheels revolving ever faster, the wagons rattled and shook and thundered in unleashed force until the ground trembled. No-one could resist them, no-one could stop them, they ran until they reached the end of their journey, until they hurtled and ploughed with a roar into the ranks of the enemy, scything down swathes of men, battering, crushing, killing. If the wagons themselves overturned they played dreadful havoc even in their fall. And before the enemy could recover and remuster, Žižka had already given the order for the attack to his own men, as happened at Malešov against the Praguers in the year of our Lord 1424.

Žižka himself rode a white horse; at this time he was already a middle-aged man, of middle height but sturdy and broad-shouldered, with a round, broad face, a shade over his left eye, and a closely-trimmed brown beard. In time of war he rode in armour, with the truncheon of a general in his hand. At other times he wore a round cap hemmed with fur, and beneath it his hair hung down to the shoulders of the dark sleeveless cloak he wore over his gown. On his feet he wore high riding-boots.

When he rode surrounded by his captains a priest walked before them carrying a wooden church vessel on a pole. This priest wore a surplice, as indeed did all Žižka's priests, and served Mass in full vestments; he did not like it that the priests of Tábor did their office in ordinary clothes and without surplices, and wearing

248

their riding-boots. For that reason, they say, he called them cobblers, and they in turn called his priests the linendrapers.

He stormed and captured many towns and castles, but always he gave whatever booty he took to the brotherhood. He kept nothing for himself, only, as they say, 'the cobwebs'. It's said that in captured towns, let the brothers go running after plunder as they would, he would only sweep up 'the cobwebs'. These were the joints of smoked meat from the chimneys. All these he swept up, all the cobwebs of huge shoulders of pork, joints and hams and sides of bacon, and had them loaded on to carts and drove them away with him, so that in time of scarcity he might have the necessary supplies for himself and the brethren.

III

Brother Žižka took a stern revenge for John Huss. More than one church, more than one monastery and castle of his enemies, he burned and sacked without mercy. But he could also show pity. Thus it happened in Prague, when he came with his men to the cloister of Saint Anne, to destroy it. There a nun of the convent who was related to him fell on her knees before him on the threshold of the cloister, and for the love of God implored her kinsman to have mercy on her and her sisters of the order, and to spare the convent. And Žižka pitied her and showed mercy, leaving the convent untouched.

The great monastery of Sedlec, by Kutná Hora, fared worse. Žižka gave it as booty to his men, but ordered that they should spare the splendid church of the monastery, which was a great building and a fine one. But one of his soldiers crept up under the roof and set fire to it, and the flames seized hold on the whole church. Žižka was enraged when he saw the smoke and the flames licking upwards; he asked at once who had set fire to it, saying that the man responsible should declare himself, and promising a reward in gold to whoever had done it. And the soldier came and boasted of his deed. Then the angry commander ordered that they should give him the promised gold, but should first melt it down, and then pour the precious molten metal down the man's throat. This was the measure of Žižka's grief and anger for this beautiful church.

Žižka found himself in great difficulties at the castle of Vlčinec, to which he laid siege when he was marching to the mountain of Ostaš, beyond Police on the river Medhuje, where the Silesians had so cruelly tortured and murdered the Hussites of Police.

The castle of Vlčinec stood among forests on a high spur above where the Medhuje and the brook Žďár meet. It was strong in itself, but in addition it seemed that it was protected by some magical power, for cannon balls could make no impression on its walls. The Hussite forces aimed well, their cannon were booming all day long, often well into the night, until all the forests reverberated as though with thunder, but without effect. The shot rebounded from the bastions, ramparts and towers like peas.

There was no point in continuing; they ceased their fire. And as the guns fell silent the soldiers in Žižka's camp heard music from the castle. Someone within was playing a violin. It was a musician in a window of one of the towers, whom they had seen playing there even earlier, while they were firing. Žižka ordered his best archer to aim at the musician. The archer took his bow, aimed and loosed the bolt—the violin was suddenly silent, and the musician had vanished from the window. Then Žižka ordered that all the cannon should fire on the castle; and with the very first balls spurts of dust flew from the walls, stones fell in showers, and before long a great breach yawned in the wall. Before the sun had set the cheering of the victorious brethren rang through conquered Vlčinec.

They sacked and burned it; the glare gave them light all night long, and flooded the forests and hills around with a red glow. The castle was burned out, and everything in it, including the musician-sorcerer who had protected it by his arts.

Only ruins remained, and in time foul weather and the growth of trees destroyed even those. Vlčinec was overgrown and overthrown by the forest, and where the enchanted violin sang and Žižka's cannon roared, nothing is heard now but the murmur of the woods.

Thus Brother Žižka marched in arms through Bohemia against the friends and allies of King Zikmund. Many a city surrendered to him, and many a castle he captured. In the year 1421 he besieged the castle of Rábí in the region of Pilsen. Once already before this he had taken this castle, but he had left no garrison in it. And now, when he led his men to the attack and the first shots were launched at them from the ramparts, he was seriously wounded by an arrow which struck him in the eye, his single sound eye. The name of this archer is said to have been Sezema Kocovský, or Sezema of Kocov. But there is another account which says that at this attack a splinter from a pear-tree, which had been split by an enemy arrow, flew into Žižka's eye, and he was wounded so severely that he scarcely escaped with his life. He was carried to Prague for treatment, and with him went Matthew Louda of Chlumčany, a captain in the forces of Tábor, and a learned man, who installed Žižka in his house in the Old Town of Prague, which is said to have been called the Black Lamb.

Here doctors removed the arrow from Žižka's eye, but they could not return him the light of day. He was blind in both eyes.

At the castle of Rábí, where this misfortune befell, they later painted a picture on the gate. On the left in this picture Žižka could be seen in his coat of mail, on horseback with his truncheon in his hand, leading his armed ranks to the attack. On the right was painted a tower with a gate, and Kocovský could be seen on the tower in the act of loosing the bolt from his bow. Beneath the painting was written the conversation he had with Žižka.

'Is it you, Brother Žižka?'

'It is I.'

'Cover your nakedness!' By which he meant his face, which alone was unprotected.

From that time forth Žižka was unable to lead his people into battle in person, riding on horseback at their head as in the past. Yet he still directed their battles and skirmishes with great skill. Sitting high on a wagon beside the great standard with the symbol of the Chalice, he was driven into war with his army. Those who sat with him, and his captains, especially his 'dear and faithful brethren' Victor of Poděbrady, John Bzdinka and Kuneš of Bělovice, described to him all the lie of the land, told him where there were rocks or hills, where forest and meadow, and where lay valleys, plains or uplands. Before the battle they told him everything in great detail, and also described the course of the battle, keeping him informed of every event in relation to the enemy forces.

In accordance with what he thus learned Žižka gave his orders—and triumphed over the allies of the Hungarian king in both Bohemia and Moravia. On one occasion he even prepared to make a direct attack against King Zikmund himself, and this was in the year of Our Lord 1423, in autumn, at the beginning of the month of October.

Preparing four columns of wagons and as many cannon as he could muster, he crossed the mountains on the frontier of the Czech kingdom and entered Hungary. Wherever he passed he ravaged the country, repaying the Hungarians and their king for the unchristian cruelty and violence with which they had conducted themselves in Bohemia, especially in the year 1420, sparing neither women nor children.

Žižka penetrated into Upper Hungary as far as the Danube between Komárno and Ostřihom. Everywhere the inhabitants fled before him, and drove off their cattle with them; and so it happened that he ran short of supplies, and especially of meat. During this expedition he came once into a village on the Danube above Ostřihom. The place was deserted and empty, not a man had remained in it. To hunt the inhabitants down was not possible; they had fled in boats and rafts to a nearby island in the Danube, and there they had taken all their stock also, leaving in the cowsheds and sties only a few calves and young piglets which they would not have found it possible to drive across the water to the island.

The Hungarians on the island were congratulating themselves on saving all their cattle from the Czechs, and grew exuberant in the assurance of being safe. They shouted from the island, hallooing across the water at the village, waving mockingly at the Czechs and calling to them to come over to them, for here they had cattle and to spare. They knew very well that the Hussites had neither boats nor rafts.

But Žižka needed none. He had other means of getting the better of the Hungarians. When dusk came down, he ordered the brethren to take the calves and the little pigs they had found in the village and lead them down to the edge of the water, and there to beat and goad them so that the calves would bellow and the piglets would set up a piercing squealing.

The young things responded by raising their delightful voices in a chorus of bleating and squealing and wailing that made the ears ring. It floated across the waters of the Danube to the island, and had an instantaneous effect, especially on the cows and sows. Driven by instinct they gathered themselves suddenly and leaped into the water in wild haste, like frenzied creatures. In vain the Hungarians shrieked and cursed, in vain they ran to try to intercept them. They could not prevent them, for all their cursing and shouting, nor even halt the remaining beasts, which rushed into the river as soon as they saw the first few swimming strongly away ahead of them. The river teemed with cattle, and above the water and the shore rose the babel of animal voices, lowing, bleating, bellowing and squealing, until all these were quenched by the joyful yells of Žižka's men, as they herded the streaming, glistening cattle they had captured so easily, and drove them into camp, to the blazing fires.

Until this time the Hungarians had offered very little resistance to Žižka, and had nowhere blocked his path with arms. They wanted him to feel sure of himself and venture deep into the country, where they could fall upon him with their much greater numbers and crush him. But he, fully understanding that it would not be wise to penetrate farther, turned his wagons and withdrew towards Moravia.

But now he found himself making a hazardous journey. The great Hungarian army, almost entirely of cavalry and with large numbers of cannon, was snapping at his heels. They closed in on him from all sides, and tried to harass him in camp as often as they could. They also made it difficult and dangerous for him to cross the rivers with all his men. But the blind general foiled them by his wit. Everywhere he stood them off successfully, and brought his host safely back into Moravia.

This Hungarian expedition was one of the most splendid military feats Žižka ever achieved, for it presented him with more difficulties than he had ever had

to overcome since the beginning of his fighting career. 'But the Lord God helped him to withdraw from Hungary.'.

When he was returning from Moravia into Bohemia, and had passed through Litomyšl and reached Vysoké Mýto, he halted his army. Noon was approaching, the hour of rest and food, and he himself was weary. Here the brothers, wishing to prepare a pleasant surprise for their beloved leader, made a special place where he might rest and eat in comfort.

Every soldier filled his helmet with earth, making several journeys, and emptied it on a chosen spot. Hundreds and hundreds of helmets of earth they piled up here, and in a very short time they had fashioned a small mound, and levelled the top of it. Then they led Žižka to it, and here he sat and ate his dinner. When the meal was done the army marched on. But the mound of earth they had shaped did not crumble away; it remained and preserved its form to this day, and to this day all the people from the country round call it Žižka's table.

I V

When Žižka was marching in arms to Moravia, he besieged on the journey the town and castle of Přibyslav. Here in camp he fell ill of a malignant disease. But his illness did not last long. Seeing that he would never rise again, he confided the guardianship of the faith to his beloved and faithful Czechs, especially the lord Victor of Poděbrady, to whose son George Žižka is said to have stood godfather, Kuneš of Bělovice and John Bzdinka, bidding them always defend the sacred truth.

During these sorrowful hours Žižka had with him also John Laudát, his clerk, and Michael Koudel of Žitenice, in whose arms the general died; and this was on the Wednesday before Saint Havel's day, under a pear-tree, as one ancient account bears witness. But others say that it was under an oak-tree, as he had been born under an oak.

Bitter grief gripped the hearts of all his men. Bearded, hardened and heroic soldiers shed tears at the news, and Žižka's people took to themselves the name of the Orphans, as though their father had indeed died.

The body of the dead general was buried in the church of the Holy Spirit in Hradec on the Elbe. Later his remains were removed to Čáslav, and laid there in the parish church of Saints Peter and Paul. His tomb was close to one of the church pillars, near a side altar.

Opposite this tomb a stone plate hung. Of this plate it used to be said that Žižka had eaten from it; but others say that it was on this tablet Žižka's priest held the Holy Sacrament when he celebrated Communion in both kinds.

So departed Brother John Žižka of the Chalice, victor of Sudoměř, Vožice, Žižkov, Kutná Hora, Německý Brod, the mountain of Saint Gothard by Hořice, Malešov and other battles, the creator of the Hussite military science, to whom so many cities and castles had succumbed, and who himself never knew defeat, for he fought 'not only for the law of God, but in particular also for the liberation of the Czech nation and the Slav race'.

When he died the people of Hradec had his image painted on their standard, on a white horse, in knightly harness and with his truncheon in his hand, just as he used to ride during his life; 'And while the people of Hradec fought beneath this banner, they never lost a battle.'

Not one of the figures renowned in Czech history has fixed himself so vividly and deeply in the memory of the people as the hero of Trocnov. The place of his death also remained long in memory. They called it Žižka's field, and still call it so, and they left it unploughed. During more recent times, when the memory of the glorious hero became dulled in various ways, they tried to plough this field. They ploughed a small strip, but they never finished the work. The cattle which were yoked to the plough fell ill and died.

So Žižka's field still remained fallow, and later an elder-tree grew in it, of such rapid and lavish growth that the farmer who owned the land wished to dig it out. But as soon as they tried, the tool slipped and dug deep into the foot of one of the workmen. Then they took an axe to it, but at the first blow the head of the axe flew from its handle and wounded the man who was wielding it. So the elder-tree was left standing. The spot near to the farm of Trocnov, where Žižka was born beneath the oak-tree, also held its place in the public memory. The oak stood for centuries, and people treated it with reverence. Later, after the battle of the White Mountain, the people were told that Žižka was a cruel and bloodthirsty tyrant.

But the people remained unshaken in their conviction that he had been an invincible warrior, seemingly fortified by some strength above human; and the source of this strength they sought in the place of his birth, and in the oak-tree itself. They went to Trocnov for the sake of this tree, cut off branches from it and hacked segments from the trunk to make handles for axes and hammers. They believed that such handles would ensure heavier and stronger strokes and would last longer. When the tree died as a result, and the trunk remained standing like a dead log, blacksmiths and country people used to come here and hammer nails into it, convinced that this charm would gain for them strength and vigour. At the same time they destroyed even the trunk, by carrying away pieces of its wood to make handles for the tools of their craft; so the remains of the mighty oak perished, until only a stump remained. And when even this began to disintegrate, people came for splinters, so as to reinforce with these at least the powers of axes and hammers, by embedding the fragments in their handles. Not a trace of the oak is left now. All the buildings in the country, especially monasteries and castles, which have been destroyed in war, and particularly in the Thirty Years War, fell victims to Žižka's strength. So people believed, and so many of them still believe. And wherever there is an ancient rampart or earthwork to be seen, even from prehistoric ages, that is also attributed to Žižka's times.

Thus the old ramparts in the region of Luž are said to be connected with Žižka. If you visit the gigantic earthworks at Kopidlno, and ask the people living in the neighbourhood what they know about this extremely ancient enclosure, you will get the reply: 'Those are old Czech fortifications from when Žižka was fighting hereabouts.' Even the places where he halted on his campaigns, from which he launched his attacks, or where he rested, people have kept in remembrance, and preserved their story from generation to generation.

Near Rychmburk is the mere of Spálinec, or the Place of Burning. They will tell you that it got its name because there Žižka burned the monks whom he had taken captive at the monastery of Podlažice. In Rychmburk itself they will show you Žižka's rock, a steep outcrop directly opposite the castle, divided from it only by a narrow ravine. They say that Žižka had the middle part of this rock hollowed away, and then placed his cannon here, and from this spot directed a powerful fire into the castle, in which to this day two stone cannon balls from the Hussite wars are embedded. Far away from here, in the north-west of the country at Blšany, there is a hillock still called Žižka's mound, because they say the general of Trocnov once made camp there. And beyond the frontiers of the present Bohemia, in the region of Kladsko, which at that time formed a part of Bohemia, on the way from the town of Radek to Vambeřice, there stands a rock at the edge of the forest, and on the rock a stone which resembles a helmeted head, with a patch over one eye. They still call this rock Žižka's Head.

In Náchod they have another Žižka's table, a large round stone on a rough sandstone base, beneath the white tower of the ramparts on the castle hill. Once there used to be a stone bench beside this table, but now it stands a little lower down the slope. At this table Žižka is said to have eaten when he had returned through Kladsko from Moravia. He did not storm the castle of Náchod; he is said to have examined it and said that that wasps' nest wasn't worth his trouble.

In addition to these tables of Žižka there is still one more in the region of Hradec. Near to Všcstary, Rosnice and Probluze by Hradec Králové lies the forest of Bor. In its slopes rises the low hill of Homol, and its highest summit, open and grassy, is called Žižka's table. At each of its four corners stands a lime-tree, and in the centre of the expanse grows a mountain ash. On this spot Žižka halted when he was on the march from Kutná Hora to Hradec Králové. The army then lay round Homol, and on its highest spot they laid their general's table. It was of gold, they say, with dishes of silver, and while Žižka ate at this table the soldiers all round sang. After the meal they buried the table and the precious dishes, as their general ordered, and went on to Hradec.

And to this day the golden table and the silver service lie where the army left them. But no-one has yet succeeded in digging them up.

Plenty of 'Žižka's' horseshoes have been dug up, however. Wherever an old horseshoe is found deep in the earth it is sure to date, so people believe, from Žižka's times. They know it certainly from the holes, for the nail-holes in shoes of Žižka's day are round.

As there are Žižka's tables, ramparts and rocks, so there are Žižka's trees. Most often lime-trees, beneath which the tired general sat down to rest in the cool shadow, as under the old lime-tree in Krčína, and elsewhere.

What the ancient chronicler wrote of Žižka has been fulfilled:

'His legend is sounded abroad into many and distant regions of the world, it endures to this day, and still will endure.'

The Miners
of Kutná Hora

I

Lt was during the time of Žižka that Kutná Hora found its way into Czech history. At that period they say that, in the Italian court there, they were minting coins with the Czech lion on one side with the inscription: 'Penny of the Czech people'. And on the other side, with the image of an ark and the chalice, the inscription: 'To the glory of the God of Battles'.

Then came a further fulfilment of Libuše's prophecy about Kutná Hora: it declined for the second time, and for the second time rose to prominence again. This happened particularly in the reign of King George of blessed memory, and after him in the reign of King Vladislav of Jagellon.

More than one new vein was discovered, more than one new mine founded, many shafts deepened and many galleries cut in the rock. The company of the craft increased, the mines teemed with miners, and their devout songs rang out from many lodges where they waited for their shift. Even in the town they appreciated the blessing of the metal and the work. Kutná Hora was flourishing on a rising wave, and as the mines prospered, so the crafts prospered. There were good profits and plenty of money. Many houses were being built, and at this same time Matthew Rejsek was building here at Kutná Hora his glorious work, the church of Saint Barbara. Country gentlemen were coming to settle in the town, and foreigners and merchants in large numbers flocked there. The scene in all the streets and squares was lively and noisy. And busiest of all was the Italian court, where the principal Master of the Mint of the Czech kingdom had his offices, together with the high overseer of the mines and his officials, and the clerk of the mines and his deputies, and where the royal treasurer conducted his business, and occasionally even the king himself resided for a time.

Beneath their offices and beneath the splendid rooms of the royal suite were the cellars and vaults full of precious metal, and the workshops of the minters where, from the silver smelted in the furnaces and fashioned into rods, they minted shining Czech pence.

Kutná Hora was in full bloom, the first city of the realm after Prague. At that time, in the reign of Vladislav the Second, the people of the town remembered the faithful Czechs who some years earlier had been seized by the Germans, who then ruled the town, for their crime in administering and receiving Communion in both kinds, and had been mercilessly thrown down into the mines, most of them alive. They were digging out from the old mines the bones of these Czechs, most of all in the shaft beyond the Kouřím gate, in order to give them honourable burial. In this same shaft, wonder of wonders, they found a body, not intact but nearly so, which had the pure and fragrant scent of fine myrrh.

This caused great excitement and wonder through the entire town, and it was generally agreed that this body, which had lain there in the deep shaft for years, must have its perfume as a sign of the grace of God, and that it must surely be John Chodko, sometime parish priest at Kouřím, who after torture had been cast down here into the shaft along with his three priests, like hundreds and hundreds of other Czechs.

This marvellous discovery happened in the year 1492; and after this devout storm of emotion there soon occurred some very different disturbances. Storms burst upon Kutná Hora, and they came out of the depths of the earth, where discontent was seething, where the poor man with his heavy labour dug out wealth and luxury for the rich and powerful. The earth gave up so much ore that the royal revenues could have their fill of silver and the people a substantial profit. But the greed of certain men was offending against both the king and the workmen. The officials of the mines did not send all the silver to Prague, and at the same time they cut down the wages of the miners.

Deep in the earth, in the barren dark galleries, by the flickering reddish light of his smoking lamp, the miner in his hooded cape worked diligently and untiringly, hewing out the precious ore with his hammers and sharp iron pick. Until now he had had carried out this heavy work quietly and steadily. He had had no serious cares, except that some day in this solitude, in the dimness and the flickering light, he would suddenly halt and incline his ear, unexpectedly catching through the dead stillness the sound of an unknown voice calling him by name, slowly and sadly three times over. Or perhaps he might look round warily to make sure that the 'knocker' was not hopping suddenly out of the depths of the dark galleries, the little dwarf in miner's clothes, with his lamp at his belt and his hammer in his hand, the imp with the glittering eyes who loved to tease and torment the miners, but also led them to the good ore.

But now the miners had other anxieties. They were angered by the harsh injustice inflicted on them by their masters, in constantly forcing down their wages for such hard and laborious work. They were now receiving barely half of the wages they had formerly earned, though their work had not been eased at all. On this miserable pittance they could no longer provide properly for their families, and some of them were already living in want.

This grievance smouldered in the hearts of all of them. They complained one to another, and not one concealed the anxiety that was consuming his mind at work, or the conviction that was fiercely possessing him, that this state of affairs, with the working men growing poorer and the officials and owners of the mines growing ever richer, could not and must not go on. They were also concerned about the king's rights. They knew how much ore and pure metal they were winning from the mines, and how much it should amount to in smelted silver, and they knew how far short of this was the amount the officials were sending to Prague.

First of all they asked for reform. But neither the mine officials nor the councillor-overseers and the elders of the town would listen to them. Worse, they took strict action against them. When the miners met to discuss their grievances the mayor of the town drove them out of the Italian court with his sergeants or the soldiers. So the miners conferred secretly, and agreed that they would send ambassadors to the king, who was then staying in Hungary at the castle of Budín.

In excitement and eagerness they waited to see what answer their envoys would bring back with them. They hoped and expected that the king, when he heard about their troubles, would at least have an investigation made, to find out for himself whether the law was being observed.

As the miners' ambassadors had departed secretly in the night from Kutná Hora, so they returned in secret; it was evening, in the month of July in the year 1496.

Everyone hurried to the open space before the Italian court. All the men who were not at that time working in the mines ran to the meeting place, and many women. Many were already hopeful that their lordships in the court were about to hear unexpected news, after which they would act more carefully.

But their lordships did not change their ways; neither, however, did the miners, though the news from Hungary was a reverse for them. The king had done nothing for them, had not taken their part in any degree, for he had not even heard what the envoys had to say. They had refused to let them in to him. This was news from Hungary which they had not expected; and the envoys added that they were being so slandered to the king that they were in disfavour with him, and the courtiers had told them that they had best be off home in haste, if they did not want to stay there in prison.

The ambassadors had not so much as finished speaking when it was as though a storm had broken around them out of a clear sky. A furious cry of disappointment and anger burst from every throat. Hundreds, thousands of fists were raised and shaken at the Italian court, a thousand voices cursed and abused it, calling those within traitors and liars and thieves, good for nothing but to oppress and slander better men than themselves.

When the clerk of the mines appeared on the battlements of the castle wall and wished to speak to the crowd, the storm burst out again, and so violently that the clerk made himself scarce in haste. Not even the Master of the Mint himself could restore order. When he appealed to them to disperse they shouted at him to get them a hearing with the king so that they could have their rights, otherwise they would leave the mines, and their lordships could dig in them themselves.

Everywhere in the town people closed their doors and shutters, everywhere they waited in fear and tension, and the whole night long scarcely anyone closed an eye.

All night long the miners were up in angry activity, preparing for their journey, marshalling the women and children out of their dwellings, running to call the miners who had been below at work in the galleries.

Not even the royal officials or the councillors could turn or disperse them. Their men-at-arms were not enough to confront so many thousands of excited and enraged men. Indeed the elders of the town and the lords' officials in the Italian

264

court were only too glad that the miners had calmed down. They had feared that there was going to be bloodshed, and that they might even burn down the town.

Like a dark torrent in flood the miners rushed through the streets of Kutná Hora in the morning twilight, beneath their banner and carrying their tools, many of them also bearing arms; out to the gate they went, all singing a proscribed hymn together in such a thunderous chorus that the windows shook: 'Come, all true Christians, place your hope, In the supper of the Lord.' They sang it, although by royal decree it was forbidden to sing it under pain of death.

Out of the town went the miners, six thousand strong, and marched until they came to a halt on the summit of Špicberk, between the hills of Malína and Kaňka. There they made camp, and at once, on the advice of their elders, began to dig a ditch round their position and build an earthwork.

It had grown quiet in Kutná Hora, but the tension remained. They still went in fear of the miners, and in dread that a great disaster had overtaken the mines, that they would be left without workmen. And the lords in the Italian court, and the councillors who were responsible to the town for the administration of the mines, were angered by the boldness of the miners. They wished to force them back to work, but they also wished to punish and humble them. So they wrote letters in haste, both officials and councillors, and sealed them, and sent them out by mounted messengers on fast horses, who distributed them on every side throughout the district.

II

A day passed, a second and a third, and yet another day, and all this time the miners were encamped in their earth rampart on the hill. Constantly they expected that the lords from Kutná Hora would send after them to tell them to return and go back to work and would promise them reforms in return. But nobody came, no-one appeared on the road riding towards them. The evening of the fifth day was approaching. On the ramparts round the camp young miners stood on guard in arms, keeping steadfast watch.

In the camp the miners, especially the elders, were pale with anxiety. They were afraid that the people of Kutná Hora must be up to something, and they calculated that they could not hold out very long on their hill, for their supplies were running low. They went to sleep late, but even so they did not sleep through the night.

Towards morning there arose a sudden outcry. The guard on the earthwork called them to the alert, with the news that he had sighted a great company of

265

men approaching. As the elders ran to the ramparts they saw in the dim half-light of the morning a sombre crowd of men, both mounted and afoot, coming from the north, from Kolín.

At that moment there came a cry from the other side that another company was moving towards their flank from Čáslav and, before the news was fully grasped, they saw a large assembly coming towards them from Kutná Hora to take them in the rear. They could hear the roll of drums and blare of a trumpet from this group, and see a banner fluttering over them, as over the companies from the neighbouring towns.

Now it was clear that all these were converging on the miners, compassing them about on all sides. For the citizens of Čáslav and Kolín had received from Kutná Hora horrifying reports about the miners, how they were preparing for murder, and intended to destroy all the shafts and ruin the mines.

These attendant companies were still marshalling their ranks at the foot of the hill when a new and strong detachment of men-at-arms appeared; these were from Poděbrady, and numbered a strong proportion on horseback. When they halted at the bottom of the slope it was already growing light, and the miners on their mountain could see that this new detachment was led by the castellan of the royal castle of Poděbrady, Oněk Kamenický of Topice.

The lofty camp of the miners was surrounded, the foot of the hill was black with their opponents, a teeming army. Almost four thousand armed men were massed there against them. The miners on the hill took station on the earthwork in companies, as their elders had divided them, with weapons and hammers in their hands, awaiting the onslaught of their enemies. They had resolved that they themselves would not begin the fighting; but neither were they willing to beg or to surrender.

But the idea had occurred to one of them that they ought to try to parley, not with the people of Kutná Hora, but with the castellan of Poděbrady, for he was the king's deputy, and had the ear of his Majesty. They were certain that Oněk Kamenický did not know what had happened in Kutná Hora, and why they had withdrawn their labour. If they explained everything to him, perhaps he would take their part and help them to gain audience of the king, or perhaps he himself would inform the king of their grievances.

And behold, the castellan of Poděbrady, fully armed, rode out alone from among his company, and came straight to their ditches. The elders went out in front of the rampart to meet him, and one of them, the grey-bearded Opat, who always spoke for the miners, told the castellan that they had no wish to cause bloodshed, all they wanted was their rights, and in particular they wanted his Grace the king to listen to their complaints.

266

'If that is so,' said the castellan, 'come with me to Poděbrady, and I will obtain for you from his Majesty the hearing you desire.'

'We would gladly go with you,' said Opat, 'but we're afraid for our lives.'

'Nothing will happen to you; take my word for it and come.'

So the elders, relying on his word as a nobleman, agreed that they should go. They informed the other miners what they had decided, took their leave of their families and went: Opat and his brother Victor, Simon and Průša, also brothers, Duchek, Černý, Kůžel, Holý, Želva, Ondřej Němec, Vít Krchňavý, Lana of Hlouška, Mládek and Klad. All the remaining miners with their families set out on their way back to Kutná Hora, to wait there until their cause should be settled before the king, as they had been promised.

The elders of the miners took the road to Poděbrady with Oněk Kamenický and his men. More than once they cast glances aside in the direction of Kutná Hora; they looked ahead in no very gay spirit. They were not travelling with complete faith, they had no security and they were placing themselves in the power of the lords.

But they believed that a knight would hold by his word.

When they came to Poděbrady the castellan offered them the servants' quarters of the castle as their dwelling, and had them suitably provided with all that they needed. In the courts of the castle they were allowed to go about freely, but they could not leave the castle and go into the town. They were not permitted to do so, nor could they, for the drawbridge was kept raised all day long.

On the third day the castellan received them in a brief interview, and promised them that he was sending two mounted messengers to the king at once with a written report, and in the meantime they must have patience. As soon as word came from the king, if God was gracious a favourable word, he would inform them at once.

He had, in fact, already sent a report; but having been bribed by the authorities at Kutná Hora he sent an account similar to the one which the royal officials had already dispatched to the king from the Italian court. Oněk Kamenický described the miners as dangerous rebels, who had been fully prepared, if need be, to ravage and destroy Kutná Hora, that jewel of his Majesty and of the entire Czech kingdom. Before his messengers returned he rode to Kutná Hora and there reported to the lords in grateful acknowledgement of their liberality what he had done and what was happening, saying that on the strength of his account the king would certainly condemn the miners to death, so their lordships would do well to start preparing shrouds for them.

And so they did, but first they paid over a substantial sum in silver to the

267

castellan of Poděbrady. Then secretly they provided thirteen shrouds such as were worn for execution, of white linen, for the elders of the miners' craft.

When the castellan returned to Poděbrady the messengers were already riding in from Hungary. They came late in the evening, and the miners knew nothing of their arrival. The next day the castellan called to him Holý, Ondřej Němec and Vít Krchňavý. He asked them to make ready to go to Křivoklát, for he said they had found ore there and they were anxious to know what was in it, and the three miners were to examine it, since they knew all about ores and stones.

Thus deceived, the three had no suspicions, and taking leave of their companions in the hope of an early and happier meeting, set out on their journey. They could not guess that they had looked their last upon their fellows, that their guide was carrying to the burgrave of Křivoklát about them such a letter as King David sent concerning Uriah, informing him that they were to be put to death at Hrádek, and for that reason he was sending with them in the wagon three execution shrouds.

When these three had departed, on the third day the castellan had the remaining ten called to him. Until that moment they had no idea what news the messengers had brought back from Hungary. It was early in the morning when he sent for them, on a Friday, the day after the feast of St Lawrence. The elders of the craft wondered why he should send for them at such an early hour, and thought that perhaps the envoys had just arrived. So they went with eagerness and hope.

But they were not led to the office, but into the courtyard in front of the balcony which was raised on three arches close beside the castellan's room. And round the courtyard, on which the morning shade still lay though the towers and roofs above it were already flooded with the golden sunlight of the August morning, stood troops in full arms, lance in hand. And there was a great force of them.

The elders were alarmed, especially when they were ordered to stand here in the courtyard in front of the balcony. But they had not long to wait. Oněk Kamenický of Topice came out from his office in a black velvet hat with a black plume and a gold chain, and black coat and hose; and on his heels came Žďárský, the mayor of the town of Poděbrady, and the officials of the castle.

The castellan, holding a parchment in his hand, announced sternly to the miners that his Majesty the king had been pleased to make known his will, and he ordered that all those standing there, together with those who had been sent to Křivoklát, should be put to death as rebels.

The miners, old and young, stood mute, the blood frozen in their veins; not

with terror, but at this injustice crying to heaven, and the monstrous wickedness and treachery with which the castellan had used them. Then one of them cried out, and they all took up the cry, casting it in his teeth in their indignation that he was a shameful traitor, that he should stand to his word if he was a true man.

Oněk, scowling like a thunder-cloud, motioned silently, and his soldiers seized the miners and led them back into their quarters, where two executioners were already waiting, Sochor, the castle headsman, and Kolouch, the executioner from the town, both with their assistants. There the condemned were made to put on the white shrouds, and there two priests came to them to prepare them for their last journey.

Not long afterwards, it was at nine o'clock in the morning, they fettered them two and two, and led them from the castle. The castellan Kamenický on horseback led a large detachment of his men-at-arms, and with them walked the mayor, Žďárský, with his sergeants.

Meantime word had flown through the town of what was happening in the castle, and already a great crowd of people had assembled, and walked behind the sorrowful procession.

One and all they were muttering against the judgement, and still more against the castellan, and they all sincerely pitied the unhappy condemned men, who paced out their pitiful journey barefoot in their white shrouds. There was darkness before their eyes, and the death-bell's mournful sound came to them only dully, as if through thick mist.

They walked one behind another as in a dreadful dream. This appalling ending had come upon them so suddenly, so unexpectedly. Not one of them had even considered this, for the castellan to the last moment had been encouraging them that all would be well.

On top of all the injustices they had suffered, to be put to death! And their poor children and wives at home! Such terrible cruelty! It was impossible! In the turmoil of their minds they clutched at that thought. But then, these fetters, the white shrouds, the tolling of the bell! But surely all this was merely to frighten them. The lords wanted to punish them with the terror of death. But when they arrived at the place, surely the castellan would announce a reprieve. So they thought, comforting themselves with the last small spark of hope.

They passed by the strong castle of Poděbrady in the plain beside the Elbe, crossed the bridge, passed the hill of Kluk and came to the sad spot in the meadows, between the villages of Polabec and Kluk. An old pear-tree spread its great crown above the place of execution, and broader still rose a gnarled oak-tree that towered high about it. The lowest of its great branches hung down almost to the grass.

270

Beside this oak the procession halted, and the castellan of Poděbrady called from his horse to the headsman Kolouch:

'Do your duty!'

With those three words he erased the last hope. The miners saw now that they were not to return. All this around them was the dreadful truth. This was their last journey, and here was their last halting-place, and then—eternity.

Anger faded from their hearts; grief and sorrow flooded them, and their minds forsook the dust of earth and were uplifted to heaven. Only there was justice to be found. As though they had agreed among themselves they fell suddenly on their knees, and with all their hearts they prayed aloud:

'O God our Father, Thou who knowest and seest every wrong, let fall the dew of heaven to wash away this our innocent blood!'

Their voices in passionate and solemn chorus rang through the deep and piteous hush. All those in the crowd were overcome with pity. Even the executioner Kolouch. He had his sword already naked in his hands, but he threw it down beneath the pear-tree, and in excitement and emotion he cried:

'I won't do it!'

So it was the executioner Sochor, who could not thus defy his lord the castellan, who advanced and did what his merciless commander ordered.

The first to kneel was Simon, the elder of the two brothers, beneath one of the mighty branches of the oak, which spread above his head like a canopy. Through its dappling of green light and shade flashed the headsman's sword.

After Simon knelt his younger brother Průša, then Černý, the Opat and his brother, all the ten one after another. When the last of them sank lifeless into the blood-soaked grass a tiny cloud suddenly appeared in the clear sky, and grew and spread astonishingly, until it had swelled into a monstrous blackness and swallowed up the entire heaven. From the darkness of the cloud thunder rolled like the voice of God's wrath, and a storm of wind suddenly swept through the old oak and the pear-tree, so that the branches lashed and rustled violently.

The people at the execution-ground remembered the prayer of the unhappy miners, which had hardly died yet from the quivering air. They crossed themselves and rushed away home in terror, repeating in fear and awe as they ran:

'The judgement of God! It's the judgement of God!'

'God heard them! He heard those innocent voices!'

The dead miners had hardly been hurried into the graves dug for them when the rain slashed down, a terrible rain storm. The castellan himself, as he rode into the castle, slipped in the gateway and was thrown from his horse.

The storm raged all day and all night, and still day and night, and so without ever ceasing once for nine days and nine nights. It poured down without easing,

271

until even dried-up brooks ran in flood like rivers, and streams of water washed away the fields and tore out a ravine between Poděbrady and Kutná Hora.

The execution at Křivoklát had been carried out at the same time as the one at Poděbrady. But not all three victims died there. Vít Krchňavý, when his two comrades had already been beheaded, burst his bonds and stunned the executioner with a great stone. Then he fled into the forests, and so he was saved.

III

But those who had dealt so unjustly and cruelly with the miners did not go unpunished.

King Vladislav, who was also king of Hungary, returned from Hungary into Bohemia, and there he heard from certain honest people the plain truth about the judgement of Poděbrady. As soon as he rode into Kutná Hora, where he stayed at the Italian court, he summoned to him Oněk Kamenický, the castellan of Poděbrady, heard his story, and listened to the account given by the officials of the mines. Vít Krchňavý, the sole survivor of the thirteen, was also called before the court and gave his evidence of how their lords had dealt with the unhappy miners. Oněk Kamenický of Topice and several of the officials, who stoutly denied the story, were stretched on the rack, and the king's castellan failed to endure the pain. He died under torture. And just punishment overtook all the others who had taken part in his crime.

But Kutná Hora did not recover from the affair of this cruel execution of the innocent miners for many years, and declined almost into beggary. And on the execution ground where the miners had died a strange wonder was manifested. On the oak beneath which the judgement had been carried out there grew from that time forth acorns of a curious and unusual shape; they resembled the hooded capes of miners. But they grew on only one branch of the tree, the one which had been sprinkled with the blood of the victims, and from that day had borne red leaves.

It happened sometimes that in a year of poor harvest there would not be a single acorn on all the rest of the great tree, but the affected branch always bore fruit. Acorns in the form of miners' capes became renowned, and people came from far and near to gather them, carrying them away as souvenirs. They even had them set in silver or gold and wore them like charms round their necks, believing that they would afford protection from spells and witchcraft, and bring luck to the wearer.

272

No similar acorns grew anywhere else, except on the oak-tree in the village of Kluk, past which the miners of Kutná Hora had been led to their death. The old oak on the execution ground still stood, beside a little chapel, until the second half of the eighteenth century, when a terrible storm uprooted and overthrew it. Its younger companion at the village of Kluk was dug up in the year 1842.

The White Lady

Day follows day, year follows year, and at the end comes death. There has always been a belief, and it still persists, that signs of the approach of death may be manifested, that strange sounds will be heard, prophesying the coming of the last hour.

The cry of the screech owl, a secret knocking, or the sound of someone lashing with a switch at door or window, these and many other similar signs foretell the approach of death. But these are general signs. To certain families, it is said, death has special ways of announcing itself.

Thus if one of the squires of Strojetice was about to die, he saw a white sparrow. One of the Příchovskýs would hear without warning the blare of a huntsman's horn, the baying of hounds and neighing of horses. When a great

274

black cupboard in the castle of Rábí began to shake suddenly without any apparent reason, and a hollow noise came from it, that was a sure indication that soon one of the Dlouhoveskýs, the Častolars or the Chanovskýs was to die. The Černíns heard before death a curious sound as though someone was scattering sand or gravel, the Lobkovic family heard the ringing of a bell; and when one of the Kolovrats was to die the grave-stone in the church of Ročov, beneath which one of his ancestors lay, was seen to exude sweat.

And to certain families a white lady appeared. To the Berkas of Dubá, the lords of Lípa and the Švamberks; but particularly to the lords of Hradec and Rožmberk. She has been seen in Telč, in the castle of Bechyně, in Krumlov, Hradec and also in Třeboň.

Whenever she appeared, some great event was sure to happen shortly afterwards, either happy or sad. Someone was to be born or to die, or else there would be a wedding celebrated in that family. And she always appeared in a white gown, a grave, tall lady, her head covered with a veil like a widow. Only when the event to come was a sad one she is sometimes said to have worn black gloves.

She appeared at various times; sometimes at high noon, but most often in the night. At the castle of Jindřichův Hradec they saw her at midday. She glimmered suddenly in a high window of an old, forsaken tower, where there was no way of access, for the wooden staircase which had once led to the spot had long since been destroyed in a great fire. When the people round about the castle gazed in astonishment at this pale, mysterious vision, and pointed at her, she did not disappear at once. The white lady remained standing at the window, and then gradually sank from sight as though she had fallen down into the tower, growing smaller and smaller until she vanished. In the night she came in the same garments, all white and wearing a white veil, grave and awe-inspiring but not terrible. Either she walked slowly through the corridors, or else she went with a rapid step from room to room, as though she were in haste, and with the keys she carried at her waist she locked this door and unlocked that one. She did no harm to anyone. If any man met her during these secret walks of hers, and gave her greeting, she thanked him gravely, either silently with an inclination of her head, or in words. And her voice had a small, sighing sound like the rustling of leaves, or the passing of a soft breeze.

For the families of the gold and red roses, the lords of Hradec and Rožmberk, with whom in her lifetime she was related, she showed a special care and tenderness.

In the year 1539 there was born to the lord Jošt of Rožmberk, who was then stricken down by a serious illness, his youngest son Peter Vok, who was born at the castle of Krumlov. And this was the last branch in the male line of his very ancient family. The child was cared for by nurses who were constantly with him. But in addition to these he had another, a careful and loving guardian.

She appeared every night when all the castle of Krumlov, towering loftily above the Vltava, had fallen silent, when everyone was asleep, even the nurses. It was the white lady. The windows of the room in which little Peter lay were closed, the door also, nor did they open or move, but the white apparition, moving where it would, suddenly stood in the middle of the room. And she brought with her such an effulgent radiance that it was like the light of the full moon flooding the chamber.

The white lady stood beside the cradle, which was roofed with a light canopy on four slender pillars, drew back the curtains, leaned down to the crib and gazed at the last heir of the ancient family of the Rožmberks.

The nurses sat close by, fast asleep, and slept on undisturbed. And when the little boy cried the white lady picked him up and nursed him, rocking and stroking and kissing him, smiling at him until he stopped crying and fell softly asleep again. Then she vanished, and when she departed the moonlight also faded.

But one night one of the nurses awoke. Her voice froze in her throat with horror. Trembling she looked at the mysterious vision, and realised at once that this was the white lady, of whom she had heard so much. But terror held her rooted to the spot, and all she could do was look on, in fear that the new nurse might do the child some harm. When the white lady suddenly vanished, the nurse woke up her companion and told her in agitated words, still trembling, what she had seen happen in the room, and at once she ran to the cradle, and her colleague hard at her heels. But there was nothing amiss. Their little lord slept soundly, flushed and rosy, and woke up in the morning lively and healthy; and all day long he showed no sign of any trouble.

In anxiety the nurses awaited the coming of night. As on the previous day they sat near to the cradle when they had lulled the baby to sleep. But they themselves did not so much as close an eye. They waited, watching the window and the door, and starting at every sound, until suddenly, just as it struck midnight from the tower of the castle, the room was suddenly illuminated, and in the pale radiance stood the white lady.

She went to the cradle and looked into it, and when the little boy began to cry she took him up and rocked him and hushed him gently, and then rocked the cradle until he fell asleep. Then she vanished as on the previous night, and the frightened nurses, though they had watched intently, could not tell where or how she had departed. Only it seemed to them that somewhere close to the wall she dissolved and disappeared. And the child was well, he slept as sweetly as in paradise.

Their horror was allayed and eased, and the next night both women waited

in a calmer frame of mind. And it happened just as on the other nights. The white lady appeared and tended the child, and then vanished, and soon the nurses also fell asleep, instead of watching in suspense until morning as they had done previously. And when the white lady walked night after night, and never failed to come and watch over the lord's son, the women no longer sat up waiting for her, but slept tranquilly through her visits, just as they had fallen asleep in the evening. They trusted the white lady now, and had no fear of her.

But it happened that one of these nurses fell ill, and they procured another in her place. This woman awoke in the night and saw the pale apparition, and was so frightened that she dared not utter a sound. When she told her companions about it in the morning they reassured her, bidding her keep quiet and sleep peacefully the next night, for the white lady would be nurse in her place. But this did not please the nurse, she repeated that she did not trust this spirit, and how could she answer for it before the Lord God and before the lord of Rožmberk, if anything should happen to the little lord?

So the next night she did not sleep, but sat up waiting anxiously for midnight, to see if the white lady would come again. And come she did. She came just as she always came, walking straight to the cradle; and when the baby cried, she took him up in her arms to comfort him.

But suddenly there before her stood the new nurse like a clucking hen protecting her chickens, and snatched the child from the white lady's arms. She tore him from her hold fiercely, and the white lady did not resist. She stood motionless and frowning, gazing sternly at the audacious nurse.

'Do you know, insolent woman, what you have done?' she said. 'I am kinswoman to this child, and I have rights in him. But you will never see me here again.'

Then the nurse saw her standing by the wall, and when the white lady made the sign of the cross over it, the wall opened, and the apparition disappeared within it. Not a trace remained; the radiance had vanished with her, darkness filled the room.

The nurse, recovering her wits a little, could hardly carry the child back to his crib, her legs were shaking so under her.

She never saw the white lady again; neither she nor any of her companions. She never came again to watch over the lord's son. When he grew up he learned the story of his secret guardian, and also how she vanished from his cradle. There was often talk about the visitation, until one day it occurred to the lord Peter Vok to have the wall of his former nursery opened at the place where the nurses had reported the white lady used to disappear. When the masons had made a small breach in the wall they came upon a great treasure.

Here was a legacy from his forefathers. The lord Peter Vok, laying in store a wealth of precious metal, thought gratefully of the white lady, who had showed him the way to this hoard of gold and jewels.

The white lady also did good service to the last in the male line of the related family of Hradec, the lord Jáchym.

In the year 1604 Jáchym fell seriously ill, though no-one suspected that he had got his death-illness. It was in winter, in the month of January. One night when it was blowing a gale outside and the wind whistled through the courtyards until the shutters rattled, the lord Jáchym's confessor was suddenly startled out of his sleep. It seemed to him that someone was calling him. He jumped up and dressed in haste to open the door, and there in the darkness before him like a pale shadow stood the white lady. She said in an urgent tone:

'Make haste, come with me!'

He wanted to strike flint and kindle a light.

'Wait for no light,' said the white lady; and she reached for the little lamp and breathed on its glass, and at once a bright, clear light was burning in it, and illuminated the whole room. With this lamp in her hand the white lady led the way out of the room, and walked quickly, evidently in haste, through the long corridor to the chapel. And the priest after her.

When they came into the chapel he gasped in astonishment. The holy place was brightly lit, the candles burning on the altar as though for Mass. The white lady indicated to the chaplain that he should take up the precious instruments of extreme unction, and then led him straight to the bedroom of the lord Jáchym. But on the threshold the light faded and the white lady vanished. The priest understood, and went quickly into the room. The nurse who should have been watching and tending the sick man was fast asleep, and her lord was in his death-throes. And the priest did his office, and administered the last rites to the dying man.

At the castle of Jindřichův Hradec they preserve a special memory of the white lady, the distribution of the 'sweet porridge', the feast of the poor. Every year for several days in succession the lofty, vaulted kitchen in the Red Tower served the poor of the entire lordship. On the Tuesday and Wednesday before Holy Thursday, and on Holy Thursday itself, a great fire burned there in the enormous hearth, and over the blaze stood an array of three-legged pots, while above them swung a large, broadbased kettle. They tended this fire from morn till night, cooking in particular great quantities of fish; and the thick columns of smoke rolled upwards to the vault, and into the five openings through which it escaped into the room above. There they had their smoking-chamber, and so it rose into the open air through special chimneys built in the form of chalices.

At morning on Holy Thursday bells were rung from the old round tower, between seven and eight o'clock, to summon the neighbours from the town, the village mayors, the foresters and the others who were to help to serve the food and to keep order. In the meantime the space before the castle and in the streets of the town teemed with crowds of country folk in furs and gowns and coarse cloaks; and always the throng increased, fed by new streams rushing in from all sides. There were always at least four thousand of them, sometimes five thousand and more, and as the years grew harsher and poverty more widespread, especially after the Thirty Years War, sometimes as many as nine thousand came.

In the crowds it was always noisy and lively; a babel of murmuring and clamouring voices, a medley of expectant sounds that rose and mingled, mounting to the castle.

The clamour and hum of the crowds grew louder still when the bell was rung for the second time at nine o'clock, signifying that everything was now prepared, and every one of the helpers in his place. Then they rang the third chime. And it was as though a great flood had burst through a dyke. Shouts and cries echoed from all sides, as everyone surged forward to the castle gate. They admitted only a part of the throng into the first court, and then all the gates were closed and guarded again.

Those who had entered the first courtyard got rolls there, and the vessels they had brought with them were filled with beer. Then they took them to the kitchen, and distributed to every one bread and a piece of boiled carp; and in the last courtyard the poor guests sat down to eat. They got fat soup, fish roes, fish entrails and meat with herbs, and last of all the sweet porridge made of wheat oats cooked with warm beer and honey, with poppy oil added.

When the first group had eaten their fill they let them out through a wicket, which they watched well to make sure that no-one should slip back again. At the same time the gate was opened again in the first courtyard and a second party was admitted to the castle. And so it continued until all had had their turn and eaten their fill.

They say the first of these feasts of the poor was started by the white lady, in the days when she was not yet a good spirit walking through the castle of Hradec, but lived and ruled there as a gracious lady and careful housekeeper.

At that time a part of the old castle was being rebuilt. The white lady, who already was in the habit of going out to the fields to look after the harvesters, came also to watch the builders; and there she urged the working people to be diligent, and promised them all sweet porridge if they would do their best. She promised it not only to them, but said also that she would prepare a feast for their descendants for all time, in memory of their diligent forebears. The building was finished late in the autumn, and the lady, as she had promised, spread a feast for them.

But when the large numbers of people for whom there were not enough places laid took their full dishes and sat down outside, suddenly snow began to fall, and fell also in the sweet porridge.

Therefore, they say, the white lady decreed that on the next occasion this feast should take place at the beginning of spring, on Holy Thursday. And so it continued for ages.

The white lady has not manifested herself for a long time now. On Holy Thursday the courtyards of the castle of Jindřichův Hradec are silent. But there remains for us a vivid reminder of the feast of the poor in the old, high-vaulted kitchen, with its broad window quartered by a stone cross, through which long ago sweet porridge was distributed to all the poor of the lordship.

And there is one more room which can awaken memories of the white lady: the ornamented chapel of the Blessed Virgin in the third courtyard of the castle, close to the apartments of the former mistress of Hradec. An ancient door leads into it, and the walls are covered with old paintings; here is a Virgin with beautiful fair hair, hailed by the angel, here the lords and ladies of the Hradec dynasty kneeling before the Mother of God, there angels and saints, and on the blue vault and the walls the arms of the lords of Hradec and their wives, and white scrolls with faded inscriptions in old Czech.

Here in this quiet holy place, before the altar with its carved images, we are told that the white lady also knelt. Here she prayed to God for all her family, and that love of hers did not weaken even in death.

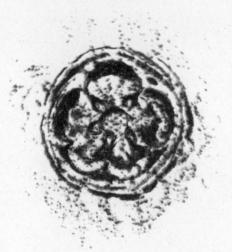

The Rose Meadow

In a solitude among fields of waving corn, beyond which pine-groves darken, a small meadow lies hidden, not much more than twenty paces long and fifteen paces wide. On its borders cluster low, thick-growing bushes of red roses. They are of a special kind. There are no others like them in all the district, and in other soil they will not thrive. Attempts have been made to transplant them, but they would not strike root. Then they wished to remove them; they dug them up, but within a year they were growing thick and green again. They still flourish, and are growing out towards the centre of the field.

It is from them that this place, made holy by the grief of our godly forefathers, takes its name. This is the Rose Meadow on the upland near the village of Morašice, a good hour's journey west of Litomyšl.

The view from here over the countryside is beautiful, towards the pine-forests, among which peers out the tower of Makov, towards the villages shining pale among the greenery, and especially to eastward over the uplands and wooded hills by Česká Třebová to the beautiful and imposing building of the old castle of Litomyšl.

There four hundred years ago, when the first castle was still standing, lived the lords Kostka of Postupice, faithful protectors of the church of Czech Brethren. Close to that castle in the town the council of the Brotherhood had its headquarters, and the majority of the inhabitants of the town were brothers.

When Ferdinand the First overcame the resistance of the estates, he took from the lord Kostka of Postupice his property and castle of Litomyšl, and the brothers from the town and the district had to go into exile. The elder of the Union, John Augusta, was himself captured. He was hiding in the neighbourhood of Litomyšl, disguised as a farmer; but without realising it he betrayed himself. He forgot his country clothes, and drew from his inner pocket, so they say, a red silk kerchief, to wipe the sweat from his brow. This was observed by the grooms of the king's sheriff Šejnoha, at that time steward of the castle at Litomyšl, and Augusta was captured and led into Litomyšl, until he was sent from there to close imprisonment in the castle of Křivoklát, with his clerk Brother Bílek.

There they were kept in harsh captivity more than fourteen years.

Years later, in the reign of Ferdinand's son Maximilian, there were easier times. The brethren returned from exile and settled again in Litomyšl and the district round. But they did not enjoy their freedom long. The great storm burst, and raged throughout the year 1618; and a time of great bitterness descended upon the Czech land during the wars of religion, and most of all after the battle of the White Mountain.

Whoever was not a Catholic or would not renounce his non-Catholic faith had to leave the country, and this same fate befell the brethren from Litomyšl and its district. But before they departed they agreed that they would all meet together and once more offer their assembled worship to God, since they were forbidden to do so freely and openly, and then would take their farewell all together of their native land. For this meeting they chose the meadow beyond Morašice, among the forests.

For safety's sake they met at night, there among the hushed black groves, under the starry vault of the eternal heavens; there for the last time on their native soil they partook of the Blessed Sacrament in both kinds, made their last communal prayers to God, and sang their hymns together.

And then they made their solemn farewell to their homeland. More than one man among them gathered up a handful of soil from his native earth as a memorial, more than one kissed the ground they were watering with their tears. And from those tears grew these roses, to bear witness to their loyalty, and their love for their faith and their country.

That same night, after their Communion was over, they buried the golden chalice from which they had received it, so it is said, and that chalice lies deep in the earth of the meadow to this day.

After a time people forgot about the brethren; but the place where they took their last leave was still held in respect. The meadow used to be larger, the forests around it darker and thicker than now. Now all that remains of the forests is scattered coppices and wide clearings. They also ploughed round the meadow until only a small enclosure remained. They wished to cultivate even that remnant and change it into a field, as all the ground around it was now under cultivation. The little meadow was merely a loss and a hindrance among them. It must go.

They began the work of ploughing up the meadow, but the plough was damaged or the horse fell.

Finally they sowed flax there. It duly grew and flowered, they harvested it, wet and dried it, and were already at the stage of braking it when the flax burst into flames. The fire spread to the drying-room and all the extensive buildings

of the farm belonging to the farmer who had sowed the meadow with flax; and in the blaze the farmer's young daughter lost her life.

No-one ever again ventured to plough up the Rose Meadow.

When the Russians came here in the year 1813, in their advance against Napoleon the First, several of them asked after the Rose Meadow. When they were directed to it they dismounted from their horses, and went forward on their knees into the meadow, and there prayed devoutly.

There is an old prophecy about the meadow, which says that a great battle will some day be fought out in it, a terrible battle, with blood flowing.

Then seven kings will meet there and make a compact of eternal peace. And that among the roses, on the spot where the Czech Brethren, opponents of war and bloodshed, took their leave of their country.

The Judgement of God

I

The important road leading through the forests of Šumava from Domažlice into Germany has been guarded from time immemorial by the Chods, a sturdy and hardened people of bold and resolute mind. Their villages and the present town of Klenčí, formerly on the very edge of the royal forests of the border, extend over valleys and highlands, and are dispersed along a strip about six miles in length, along the frontier astride the important paths and crossings.

The Chods, the ancient Czech frontier guards, patrolled this border and saw to it that their neighbours the Germans did not come across the frontier, did not ravage the Czech forests unlawfully or hunt game in them, and in general that no offence should be committed against the forests. In time of attack by the enemy they defended these pathways and roads, dug ditches to protect them, built fortifications on them, made log barricades, and fought in all the battles and skirmishes that were ever contested in their regions.

They carried the 'čakan', and it was a good comrade to them, walking-stick and weapon in one, with a sharp point at the lower end and a small hammer and hook at the upper. In later times they used long and short firearms, and as companions and helpers they had large, strong dogs. They always carried arms, even in times when the other inhabitants of the kingdom were forbidden to bear them.

Whenever the king of Bohemia entered their territory the Chods welcomed him in arms beneath their principal standard; it was white, and the sign on it was a dog's head. Paying their respects to their lord after the ancient custom with a barrel of mead, they escorted him as a guard of honour across the mountains and over the frontier.

For their hard and often dangerous services the Chods enjoyed special privileges and rights. They were free men for life, and apart from their king they had no overlords. They did no forced labour in the fields or other feudal dues, they had free use of the forests they guarded, and they could also hunt freely within them.

They had their own court of justice in their castle of Domažlice. Presiding in this court was the 'mayor of the Chods', appointed by the king. In this castle they kept their flag, seal and charters, granted to them by an array of kings, John of Luxembourg, Charles the Fourth, Wenceslas the Fourth, George of Poděbrady and others.

The Chods performed their military duties for the last time in the fateful year, 1620, building barricades on the Bavarian frontier at strategic places. The calls of the Chod guards echoed for the last time through the deep woods of Šumava, and the white flag with the black border and the sign of the dog's head flew for the last time over the heads of the keepers of the Bohemian frontiers.

Then came the battle of Bílá Hora, White Mountain.

Ruin blazed also into the mountain fastnesses of free Chodsko. On the fortieth day after the executions in the Old Town Square the Chods, by a decree of Charles of Lichtenstein on behalf of the emperor, were handed over to Wolf Wilhelm Lamminger, independent lord of Albenreuth, who had been one of the emperor's commissioners in the terrible tragedy of the twenty-first of June 1621.

Nine years later the Chods were *sold* to this same Lamminger as his absolute, bequeathable property for 56,000 gold pieces. Their new lord did not choose to recognise and did not recognise their freedom and privileges, and dealt with them as if they were slaves. But the sturdy Chods did not take this silently, and were far from willing to surrender their freedom and the privileges inherited from their forebears without a struggle. They entered on a lawsuit with their new overlord, whom they did not wish to acknowledge. The case dragged on for a long time. In the meantime Wolf Wilhelm Lamminger died, and the quarrel was only brought to a verdict under his son Maximilian, who won his case.

The Chods got the answer that they no longer had any privileges, for they were no longer valid, and that under pain of punishment they themselves were laid under a ban of perpetual silence.

This was in the year 1668.

This verdict was a terrible shock to the Chods, and for a long time there was the silence of the grave in their district. But this silence certainly was not perpetual. The Chods did not forget their privileges or their former freedom, and as their most precious treasure their trusted leaders guarded the ancient charters granted to their forefathers by the kings of Bohemia. As long as they had these they could believe that this was not the end of everything, that they could still lay claim to their rights.

The lord of Trhanov got word of the source of the Chod's hopes and ambitions, and he ordered that they should hand over their old charters to him. But this move only convinced the Chods even more surely that their letters of majesty were still valid. Why, otherwise, should their lord want them? And so they did not obey the order, but withheld the documents. At this Lamminger threatened them with force, and indeed he forced the charters from them by force, at Újezd, where they were then hidden. But he did not get all of them. Two documents, and those the most important, the Chods managed to save, and they then renewed their lawsuit against Lommikar of Trhanov, as they called Lamminger.

First they sent a deputation to the emperor in Vienna, in the year 1692. Word came back to them that the emperor had received the envoys graciously, and this raised the spirits of the Chods, and confirmed their faith that their right would triumph. Before the judgement was announced they refused all services to the lord of Trhanov, and went no more to do their feudal labour. Lamminger complained about them, and described their every act as dangerously threatening public order, so that the sheriff of the province of Pilsen, Hora, was dispatched into Chodsko.

From all the villages the Chods were called to Trhanov, to their lord's seat. All the courtyard of the castle was white with the serge overcoats of the Chods, who stood in close formation, shoulder to shoulder. Heavy black hats touched broad brim to brim, with here and there a lambskin cap between. They waited eagerly and anxiously to hear what the sheriff would have to say. The great majority of them were already expecting the joyful news that their case had been determined favourably.

In the window above the courtyard appeared at last a gentleman in a long, curly wig, and a coat embroidered with gold. This was the provincial sheriff. His deputy came to the window with him, and he it was who read to the anxiously listening Chods the verdict of the court: that their rights and privileges were long since forfeited, that they themselves were to remain in perpetual silence, that they had disregarded this injunction and thereby committed an offence for which they deserved punishment. However this transgression would be pardoned if they now forswore their quarrel and submitted themselves to their overlord.

This verdict fell upon the Chods as a crushing disappointment. It was a wonder they did not cry their defiance of Lamminger there and then. While they were debating, up spoke a young farmer of Újezd, John Sladký by name, known as Kozina. He told the provincial sheriff to his face that he did not believe what had been read out to them, for it was against all law and justice.

And so they did not obey, but carried their lawsuit for their freedom farther. Their complaints were referred to a new hearing by the court of appeal at Prague, and at the same time an order was made that they should send seven capable and honest representatives to this court in Prague. Besides old Kryštof Hrubý, mayor of Draženov, John Sladký Kozina was the most notable among them. In Prague at the court of appeal, however, they did not question them at all about their ancient privileges, but only about their insurrection against Lamminger, and about the disturbances which in his reports and complaints had grown out of all knowledge. The Chods again pressed for their rights, and as proof of them showed the two important letters of majesty they had conserved. But the court cut off the seals from the parchments and had the charters cut to pieces, laying it down that these were no longer of any value. The seven representatives were ordered to submit themselves to Lamminger as their overlord, and swear obedience and loyalty to him. When they refused to do so they were cast into prison.

In the meantime Lamminger's steward Koš, acting in accordance with his lord's wishes, had provoked the farmers of Chodsko so far by his use of force that they rose in revolt against him and his subordinates. He had burst forcibly into the farm of Kryštof Hrubý in the village of Draženov in order to get possession of several letters sent from Vienna by the envoys. When he tried to do the same in Újezd the inhabitants banded together against him. The steward Koš ordered his master's gamekeepers, who were in his company, to fire upon the people. But the Chods of Újezd disarmed the gamekeepers, captured their lord's burgrave,

and the steward Koš barely managed to escape on his horse. All this assisted Lamminger's cause. Immediately he asked for troops. And the soldiers duly came, and first to Újezd.

The people of the village left the place before the troops arrived, and gathered in the forests by Hamry, where the Chods from the neighbouring villages joined them. Thence they retreated before the much greater strength of the soldiers to Pocínovice. And there was fought out a grim battle between them and the troops who were hunting them.

I I

More than one Chod shed his blood there for his ancient and precious liberty, but in vain. They were overwhelmed by force of numbers. More than seventy of the captured were thrown into prisons in Pilsen and Týn and Stříbro, and beaten like thieves and vagabonds. The rest of the Chods, village by village, were called to the castle at Trhanov just before the harvest, and there all of them, farmers and cottagers, were made to swear on the Gospel that they were and would remain, they and their descendants after them, serfs owing feudal dues to his Grace the high-born lord Lamminger of Albenreuth and his successors; that they one and all acknowledged the invalidity of their former rights and charters, and would observe the order of perpetual silence laid upon them.

The assembly at Trhanov was hard and cruel; silent and downcast the Chods waited before the office until they were called in. They were now completely crushed in spirit, and those who were not knew that all resistance was useless. In subdued tones they repeated the oath, more than one faltering over the words, more than one voice trembling. Their representatives, Kozina, Kryštof Hrubý and the others, were still held in Prague at the New Town Hall. The lords demanded that these men also should acknowledge their serfdom to Albenreuth; and when they heard what had befallen at home, they took the oath. But not all. Neither old Hrubý nor Kozina would sign.

'Lommikar can force us to do feudal labour,' said Kozina to the lords confronting him, 'but how am I to say that our rights are invalid? Our rights are valid. Now we commit them to God.'

Those who had signed were allowed to go home. But the old mayor of Draženov and his nephew Kozina remained in prison.

But Lamminger was not content even now. The punishment the court of appeal had meted out to the Chods was not enough for him. He applied for a re-hearing, and laid a charge in the criminal court; and all went well for him.

The criminal court gave judgement that Kryštof Hrubý, Kozina and Čtverák, who had been the ring-leaders in the revolt, should be hanged, and the other leaders of the Chod people should stand in the pillory and receive harsh imprisonment.

In Vienna this sentence was abated to the extent of remitting two of the death sentences and deciding that only one man must hang. In the meantime old Kryštof Hrubý, once the most important and respected mayor in Chodsko, had died in prison at Prague. It remained to decide whether Čtverák or Kozina should hang, and the court gave its voice against Kozina, because he was a very eloquent man and therefore dangerous, and of all the most obdurate, refusing to beg for pardon.

They transferred him to Pilsen, so that the sentence might be carried out. When the day of the execution drew near Lamminger ordered that sixty-eight Chods from all the villages of the region, every one bringing his little children with him, should come to Pilsen to see Kozina's punishment, so that both they and their children should remember, and hand down the memory to future generations, how defiance and rebellion against the lord of Trhanov ended.

And he himself came to Pilsen to see Kozina die. The prisoner prepared himself calmly and bravely for his shameful death, comforting himself with the knowledge that though Lamminger had triumphed in an earthly court, at the judgement seat of God he would be vindicated, for his own cause was a just one, and he was dying an innocent man.

On the day of the execution, the 28th of November in the year 1695, an enormous crowd of people had gathered in Pilsen from the town and the surrounding district. They all flocked after the condemned man, behind whom walked his family and his fellow-countrymen, sixty-eight Chods, most of them tall and stately men, in cloaks and furs, but without their sticks. Leading their children by the hands, they marched dourly and sadly, looking with anguish at the unfortunate Kozina. He was lean and pale from his long imprisonment, but he walked firmly in the middle of his escort of soldiers, and carried his head high.

The procession streamed out of the town. The drum, muffled in black cloth, rolled dully and mournfully, and its sombre sound mingled with the sorrowful voice of the death-bell. The gallows stood on a hillock beyond the town. The soldiers took station around it, and in the space enclosed by their ranks stood the councillors and officials. There also were the officers on their horses, the provincial sheriff, and by his side Lamminger of Albenreuth.

Into this enclosure they led Kozina. It had grown silent all around; only the sobbing and weeping of Kozina's family and his fellow-countrymen disturbed the grieving hush. The young farmer himself, standing beneath the gallows, kissed the cross a priest offered to him, and looked round him for the last time at his own people and at the crowd of onlookers. And there among the mounted officers he caught sight of the one man who had been the cause of all this—Lamminger. Kozina drew himself erect, looked him in the face, and cried out in a great voice that rang clearly in the sparkling air of the frosty day:

'Lommikar! Lommikar! Within the year we shall stand together at the judgement seat of God! There it will be seen which of us—'

At that the officer in charge came to his senses. His naked sword flashed through the air, the executioner plucked away the ladder, and Kozina's voice fell silent. John Sladký, called Kozina, no longer lived.

Lamminger sat gazing at him, pale as death, then quickly turned his horse and galloped away to the town. The Chods and the people watching fell on their knees, and prayed in agitation and compassion for the dead man. Not only the people from Chodsko were in tears, but even the strangers, and in wonder and excitement they repeated to one another how the Chod had summoned the lord of Trhanov to the judgement seat of God.

III

Lamminger did not return from Pilsen to the castle of Trhanov. He sent a swift messenger to his wife to bid her come after him, and he would be waiting for her at Pilsen. He came again to Trhanov a year later, in the autumn. All those who saw him reported that he was greatly changed, and had lost flesh. He was also more irritable and severe than before. He never rode out alone now as of old, but always with an escort. He did not trust the Chods.

And at home, when he was solitary, he often spent hours pacing his room, obviously uneasy and thoughtful. Sleep had forsaken him; if he did fall asleep he moaned and cried out, tortured by horrible dreams. Kozina's words had never passed out of his mind, and he was counting the days. The year had almost passed now, and nothing had happened. Already he was beginning to feel reassured that the farmer had merely uttered a wanton threat against him. But other moods came upon him, when he could not get Kozina out of his mind, when the dead man appeared to him in dreams, pale, with flaming eyes, calling him to the judgement seat of God.

To rouse himself out of his thoughts Lamminger invited many guests to Trhanov castle, and arranged great hunts, and noisy parties after them. But he did not set the Chods free or make their lot easier. They had to do forced labour for him, and when he hunted with his guests the Chods had to beat game for him in the same forests in which their fathers had themselves hunted like lords.

October passed, and November came on. One evening after a day of hunting, Lamminger sat at table with his guests; outside a storm was brewing. Lamminger was in good humour, for during the previous days he had convinced himself that Kozina had certainly spoken at random. If nothing had happened so far, nothing would happen now, and he would weather November as he had weathered all the other months. He was also exhilarated from much wine. At last he began to speak openly of the preoccupation of which he had never before spoken before other people: of the term Kozina had set for him. He was laughing at that ultimatum now, and arrogantly he cried aloud:

'A bad prophecy, Kozina! The year's gone—and you're there and I'm still here!'

The words were barely out of his lips when he collapsed abruptly backwards into his chair.

At that same instant the storm burst outside, and the trees heaved and threshed at the windows. In the room where the nobility sat the door flew open of itself, the windows clinked and rattled, and a pale figure passed slowly through the dining room.

The lord of Trhanov spoke no more. He lay senseless, his eyes fixed. He had gone where Kozina had called him. The lords and ladies round him stood transfixed and trembling with horror.

The report of Lamminger's death flew through Chodsko; everywhere people praised God's justice, and thought ardently of Kozina, saying to one another:

'The judgement of God! The judgement of God!'

In the church of Klenčí they laid Lamminger of Albenreuth in his grave, and the curses of the Chods followed him to the tomb. Immediately after the funeral his widow left Trhanov with her daughters, and never again returned to it. Within a year she sold it, together with Kout and Ryzmberk and all the rest of the lordship.

But steadfast John Kozina remained in the memory of all his countrymen, reverenced and blessed, and from the time of his death they began to wear black cords on their white serge coats in token of mourning. To this day the Chod people will tell you that Kozina 'was put to death unjustly, and he is a saint'.

The Story of Janošík

I

Králova Hola, Mount Royal, soars out of wide forests above the beautiful valley of the Upper Hron, a high mountain, a memorable mountain. Its mighty crest is bare of trees, and stands open; the torrent of the wind is hardly ever stilled on that sunny summit. And in the sun and the wind, in mists and thunder-storms

297

alike, lonely on Mount Royal stands a stone table, moss-grown, ancient and forsaken, jutting out of the grass and heather and dwarf pines. Once upon a time, long, long ago now, it had its guests, and all the wide open space around it rang with shouts and laughter; and that was when the lord of Hungary himself, merry King Matthew, used to come here.

Whenever he came hunting in the neighbourhood, in the mountains of Liptov and the forests of Zvolen, after bears or wild boar, he made a halt here with his large retinue: the king in hunting gear with a golden horn, his lords magnates in rich dolmans and gleaming belts, in plumed caps of costly furs and with lance in hand and sword on hip, men with smooth, sunburned faces and huge moustaches. They came and sat here round the stone table, and their coupled hounds lay down panting at their feet, beasts of ancient breeds, wolfhounds and boarhounds, gulping the cool air. The servants and the people of the valley brought food in hampers and laid on the table meat and drink, and the king dined high above the world with his nobles. With keen delight he gazed out over the mountains, following the wide sweep of their slopes, and down over the darkness of the forests to the green valleys drowned in the golden sunlight, where castles gleamed white, and the red roofs of their towers loomed over the cottages of the hamlets and farms. His Slovak land, a beautiful land.

So it was in the days of King Matthew.

After his death, however, Mount Royal lay silent, and the stone table stood forsaken for a long, long time. Meantime below the mountains, in the valleys and plains, many things were changing. In the castles and mansions the despotism of the lords ran riot, and in the villages there was oppression and slavery. Great wrongs were being inflicted upon the people; their lords and masters burdened them ever more grievously with forced labour, extorted ever more greedy taxes and tithes from them, and the well-grown young men could not even sleep easily in their beds for fear of the press gangs of the military.

It was so bad that it could hardly be worse. Many a young man fled from the tyranny of his lord, quitting the quiet village for the fastnesses of the mountains. There the serfs became 'mountain boys', the forests were their dwellings, and the bare mountain in the Carpathians was their free field.

In this distressful time there was life and bustle again on Mount Royal, and once again round the stone table sat a retinue with their leader. But he was no king, but the mountain boy Janošík of Tarchová in the Upper Trenčín, and his companions were no magnates, wealthy and powerful gentlemen in dolmans and belts hammered with metal ornaments, but the 'fellowship', the eleven 'brave boys' in broad-brimmed hats decorated with embossed patterns, in green shirts and white linen trousers, with wide belts, and shoes fashioned each from a single

piece of leather. And not with swords or elegant arms, but with sheathed knives slung at their belts and two pistols thrust into them, with the 'valaška' in hand, stick and axe in one, and rifles slung over their shoulders.

It was not only in the autumn that they halted here and sat round the stone table; their hunts continued from early spring to the desolation of winter. Janošík led them in a life of banditry to right wrongs and protect the poor and wretched. Grief and indignation possessed him at the burdensome lot of the enslaved Slovak people, from whom he was sprung. If he could not help them at least he avenged them.

And himself also. For he, too, had been ill-used by lords, he and his father, who all his life long had never known what it was to live decently, and who had had only one wish, that his son should have a better life than he had had. Therefore he sent the boy, who was bright and intelligent, to school, as he was advised by a relative of his, the priest of his mission. So Janošík was educated—in Kežmarok, as they say—in Latin and all the learning he needed to become a priest himself some day. His father devoted all he had and all his hopes to the boy, and took the bread from his own mouth.

But his overlord was angry at that this old farmer should try to turn his son into a gentleman, and withdraw him from serfdom. He persecuted the old man by every means at his disposal. And the overlords at that time did not lack the means; everything was open to them, even injustice and wrong, and no-one brought any charge against them for it, no-one punished them.

When Janošík's father was hard at work in his fields it often happened that he was forced to leave everything immediately, and always when the work was most urgent, when he was scything a meadow or drying hay, or when he was cutting or binding grain. Then the lord would demand his attendance, and the farmer had to go to the great house. And there they kept him so long at forced labour that the hay would get wet and overheat, or the corn would begin to shoot. He had trouble also over his tithes. Nothing pleased his lord, he could never do anything right for him; whenever he took a hen or a goose to pay his dues, they refused them and drove him out of the castle, saying that his offerings were thin or small, and demanding that he bring a better one, well fattened.

In these and many other ways his overlord made things difficult for the old farmer. But for his son's sake he endured everything with patience, and when sometimes bitterness overwhelmed him and he did not know where to turn, he always took comfort in the thought of Janošík; for he was to be a gentleman, over him they would have no power. And perhaps some day the boy would be able to repay him, so that at least before he died his father would know a better life.

Meantime young John studied with passion, and prospered well. But suddenly he was withdrawn from the school. From his native village a messenger came running for him, saying his mother had fallen dangerously ill, perhaps with her death-sickness, and bidding him hurry to take his farewell of her, for her one longing and prayer was to see him again before she died.

At that time Janošík was twenty-one years old. He set out at once and in haste on his homeward journey. He had scarcely arrived and entered the room where his mother lay, and greeted her tenderly, when in after him strode the overlord's bailiff, black-moustached and sunburned, and sternly commanded that on the next day, early in the morning they should present themselves at the overlord's place to make hay; and the order was for both of them, the old man and the young, the farmer and the student. Janošík in his passionate grief over his mother's grave sickness scarcely even noticed the bailiff's entrance, let alone paying any attention to his orders.

The old father understood, he heard very well, but on this occasion he hesitated, although previously he had always obeyed the summons. His wife was sinking, she might die at any moment. The bailiff could see that for himself, and surely he would say so at the office. Perhaps it would do no harm if he disregarded the summons this once, and for so grave a reason. And Janošík? It was not for this had he been called from the town, not to let him go to a serf's labours, and he a student, almost a priest. And to leave his dying mother! Even the overlords must have a spark of feeling, and perhaps they would make this one small concession.

But they made no concessions.

At noon of the next day the bailiff came again, and not alone this time, but with several men. He shouted and abused them, brutally disregarding the dying woman; before her eyes he shackled her husband and son and dragged them away to the castle, which lay three villages away. There in a vaulted room they already had benches laid out, and bundles of supple hazel rods lay on them. And there the overlord was already waiting. As soon as he saw the farmer and his son he blazed at them in fury, cursing and reviling them, and had them stretched on the benches and bound there with straps; then he sat down and made himself comfortable, lighting his pipe and crossing his legs, and when he was ready he ordered:

'Now lay on, and you, steward, count! A hundred strokes each, and meaty ones! And you,' he growled, turning on Janošík with a savage grin, 'you'll see! This will be Latin for you! This is how I'll teach you to be a gentleman!'

The bailiffs struck mercilessly, inhumanly, until the old farmer lost consciousness; before the steward had counted the full hundred the old man died in agony. The son survived the blows, but after them he could not rise, nor stand on his feet when he was dragged up, so they laid him on a dung-cart, and the corpse of his father beside him, and so sent them home to their native village. The mother was still breathing, but after the terrible shock of this meeting with her husband and her son she died of grief.

As soon as he had partially recovered, and began to regain his strength, Janošík vanished from the village. Nor did he return to the town and the school. He stole away into the mountains.

There he hid among the shepherds in their solitary huts, and there he gained a wonderful power.

Once he had gone out from the hut to a lonely spring, to draw water in a wooden pail. His faithful dog, the only legacy left to him from his home, went after him. The spring gushed out beneath a rock, and was surrounded with a thick growth of bushes and briars. Janošík's dog flew excitedly into this thicket while his lord was kneeling at the spring drawing water. When he heard his dog barking so fiercely and burrowing into the bushes Janošík looked round, and it seemed to him that he heard a faint, small moan in the thicket. He jumped up with a shout and called off the dog, and then he himself threaded his way in among the thorns and briars.

There in a tangle of wild roses he beheld a fairy woman, all in white, beautiful to see and of a gentle countenance. White and lovely she stood before Janošík and thanked him kindly for calling off his dog; and then she asked the young man what he would like from her, for she would be glad to do him a service in return. Janošík did not ponder long.

'Strength!' he cried. He had great need of it, for he was resolved upon punishing the cruel overlords for all the oppressions they visited upon the people. Then the fairy gave him a belt with a magic thread in it, and a 'valaška', the mountaineer's staff with an axe-head, by means of which he could gain the strength of a hundred men. When he held this valaška in his hand, no-one could overcome him.

I I

From that time onwards Janošík lived a bandit life, to avenge himself and the wretched Slovak people. In return all the serfs called him and his comrades good fellows, and everywhere the common folk wished them well.

In time of danger they offered them a safe refuge in the mountain huts or below in the villages. There also, when frosts set in and mountains and forests lay under heavy drifts of snow, the mountain boys passed the winter like servants in the households of kindly farmers or in some other disguise. But as soon as the trees began to bud again they were off, back to the mountains to their bandit life. But Janošík wanted no bloodshed. He never killed anyone himself, and never had anyone killed by others. The only people they preyed upon were the rich and powerful.

'Your soul to God and your money to us!' Thus they challenged, their arms flashing warning. Janošík set his aim in particular on the harsh overlords and country landowners. Confronting one of these he would block his way face to face, and thunder:

'Here, my lord, these scarred and calloused peasant hands!'

Whatever they received or took Janošík divided into piles, and distributed among the fellowship; but his share he gave to the poor and needy, or laid it away in rocks, caverns or hollow trees, so that he would have hoards of money, clothes and arms at need. A large amount in well-minted Kremnice ducats he is said to have buried in holes in the ground, so that neither lords nor bandits should spend it. He often stayed in a cave in the mountain of Vapor, and there he had a treasure hidden, and they say that from Vapor to New Castle he had a bridge of leather thongs.

He loved music and singing. Often in the evening he sat by the hut among the shepherds, and listened with delight as one of them began to play on the fujara. And he loved to hear the girls singing as they cut grass; if they were not singing he would ask them to sing to him, and then he paid them lavishly for their music, sometimes even in gold.

When he was alone with his mountain boys, and they had kindled a fire in a safe place, in the forest, in a dark gulley or high on Mount Royal, he would always bid cunning Ilčík to set to work and play his pipes. Ilčík carried sonorous pipes with three drones, and he played and played until the music swelled through the night over forest and mountain, and all the fellowship grew merry. Then even Janošík, smoking his wooden pipe inlaid with fish bones and beaten copper and brass, grew gay with them, and his grave, cloudy face cleared and brightened.

But sometimes at these late hours it was quieter on Mount Royal. And this was when one of the fellowship had brought in with him some travelling or vagabond student, whom he had stopped on his journey in the forest, and taken captive. Every one of the brotherhood did this when he could, for he knew that nothing pleased Janošík better. Whether he was very young or an older man, the student paled and trembled with fear when he saw on the solitary mount at the stone table the armed mountain boys eyeing him by the light of the fire, and round them their wolfhounds, terrible dogs, growling and barking with erected hackles. But the dogs were sharply bidden to be silent, Ilčík laid his pipes on the stone, and not one of the companions uttered a word. Only Janošík spoke with the

306

student. He did not storm or thunder at him, but began like a priest, in Latin. He questioned and tested him, delighted at the student's astonishment and embarrassment. He laughed when the student could not answer, but praised him when he made a good reply. If the young man was well advanced in his studies, he bade him preach to the company.

The brigands made up the fire, the brushwood crackled, the smoke rolled up into the darkness, the flames leaped high and lit up Mount Royal and the darkness of the great hills around, their flickering outlines melting into the night. The student, climbing on to the rock, had to begin his sermon whether he would or no. He spoke gravely of the Christian life, of good deeds and of eternal rewards.

Silence fell on them all as in a church. Sometimes during these interludes of worship the mountain boys were moved to tears, and their leader himself bent his head in deep thought when the preacher began to speak of death, which is the end of all. And when the student had finished and they all said 'Amen', Janošík would remind his companions, remember the task they had taken upon themselves: to do no injury to any man without cause, and to right wrongs.

Then he did honour to the student preacher, and entertained him with what he had; and in the morning when they let him go, Janošík poured money into his hat, or ordered his comrades to measure the young man for a new suit. And the boys brought a roll of cloth and measured indeed, but with a vast and monstrous measure: from one beech-tree to another. These beeches were old and very thick, and stood a long way apart, so that the preacher could hardly carry away his reward.

It was on Mount Royal that Janošík loved best to linger. That was the spot he held most dear, and there also he fought with three companies of bailiffs and soldiers whom the lords had sent after him to capture him. But they did not take him, they were put to shameful flight. Janošík routed them himself, single-handed with his valaška rod, which swung and thrashed like a hundred such sticks.

Sometimes he removed for a time to other places, in the valley of Prosečná or Rimava, where in a battle he killed the general leading six hundred soldiers. When their general had fallen they all took to their heels. Janošík also often went in disguise. Here he roamed from village to village as a beggar, there he entered a town dressed as a monk; more than once, on horseback and habited like a lord, he rode into some castle, exacted entertainment and respect, and then took whatever he wished, often punishing the arrogant owner into the bargain before he rode away again with his comrades disguised as grooms and bailiffs. He was here, he was there, all in an instant.

When they had set a trap for him in a certain place he would slip through their fingers like an eel, or he would be sitting somewhere in an inn in one of the nearby villages, making merry with the young men. He drank with them, he sang with them, then suddenly he vanished. Only then did the authorities learn where he had been, what he had been doing, and how they had so nearly had him in their hands.

So he roamed through the mountains for a number of years, taking vengeance on the overlords, helping the poor, protecting the oppressed. While he roamed at large, in many a castle and manor they dealt more moderately with the serfs, not from compassion or kindness, but because they feared Janošík's avenging hand.

Until at last treachery brought about his downfall. His piper betrayed to the lords where he was hiding, and how they could capture him. In return for blood-money he got the help of a certain farmer in this treachery. This farmer knew Janošík well, and he invited the mountain boy to his farm once in winter, and himself went with a wagon to fetch his guest. Janošík trusted his host absolutely, and got into the wagon with him, never thinking of treachery. As they were descending the mountain the farmer got possession of Janošík's powerful valaška stick by stealth; and in his house the bailiffs and soldiers were already lying in wait.

As Janošík entered the room he slipped and fell. They had scattered peas under his feet. As he sank to the floor they hurled themselves upon him, over-powered him and fettered him; but in a moment he leaped to his feet again and burst his chains, and struck out with his enemies all round him at his antagonists, jeering at them: 'How many bailiffs go to make a half-barrel?' Things were going very badly with them and they were retreating in disorder upon the doorway when a wrinkled old woman piped up piercingly from the chimney-corner:

'Hack at his belt!'

At once one of the soldiers struck out with his sabre, and by chance cut through the enchanted thread in the belt the fairy had given to Janošík. As the thread was broken Janošík's strength was gone, and without his valaška he could not defend himself against so many men. This happened in Klenovec, near to Tisovec, at the house of the farmer Blaho. They shackled Janošík, thrust him into a cart and carried him away to prison, first at Hrachovo, an old castle in the valley of Rimava, and then at the castle of Vranov by Saint Nicholas. There he lay in close imprisonment, chained to the wall of his cell, and they never set him free again until they led him to torture.

In this harsh confinement he suffered intense heaviness and grief, not for his life, not for himself, but for his comrades, and most of all for the unhappy poor. He thought sadly of the fellowship and of his freedom, how he had sat at ease on Mount Royal with his men, and walked with them through green forests and over mountains and valleys, in the red of the morning and under the stars, by daylight and by moonlight. But as he thought of the Slovak people he heaved a deep sigh.

'Oh, my miserable people, who will take your part now? You, Almighty God, you will still be with them, you deliver them!'

So he lay grieving until they put him on trial in Saint Nicholas in Liptov; and there they condemned him to death, on the thirteenth day of March in the year 1713. Surrounded by soldiers and accompanied by great crowds of people he walked to the gallows. He looked for the last time on the mountains and forests, lifted his face for the last time to God's sunlight, he, still young and full of life. But his spirit never flagged; he marched firmly, and carried his head proudly, and four times he circled the gallows in the dance of the mountain boys, that the lords might see that he went in no awe of death.

So perished Janošík, the 'brave mountain boy'.

III

And Janošík's wonderful valaška?

As soon as they had got possession of it the lords put it quickly out of sight behind seven locked doors.

But the valaška did not remain in its prison. Of its own accord it began to hack at the door, and hacked and hewed until it had cut its way through. When it had cut through the first door it attacked the second, and then the third. And so it hacked a passage through all the others. Just as it began to hack at the seventh door they led Janošík to his death; and when the valaška had broken through this last door it was already too late. Janošík had departed into the truth of God. Then the valaška vanished into the mountains, the free mountains, and there, where Janošík loved best to pass his days, it is buried deep in a poplar tree on Mount Royal.

And the fellowship?

Its end was tragic. When they no longer had Janošík to lead them his men could not resist the far greater forces launched against them. They were trapped one after another and thrown into prison, and in prison they died, or on the gallows like their leader. The worst fate befell Jacob Surovec; he was broken on the wheel, and there was no help for him then from his famous rifle with two barrels with only one trigger between them, which he made himself, and which used to strike terror into travellers and opponents with its thunderous double report.

The mountain boys died, but their names are kept in remembrance among

the people, and most of all, with deep gratitude, the name of their chief, Janošík. The places where he walked, the haunts he loved, his paths, his caverns are still remembered. But above all they talk of his treasures, which he dropped into the trunks of ancient trees, or hid in steep ravines.

In many Slovak villages you will find pictures of the 'good fellows' hanging on the walls of the cottages, pictures painted on glass; there they stand in their green shirts, wide belts and white trousers, valaška in hand and rifle on shoulder.

310

And in the long winter evenings when the old farmer lets his mind wander back into the past he will surely begin to talk of the mountain boys, and point at the picture on the wall, at the piper, at Surovec twirling his valaška above his head, at Hrajnoha leaping over small beech-trees and firs, at every one of the eleven, but above all at Janošík. And the old man will tell you about his strength and his achievements, how he avenged his people and what he got for it, how the lords put him to death.

And the grey-headed farmer waves his hand and concludes:

'Dear God Almighty! That's what he got for taking the part of his own Slovak people. But there's an old prophecy, children, believe me, that Janošík will come again to the help of the Slovaks. And then things will be better. If only he'd come soon!'

From the Ancient Prophecies

WHEN THE HARSH YEARS FALL HEAVY ON YOUR SPIRIT
AND WITH DESPAIR YOUR EYES BRIM O'ER,
THE ECHO OF MY PROPHECY — OH, HEAR IT! —
CALLS HOPE TO PUT FORTH BUDS ONCE MORE.

Erben

*T*he book of the ancient legends is closed.

The glory of the past shines out of them; and the great tragedies of past storms and disasters still leave behind them a sombre echo. The black shadows of harsh times have fallen across the ages and lingered long, and many a man feels them to this day.

315

There were evil times in the territories of the Czech crown, times of anxiety and dread, worst of all when the people were reduced to servitude. Deprived of their freedom, oppressed beneath cruel extortions and forced labour that drained them of their strength, subdued and abased they bent their necks, and looked humbly for a gleam of relenting and consolation.

In that age of man the subjugated people were plagued with fines and blows, wars and hunger, and their native tongue was ridiculed and despised, driven almost out of use, and seemed doomed to certain extinction.

Those were evil times, times of anxiety and despair, so that the spirit broken with suffering looked for no help but by a miracle of God. The root of this hope was nourished by the old chronicle and the account of better times, and on the secret tree of the ancient prophesies new shoots budded.

They budded in the summer nights when in the shelter of old lime-trees the village people lamented over their hard lot; they budded in the winter evenings, in the gloomy twilight or beside the glow of the humble hearth, where some grandfather began to recall the old times. They budded in the hours of darkness, or in the holy quiet of Sunday afternoons, when the old Bible reader recounted to his neighbours the story of things past, and proclaimed what signs were still to come, what further terrors would afflict the land and the people before the new and better time dawned.

And those who heard trembled in spirit. But in this affliction the flower of consolation was already budding, a flower of magical fragrance and power, and from the mist of these ancient prophecies a wind of coolness breathed, and would not suffer the fire to be quenched on the hearth of our native land, however crushed beneath the burden of its distresses.

The prophetic voice from the plough of Stadice, the oracles which Libuše revealed in the blaze of inspiration, the words uttered by the Sibyl, the shape the blind youth saw in the future, and the inextinguishable hope in the sacred inheritance of the Czech land, all these were comfort and calm and strength to the poor and oppressed.

Hear, then, these auguries, even those which gushed forth like a living spring from the dry rocks only in certain regions. Generation after generation has come to this source to refresh in the dew of prophetic comfort a mind withering and dying in the drought of those harsh times.

Come, hear these ancient prophecies!

The Prophecy
of Sibyl

I

Sibyl, Queen of Sheba, a virgin of sagacious and enlightened mind, hearing from many people how King Solomon was wondrously wise, longed for him in her heart, and wished to see and hear him. Therefore she resolved that she would go and visit him in Jerusalem.

317

Preparing a numerous and richly furnished train of virgins and men-at-arms to accompany her, she ordered them to load upon camels many rare gifts, and set out on her journey.

Her kingdom and city of Sheba was two hundred and forty-one miles distant from Jerusalem, to the south in Africa. She journeyed from this city and empire of hers through the land of the Moors, through Egypt and the regions of the Red Sea, through the Arabian desert, until she reached the kingdom of Solomon.

When she came to Jerusalem itself, the young queen descended from her carriage and went barefoot, to make clear to all that she held this place to be sacred. Thus she walked barefoot as far as the brook Kedron, across which lay a log of wood. But the Queen of Sheba did not cross it, as all her train did, but kneeled and kissed it, and crossed the brook at another place.

And when thereafter she stood beneath the mount of Calvary, she fell to the earth like one overwhelmed with grief, and lay so with clasped hands for three hours. Then, rising, she looked at the mount of Calvary and cried with tears:

'Hail, most holy place! Holy you are and holy you will be to all ages, even to the end of the world.'

Solomon, hearing of the Queen of Sheba, came out to meet her with his household in all his glory, and received her with a gracious welcome and great honour, saying:

'Welcome, dear guest!'

Sibyl went with him to his court, and there she opened her treasures and gave them to the king, a great wealth of gold, precious stones and beautiful dishes of artistic workmanship, also precious spices and cuttings from trees which sweat balsams.

The queen remained in Jerusalem for nine months, and the king, showing her the splendid halls and airy and perfumed chambers in his palace, which lay in a delightful garden, entertained her as was fitting for a famous queen. In their frequent conversations the king recognised that the virgin queen was of a wise spirit, and when she further spoke to him on many occasions of the events of the future, he asked her to tell him something about them.

As they sat in the garden full of beauty and delight, in the shade of the old cedars, olives and cypresses, Sibyl looked into the dark future and began to speak of what she saw there.

First she told the king about his own empire, saying that after his death the kingdom would be divided in two, that the people and their kings would forsake the Lord, in requital of which the stranger would come and carry away all the people and the kings into captivity in the land of Babylon.

The glory of Jerusalem would pass away, and the temple which Solomon had built would be destroyed like all the city. But after many years, when the children of Israel repented of their sins and called upon the one God, a better time would come; the people would return to their land and rebuild Jerusalem and its temple.

'But they will not have their own kings then, but foreign kings, pagans, and at the last from the Roman nation. And then, king, know that the Messiah will be born, who will perform great wonders and miracles. But he will not be recognised by his own, but rejected and condemned to death. He will die on a cross of wood, and will carry it himself to Calvary, that sorrowful mountain. This cross will be from the tree of Adam, that grew in paradise; a log of that wood lies now across the brook Kedron. And because of the Messiah and his death many places will become holy like the mount of Calvary, on which the Saviour will render up his spirit to God.

'After the passion of the Messiah the revenge of the Lord will fall upon Jerusalem, and the precious vessels which you gave to the church will be carried away as booty to Rome. But Christ will triumph over pagan Rome, and his teaching will be spread abroad through all lands, even to the end of the world.'

Here Sibyl fell silent, and said no more that day. And the king, when she had left him, pondered long in his mind over all these things, until he had his clerk called to him, told him all that Sibyl had revealed, and the clerk wrote down all. Then the king kept what was written, and laid it with his other books.

II

On the next day when King Solomon sat once more with Sibyl in the garden, he asked her to tell him what was in store for other countries before the coming of judgement day.

Sibyl told him how the Christians would multiply, and how they would have their own emperors and kings, but thereafter the Jews would decrease and their government would be taken from them. In course of time, however, the Christians would be corrupted and give themselves over to lewdness.

'There will be no faith or trust among them, their mouths will speak with other voices and their minds think other thoughts. Law will be for sale, the poor people will be oppressed, persecuted and forsaken. Then God will send many signs as a warning to the people to amend their ways; and when they do not obey, the Lord God will wipe out a third part of them for their wickedness.' And Sibyl expounded what these signs would be, and when she had made an end of her exposition she went away into her apartments, and Solomon again had all that she had said written down and preserved.

On the third day Sibyl came into this pleasant garden again and met King Solomon there under the tamarisks, cypresses and olives. It was morning, the sun was just rising above the mountains. The king again began to speak of the future, and then Sibyl herself requested that he would call his clerk to write down all that she was about to say, and that the account of it should be kept for ever.

As she began to speak, standing upon a staircase under the trees in her white gown the young queen's face was transfigured and her eyes shone with the prophetic fire. Carried away in the spirit, she began:

'O King, the Lord has endowed you with such wisdom that there never has been before you and never will be after you any prince of the world your equal, though there will be many emperors and kings. And they will have new empires. One of these empires or kingdoms will be celebrated and excellent, fruitful with grain. And that one is the Czech land, and there will be in it also hops and vines in plenty. The nation inhabiting this land will build many cities, but one so immeasurably great that there will be in it more than a thousand houses.

'It will be a glorious city, and the capital of that land, for their kings will dwell in it. But from this city also will come forth abominations and many sins. They will perpetrate injustices until at last God will take from them their king, and set up another, from a foreign race, over them. And he will persecute them so grievously that after a time they will wish and long to have again kings of their own race.

'And into this Czech land will flock many strangers, who will bring with them much evil. King after king will burden the people with forced labour, until they must work for their lords four days together, and have only two days left them to work for themselves. One of these kings will introduce unheard-of changes, which at first will please the common people; but under the cloak of a new order the old laws will be disrupted. For these changes the peasants will praise the king, but the lords will be displeased. And in his time it will also be forbidden for every man to avow his faith freely, for he will not be a lover of the priesthood and in his reign many lands and churches of the priests will be wrested from them.

'This same king will have all the land measured, and will lighten the forced labours of his people. But he will soon be overtaken by death and will die in his bed and not in battle. And that death will be a matter of wonder to the people, and they will say that the dead man is still living.

'After him will come a king who will abandon many changes made by his predecessor. After his short reign will come a young king, during whose rule there will be great and disastrous wars. The country people will be forced to carry their grain for nothing, and to give up almost all their harvest. Also many of them will be taken into the army, so that there will be in that land five armies, each with a different name, and the people will have to feed them and clothe them.

'At that same time there will be bad harvests, and God will send them many fires, storm-winds, hailstorms, heavy snows and great floods.

'From year to year it will be worse, so that it shall be a burden to young men and old to be living in this world, and especially to the common people, and the more since there will be quartered upon them such great armies that from many a farmer shall be taken even his last remaining son to serve in battle.

'But even for all this the nation will not amend. It will continue in its vices and follies, and there will be a great transformation in clothing and in customs. Then the Lord will be in anger and offence against them, and will punish them so heavily that all their cities will be ruined. Only Tábor, Ústí, Soběslav and Mělník will escape this destruction, if they hold fast by truth and law. Kutná Hora will decline, Pilsen, Hradec Králové, Kouřim and Čáslav and many another royal city will fall before the assault of enemies.

'But the Lord will punish Prague above all other cities. With fire and a terrible flood he will chasten her, and an enemy will complete her ruin. Her remnants will be overgrown with pines and thorns, and the marten and the fox will make their lairs there. That once glorious city shall be so forsaken that in course of time a carter driving through it shall halt on the Stone Bridge, crack his whip in the dead silence, and say to his son: Here was once the great city of Prague, and there stood the Old Town Hall.

'But before these things come about and that sorrowful time falls upon her, there will be various signs manifested plainly: the people will behold the days shortened, the sun will not shine as formerly, and winter will follow hard on the heels of winter, so that men will wear furs to cut the grain.

'Then will come these wars, and out of them will arise such unheard-of levies and taxes that the people will have no means to pay them. And therefore they will be ill-used, driven with whips and imprisonment, until they cry aloud: Lords, we have given you all that we can. Now we have nothing, you have taken everything from us, and left us not so much as will fill our children's mouths and our own.

'But such speeches will be of no effect, for the lords will surely exact their taxes without mercy. Then the common people, faithfully standing by one another, will say: My lords, pay these dues for us yourselves, for you have already amassed great wealth out of our labours. We can pay no longer, for we have nothing left. Thereupon the lords will cast many of the men into prison; but the people will rise and there will be bloody war, in which the people will cry: Better to die in battle, at least we will not watch our children die of hunger.

'Such punishment will the Lord let fall upon the nobles of that land, because they oppressed their subject people with great taxes and harsh labour.

'When that land is thus disquieted, and its inhabitants locked in quarrels and struggles, it will be encircled from the four quarters of the world by powerful enemies suddenly invading the land. Then will begin a battle with all those armies from all four sides. This terrible battle-field will stretch from the capital city to the mountain of Blaník, where the armies will lie between Blaník and Načeradec at the village of Bejkovice. And there the battle will begin.

'But even before this fight, marching to Blaník, the enemy will have slain so many of the unrighteous that only a few people will remain alive, such a handful as could hide beneath the cover of a wagon.

'In the place where that great battle is to be there lies a mere. But before this time the storks and other birds will have carried away from it all the thorns and reeds, and for some years before the battle of Blaník it will be empty and dried up. During that battle it will fill with blood until it overflows the dyke. There will be a great noise of crying, the neighing of horses, the voice of the drums, and such firing from great and small arms that the terrible tumult will be heard twenty-four miles away. The battle itself will last for twelve days. But on the thirteenth day God will send help to his faithful; out of the mountain of Blaník will burst the army that God has hidden there. As soon as that host is seen the enemy will turn to flee in terror. The army of the Lord will do wonders, and put the enemy to rout, but in their flight they will do such destruction upon Prague that not a trace of that city will remain. But they themselves will be driven out of the land and will flee as far as Cologne on the Rhine; and there the army of Blaník will vanish—only God knows whither, for they will not return into Blaník, and no-one will ever see them again. After the battle of Blaník the mere will again dry up; and on the sixteenth day the faithful who are left alive will begin to seek for one another. And they will rejoice and embrace one another, marvelling that God has so spared them. Then they will go all together to the mere, and there they will see the desolation of the slain, both men and horses, which the birds of heaven will disseminate, for there will not be so many people left alive as could bury all that multitude of corpses.

'The faithful thus being gathered together, a priest will serve Holy Mass on the stump of a tree in the middle of the mere, and they will praise God.

'Then they will return each to his own dwelling, and there will be among them concord and true love, and they will be all of one heart together, lords and common people. There will be fifty good and fruitful years, and in the Czech kingdom there will be plenty, and for low prices: a bushel of corn for seven pence, a bushel of wheat for twelve pence, an old Czech pint of beer for two farthings, and a pound of venison for two farthings. Plenty of everything, and everywhere peace and the blessing of God.'

Queen Sibyl fell silent. King Solomon, eager to have word of all that was to come, then asked her to reveal to him yet one more thing: when would come judgement day? But Sibyla replied: 'O King, I have no knowledge of this, for God has not revealed it even to his angels. But tell me this, my lord king: You have servants both good and bad. Do you give to the bad the same recompense as to the good?'

'The good receive good, the evil are punished,' replied the king.

'Well said, O King!' said Sibyla. 'If, therefore, the people will do righteously, the Lord will extend the time. But if they anger Him He will shorten the years and the days he has ordained from the creation of the world. Only so much is known to me concerning judgement day, and this also, that there will be many signs and wonders in the sun and the moon, the heaven and the earth, before the Lord God comes.'

And having said this, she concluded: 'Such is my prophecy, King Solomon. Let it be written and preserved. When the ages have passed my words shall be fulfilled, and the last generation shall bear witness that in these her prophecies Sibyla told truth.'

King Solomon, the wise and experienced, bowed himself before the young queen who stood high on the staircase above him, there under the tamarisks, cypresses and olives of his delightful garden. A pleasant breeze was stirring in the morning air, bearing enchanting sweetness of flowers, and the dawn sky grew rosy above them.

The Prophecy of the Blind Youth

The Emperor Charles the Fourth, King of Bohemia, was returning in the year of Our Lord 1362 from Germany through Nuremberg to his own native country; when he came to the frontier in the forests of Šumava he received word that in the village of Kout, not far from Domažlice, lived a young man blind from birth, a devout soul and of a prophetic spirit, highly esteemed by all the people of the whole district.

Charles the Fourth rode to the village, and when he came to the cottage of the blind youth he dismounted from his horse, and entered the room where the young man was, and there found him sitting at a table.

'I give you greeting, worthy youth,' the sovereign said to him.

The young man thanked him and replied:

'Hail, my lord emperor, saint and king!'

'Why do you call me a saint, sinful man as I am!' asked the emperor. 'And how did you know that I am the emperor? You cannot see, and you can have had no knowledge of my intent to visit you.'

'You are indeed a man of God,' replied the blind youth, 'for you show it by your deeds. The poor people bear witness to it, for you take their part. The sublime churches you have built and are still building bear witness to it. You cherish and bless this whole land like a benevolent father to the Czech nation. You care for them and for the tongue they speak. And yet before three hundred years have passed the Czech language will be brought to humiliation and shame.'

So saying, he invited the emperor to sit down with him at the table. Charles did so, and spoke with the blind youth on many subjects, until at length he said:

'Gentle youth, as I judge, God has taken the light from your eyes in order that you may see into the darkness of the future. Explain, therefore, what you suggested a while ago. What is to happen to my beloved country, and how long will this kingdom of mine still endure in glory?'

The young man said not a word, but taking a chalk he wrote on the table the following letters, one after another with spaces between them, thus:

K. V. Z. A. L. J. V. L. F. M. R.

When he had done writing, he said:

'As many letters as there are kings. There are the names of your successors. After your death, in the reign of your son, a civil war will arise, and great bloodshed. But military glory and military booty will all remain within the country, and the Czech land will take no hurt, but defend herself gloriously against many enemies.

'But in the course of time the Czechs will abandon discipline and unity, and their manners and ways will decline sadly. Foreigners, Germans, Italians and French, will be dearer to them than their own kin, and Czechs will be seen in clothes of strange and proud conception. Councillors will take bribes, and justice will fall into disrepute, for the judges will determine causes only according to estate, wealth and power.

The cry of the poor will dwindle unheard, and all order will be disrupted. And God will grow angry. People will still cultivate their fields, but there will be no increase of bread, for the blessing of God will be withheld from the land. Then will come taxes and levies and forced labour such as never yet were known, war will follow on the heels of war, and wives will mourn their husbands and children their fathers, torn from them to serve in the army. Then the lords temporal and spiritual will hate the Czech tongue, the Germans will rule in Prague, and many Czechs will so far forget themselves and offend against their origin as to deny their mother-tongue and cast it off with shame.

'Then on a certain hill-top in the region of Kouřim the trees will wither and dry up, and there will be great famine. And after it numberless enemies shall fall upon Bohemia, like a great storm, like a stampede of wild horses. Only between Úpa and Orlice there shall no harm befall even a hen. But whosoever survives these terrors shall then enjoy a time of blessing and happiness.'

'Dear youth,' said Charles the Fourth when the blind young man was silent, 'what you have revealed is sad news. But tell me also, what did you mean by these letters?'

'My noble lord, these letters signify:

K. That is Karel, or Charles; by this I mean you yourself.
V. Václav, or Wenceslas, your son.
Z. Zikmund, your second son.
A. Albrecht of Austria, his son-in-law.
L. Ladislav, Albrecht's son.
J. Jiří, or George, a Czech-born king.
V. Vladislav, a Pole.
L. Ludvík, a Hungarian.
F. Ferdinand, a Spaniard.
M. Maximilian, a Czech.
R. Rudolf, Maximilian's son.'

'And then?' asked the emperor, as the blind youth stopped.

'Storms and inconstant princes. But it will be worst of all when the royal house dies out in the male line and a queen succeeds. Great numbers of enemies will conspire against her, and the kingdom of Bohemia will draw near its fall. The nobility will be violent and wicked, and the poor will be subjected to such oppression as never yet was seen from the beginning of the world. And then God will punish the Czech land.'

Charles the Fourth was greatly saddened by this. 'If it were only possible,' he said, sighing, 'to avert all this misfortune! I would sacrifice everything, even my life, for my kingdom. God grant it is not I, sinful man as I am, who am the cause of all this evil!'

'I have said,' replied the young man, 'that you are a man of God. You fast and do penance in your castle of Karlštejn, and pray for your nation. You will be a saint, and the golden bed in which you rest there will be consecrated for ever, for it will not endure to carry anyone unworthy, not one, though he were your own son.'

Then, taking the chalk again, he wrote these further letters:

N. S. E. F.

'*N*. The Northern nation, neighbours to Bohemia, will invade us, and devastate and plunder our land.

'*S*. This signifies the nation to the South, the Turks and other unbelievers, with whom the Holy Roman Emperor will have many and cruel wars. In these wars the Czechs will help him, they will shed much blood in them, and spend much money.

'*E*. The nation from the east, a mighty nation which will wage war against its neighbours, but do no hurt to the kingdom of Bohemia.

'*F*. This last letter stands for a monstrous horde of armed men that will sweep into Bohemia like a flood, chiefly French, then also Germans and others from the west. Then will come the last and greatest battle. And then in their dread the people will turn to God, and call entreatingly for aid.

'And the Lord will have pity on Bohemia, and send help. From the mountain of Blaník the army of knights will sally forth against all enemies of the Czech land, and Saint Wenceslas on his white horse will lead the chivalry of Blaník to a terrible battle which will continue for several days. In that battle the foreign foe will be defeated and destroyed. Such as survive will be driven out of the land. Many a one will creep into hiding, but all these Saint Prokop will drive out with his crozier. Then the kingdom of Bohemia will be rid of all its enemies, it will be free and remain free.

'Then will come the time of constant and blessed peace. All Czechs will be united, showing forbearance one to another, and their language, which was discarded and humbled, will be exalted, and no-one then will deny his tongue. For all men will be proud of their origin and their forefathers, and their gallant defence of their land and faith. It will not be wearisome or hard then to them to labour and sacrifice for their land, for they will profess less and perform more, and that out of sincere love. Such a love as moves you, our lord and king, to glorify this land.'

Charles the Fourth sighed, and said: 'Dear God grant that then, at least, my Czech land may be happy.'

And rising, he took the blind youth by the hand, and said to him:

'Come with me to Prague, to my castle. There you shall be well provided for.'

To this the young man gladly assented, and he rode with King Charles to Prague, where he remained at the royal court until his death.

The Prophecy of Havlas Pavlata

When Havlas Pavlata, a citizen of the little town of Vysoký under the Giant Mountains, came to die, he was a hundred and fifteen years of age. Round his death-bed there stood his sons and daughters, grandchildren and even great-grandchildren. And the old man, blessing them all in departing, said:

My sons and daughters, my children all and my friends, I am taking my leave of you for ever, before I set forth into eternity. I have lived through much in this world, God willed me to live a hundred and fifteen years. And in this long age there have been many years both good and fruitful, under our Czech king Vladislav, and we've amassed plenty of good wealth.

And you, sons, put by a little money. For presently there will be a great plague, and such high prices as never were known. Within the next fifty years there'll come a new attack of plague, so bad that even in the mountains people will die, and wolves will come into the villages and look in at the windows of the cottages and howl, as though not a living soul remained there.

But the chief plague will come after that. It will begin gradually in the winter, just at carnival time, and last until Christmas, and kill so many people that the grain in the fields will be still standing on Saint Wenceslas's day, in places even until Saint Martin's, for there will be nobody left to harvest it. And soon after that will come judgement day.

At that same time there will be a great war in Bohemia, far greater and more terrible than in Žižka's time. Czechs themselves will fight one with another, and they will take Ferdinand for their king. Strange nations, Italians, Netherlanders, French as well as Germans, will come into Bohemia, and take away from the Czechs all their good money, and go into our mountains in search of precious stones.

Before this ruin comes there will be great dishonesty in the Czech kingdom and all manner of injustices. The lords will persecute the serfs without mercy, and there will be no justice to be found in them or in their stewards. They will blaspheme against God Himself, and say that a handful of power is worth more than a sack of righteousness.

Therefore all the peasants will rise against their lords, and drive them out of their castles with blows. And also before the ruin comes there will be terrible frosts, and monstrous falls of snow, with great gales of wind. The frosts will be even more cruel than those I remember, when I, Havlas Pavlata, burned charcoal in Rokytnice. I remember that time, there was a bear that could not endure in the forest for the dreadful cold, and came to warm himself at my charcoal hearth.

It was night, and bitter frost. The bear stood warming himself on one side of the hearth, and I stood at the other side and threw him bread. All the bread I had I broke up and threw to him. And the bear came on the next night also; again I fed him with bread. And he ate his fill and grew tame. When the third night came, and he appeared again, I had already prepared a birch-fibre rope for him.

I gave him bread again, and stroked him, and then I drew this halter through his nostrils and led him home to our house in Vysoký. Afterwards I led him to Prague, and Brož of Vrchlabí was with me. Those were hard frosts that year, but there'll come frosts still more biting than that time when I was young.

What more is there I have to say to you? It's sad, what I've told you, but people have only to wait, and they'll acknowledge that I've told the truth.

It's the Czechs themselves who'll be to blame for all those penalties and pains and ruin, for there's coming a sad change in them, and they won't pay any heed to law and order, or even remember the Lord God and the terrible last judgement. My dear sons! You'll still live through a few better years. That will be while our King Vladislav still lives. But after him will come Ferdinand.

After Ferdinand those bad years are coming, they'll begin before the end of his reign. In the reign of King Matthew and King Frederick it will be at its worst. People will wish and long to be well out of this world.

And these wars will go on until there comes a king whose name is Anbestas. Then better times will come, and they'll call that king by two names: the good king and the godly king.

This is what was foretold about the adversities and dissensions of the future, and about the kings to come, by Havlas Pavlata.

Various Prophecies

A gigantic rocky boulder once jutted out of the murmuring flood of the Wild Orlice below the ruins of the castle of Potštýn. It thrust upwards out of the middle of the river, in the constant rush of the foaming waves. The people of the region used to measure by this rock the rise of the water, in the time of the spring floods, or in the autumn. Sometimes the stone flushed red; that was when the reddened flood water overflowed from the pit in the crown of the rock and ran and trickled down its flanks like rivulets of blood. And then people took fright, believing that this red moisture foretold evil times, war, famine or plague.

The rock had stood for centuries in the murmur and surge of the Orlice's wild waters; but some day its hour had to come, according to an old prophecy.

'A magpie will come and peck the stone to pieces, and then there'll be misery in Bohemia. An enemy will invade the country, and with him will come hardships for the people, and terrible diseases.'

That was what was foretold.

In the year 1866 they were undertaking some building work at the demesne of Potštýn. As they needed some rough stone, the steward of the estate had the boulder in the river beneath the old castle blasted to pieces with dynamite. The old people grieved over the moss-grown rock, and prophesied no good would come of it.

And not long afterwards the Prussians invaded the country. The old prophecy revived in people's memory, and everyone realised at last that what had been foretold had indeed come to pass. It was a magpie that had broken the rock to pieces; for the name of the steward was Straka, that is, magpie. And war did follow, and epidemics of bad diseases trod hard on its heels.

In very ancient times, in a spot above the Orlice river where now stands the town of Kostelec, there was a magnificent church. In its tower hung a golden bell. But church, tower and bell all sank into the earth when the people became too sinful.

When the church shines again in its place above the valley, and the golden bell again rings from the tower it will be to proclaim a new golden age. But before that day can come the wind must sow all the hillside beyond the river, and a pine-copse must spring there and grow into a thick forest. When the pine-tree at the edge of this forest dries up and its roots decay, a black pig will come and dig out its roots, and uncover beneath them the golden bell, which will have made a long, magical journey underground from the place where it fell to the roots of this old tree.

Oškobrh, that mysterious hill, stands green with woods and white with rocks above the wide plain. In the shade of its oaks and maples, elms and sallows, quivering aspens and ashes and smooth-barked birch-trees, in groves where hazels and sycamores flourish in thick profusion, grew an enchanted flower, and more than one rare herb of strong healing power.

Libuše once used to climb to the summit by a wooden passage-way the carpenters made for her to the top of the hill from the castle of Libice. And the interior of this mountain guards a secret; a sacred army lies there asleep. It slumbers there until the day when it will awaken and burst forth out of the dark womb of the hill, and that will be when the worst distress overwhelms the Czech people.

Then the din of furious battle will be heard from the broad plain beneath the hill. From the north, from the Prussian land, enemies will invade Bohemia, and terribly will they ravage the whole kingdom, until at last, between Cidlina and Mrlina, almost all their host will perish. There the last battle will be fought, and the Prussian king, defeated, will take to flight.

And when the Prussian king with the remnant of his army flees this land, he will rest in the shadow of an old pine-tree in a wide field beyond Náchod, near to the frontier at Hronov. He and all his army will rest there, for there will be no more men left to him than will be able to sit round a drum. Here on the frontier under a rough-barked pine-tree they will take their rest for the last time on Czech soil, then they will cross the frontier, and the Czech kingdom will have peace from them for ever.

There will be storms, there will be wars, until blood runs in the gutters; but in the end the Czech kingdom will be led into peace, and sabre and sword will be laid aside and lie at rest. And this will come about when the rose-bushes round the borders of the Rose Meadow have grown over the whole meadow. Then seven kings will meet there, and in the meadow among the roses they will make a pact of sacred, eternal peace; and all will be well with our land.

Everything is only for a while, even the world. Even its wonders will some day cease. And this will be when the stone cross on the hill at Solnice, which every year sinks another hair's-breadth into the earth, shall have vanished entirely into the depths.

High among the wild rocks on Bor there sits a stone maiden, with an unmade shirt in pieces in her lap. Every year on Good Friday, when they are singing the passion of Christ in the churches, the stone maiden makes one stitch in this shirt.

Every year one stitch. When she makes the last stitch, and the shirt is finished, everything will come to an end, everything under the sun. And then it will be judgement day.

Listen to the last ancient legend and the prophecy woven into it, which was told by the blind youth to King Charles of blessed memory.

Behold the mountain of Blaník in its gown of dark forests, flowing down from its summit on all sides. Gravely, almost menacingly it looks down on a countryside remote from the world, on hills and levels that bear but meagre fruit. The summit of the hill can be seen from far and wide, and the people of the district often look attentively at it. When it is veiled in cloud it foretells bad weather, when it is clear and bluish it promises days settled and hard.

On the summit of Blaník you may see in the shadow of the beeches, firs and pines traces of very ancient stone ramparts, for the most part fallen. They are covered with growths of moss and bushes; there is no trace left now of the wooden castle they protected.

But beneath the ramparts, deep in the mountain itself, slumbers a company of armed knights, the army of Saint Wenceslas; they slumber and wait until the day shall come when their help will be needed and they will be called to battle.

Below the rocky summit of Blaník in the eastern slope there is a rock in the shape of a pointed arch. This is the entrance into the mountain, and beside it a spring wells up, at which the knights of Blaník water their horses when once in a while, by the light of the moon, they ride out from the mountain to a meadow among the forests under the hill. On such nights the hollow thundering of hooves echoes through the air around, the muffled rolling of drums and peal of trumpets. But towards morning everything suddenly falls silent, knights and horses and all the train ride in at the rocky gate and vanish in the secret depths of the mountain. Only the meadow still preserves a memory of the wild night ride, in the countless prints of horses' hooves.

More than one person has penetrated before now into the rock vault where the army of Saint Wenceslas lies sleeping.

Thus a certain young girl was once cutting grass below Blaník. Suddenly a knight stood before her and asked her to go with him and tidy up inside the mountain. The girl was not at all afraid, and she went with him. The gate into

334

the mountain stood open. She saw a vaulted hall in the rock, and mighty columns on which arms were hung. A deep hush as in a church hung over all the space within, and the hall gleamed with a mysterious yellowish light. In stalls along the wall stood a row of saddled horses, and round stone tables in the hall sat the knights, their heads inclined upon the table. The knights were asleep, the horses stood motionless; they did not toss their heads, they never stamped hoof on the ground or flicked a tail.

The girl went in and looked round her, but no-one moved. She began to sweep the room, and worked rapidly, and in a very short time she had the whole place tidied and cleaned. Even then no-one interrupted her, no-one spoke to her, and no-one awoke. As she had come, so she departed, and when she got home they asked her where she had been so long.

She wondered at this, and said that she had come home at the same hour as on other occasions; and she was astonished when they told her that it was a year since she had last come home from cutting grass, and she had been a whole year missing. She told them where she had been, and then they all understood why a year had passed and seemed to her only a little while. But on the third day after this the girl was dead.

In just the same way an unknown knight invited the smith of Lounovice into the mountain to shoe his horse. The blacksmith went, and when he had finished shoeing they gave him dust and sweepings in a sack. He was so angry that he emptied it out in front of the mountain. And when he got home he found that they had been mourning for him, for he had vanished without trace and they had neither heard nor seen anything of him for a year.

He told them what had happened to him, and when he shook out his sack three ducats fell out of it. Only then did he realise that he had made a mistake. He ran back at once to the mountain of Blaník where he had emptied out the rubbish. But in vain. He found neither rubbish nor ducats.

They tell the same story about a shepherd who was looking for a stray sheep, and himself went astray and found himself inside Blaník; and also about a young man who spent the same period of one year in the mountain, as did the shepherd, without the least idea that he had been there so long.

But all this is long ago. Blaník gazes down, sealed and stern and almost menacing, on the solitary landscape remote from the world; it is as though the melancholy of sad meditations shrouds the mountain and all around it. The army of Saint Wenceslas is still asleep. It is not yet time for it to awaken. That will come in the hour of greatest danger, when so many enemies descend upon our country that the whole kingdom will be trampled to pieces by the hooves of their horses.

When the time comes there will be signs to be seen: the tops of the trees will wither and dry up in the forest of Blaník, and on the summit of the mountain an old dead oak-tree will put forth new greenery, and the spring by the rock will overflow so wonderfully that it will go rushing in a torrent down the slope. Then there will be a great and savage battle between Blaník and Načeradec. The mere called the Waste, beside which an old dead tree will bud again before the battle, will be filled by the streams of shed blood. There will be lamentation and great sorrow over this desperate battle, but the Czechs will defend themselves heroically against the stronger force of their enemies. And at the moment of decision Blaník will open, knights in full arms will gallop forth from the mountain, and Saint Wenceslas on his white horse will lead them to the help of the Czechs.

Overwhelmed with sudden terror and confusion, the enemy will flee to Prague, and there this dreadful battle will be fought to its close. It will be so ferocious that blood will flow in a stream from Strahov down to the Stone Bridge of King Charles; and there Saint Wenceslas on his white horse, with his standard in his hand, will place himself at the head of the Czech army, and the invaders and all enemies of the Czech kingdom will be driven out before him. And Saint Prokop, Abbot of Sázava, will take his crozier in his hand and help in the work.

Then there will be holy peace, and the Czech land will be at rest. Many Czechs, it is true, will die in those wars, but those who remain will be true men. Acknowledging the errors of their forefathers and their own, they will stand firm together, and no enemy will ever again dispute their land with them.

*S*uch are the legends of the long-past years, and the old prophecies about our land.

Dear land, be happy! May your sons be strong! May they overcome all adversities and preserve their sacred heritage: their mother-tongue and their old, good laws.

May your sons grow mighty in labour and ardour, that the generations of the future may be firm as rocks, and eternally strong.